# Chemistry for Sanitary Engineers

# CHEMISTRY FOR
# SANITARY ENGINEERS

## Clair N. Sawyer

ASSOCIATE AND DIRECTOR OF RESEARCH
METCALF AND EDDY, ENGINEERS, BOSTON
FORMERLY PROFESSOR OF SANITARY CHEMISTRY
MASSACHUSETTS INSTITUTE OF TECHNOLOGY

McGRAW-HILL BOOK COMPANY, INC.

1960    New York    Toronto    London

CHEMISTRY FOR SANITARY ENGINEERS

IV

54968

THE MAPLE PRESS COMPANY, YORK, PA.

# Preface

The training of sanitary engineers at the undergraduate level is becoming more and more a practice of the past. The trend is distinctly toward education at the graduate level, with higher degrees awarded after successful completion of one, two, three, or more years of study and research.

Sanitary engineering has depended heavily upon civil engineering for its volunteers, and it is expected that this will continue to be the case, because of the similarity of factors that motivate or attract young people into the two fields of endeavor. In many respects the civil engineer is not well prepared to enter into a study of sanitary engineering because of his lack of knowledge in the fields of chemistry and biology. However, it is the responsibility of those in the teaching profession to adapt their teaching materials and methods to fit the needs of the students who offer themselves for service in the area of sanitary engineering.

After some 20 years of association with sanitary engineers, both in teaching and in practice, I am convinced that the sanitary engineers of the future will be, mainly, civil engineers by training who will have had one year of college chemistry at the time they start graduate training. I am also of the opinion that, as the scope of sanitary engineering expands, the time available for formal courses in the various fields of chemistry will diminish.

The purpose of this book is twofold: (1) It attempts to bring into focus those aspects of chemistry that I have found especially valuable in my work in the field and (2) it attempts to lay a groundwork of understanding in the area of specialized quantitative analysis, commonly referred to as water, sewage, and industrial waste analysis, that will serve the student as a basis in all the common phases of sanitary engineering practice and research.

It is hoped that this book will stimulate the student's desire to learn more chemistry. Furthermore, it should give orientation to his thinking, aid him in his choice of areas for advanced study, and help him to develop a firm concept of what he should expect to derive from such effort.

This book was written as a textbook in the hope that it will be a real aid to students of sanitary engineering and to those teachers responsible for imparting the chemical knowledge expected of them. In order to meet the modern-day requirements of a textbook, brevity has been an important consideration throughout. For those who feel that I have been too brief, I can only beg their indulgence and recommend that they seek further information in standard references on the subject.

It has taken some courage to summarize the basic concepts of each of eight fields of chemistry in individual chapters. Perhaps the most difficult was the chapter on organic chemistry. In this task, I was aided greatly by having used Wertheim and Jeskey's "Introductory Organic Chemistry" as a textbook during the past 10 years to teach a short course in organic chemistry to sanitary engineers. In writing the chapter on organic chemistry, certain material from this book has been used with Dr. Wertheim's permission, and I wish to express my thanks for this privilege.

Special thanks are due Dr. Perry L. McCarty and Dr. G. J. Mohanrao of the Massachusetts Institute of Technology for reviewing and criticizing the entire manuscript, to Dr. Robert A. Lauderdale, Jr., of the University of Kentucky for reviewing the chapter on radiochemistry, to Mrs. Gladys D. Rand for her expert typing of the manuscript, and to Prof. Kenneth W. Cosens of Ohio State University, Dr. C. Fred Gurnham of Michigan State University, and Dr. Jack E. McKee of the California Institute of Technology, the reviewers selected by the publishers, who made so many helpful suggestions.

*Clair N. Sawyer*

# Contents

PART I

# Fundamentals of Chemistry for Engineers

# 1. Introduction

The important role that sanitary and public health engineers have played in providing us with pure and adequate water supplies, facilities for sewage and refuse disposal, safe recreational areas, and a healthy environment within our homes and places of employment is not generally appreciated by the public at large. Those who have experienced living in the underprivileged areas of the world usually return home with a new sense of respect for the guardians of the public health. Among these guardians are the engineers who are in the front lines of defense, employing their knowledge of science and engineering to erect barriers against the ever-present onslaught of diseases and plagues, the most terrible of the "Four Horsemen of the Apocalypse."

For many years the attention of sanitary engineers was devoted largely to the development of safe water supplies and the sanitary disposal of human wastes, and, because of their success in controlling the spread of enteric diseases through the application of engineering principles, a new concept of the potentialities of preventive medicine was born. Expanding populations, increased industrial operations, and new industries based upon modern technology have intensified old problems in the areas of water supply and waste disposal and have created new ones undreamed of a few decades ago. Many of these have offered a real challenge to sanitary engineers, and the profession as a whole has been ready to accept the challenge.

Over the course of years, intensification of old problems and the introduction of new ones have led to basic changes in the philosophy of sanitary engineering practice. Originally the major objectives were to produce hygienically safe water supplies and to dispose of wastes in a manner that would prevent the development of nuisance conditions. Many other factors concerned with aesthetics, economics, recreation, and other elements of better living are important considerations and have become part of the responsibilities of the modern sanitary engineer.

3

## 1-1. Water

Water is one of the materials required to sustain life and has long been suspected of being the source of many of the illnesses of man. It was not until a little over 100 years ago that definite proof of disease transmission through water was established. For many years following, the major consideration was to produce adequate supplies that were hygienically safe. The public has been more exacting in its demands as time has passed, and today water engineers are expected to produce finished waters that are free of color, turbidity, taste, odor, and harmful metal ions. In addition, the public desires water which is low in hardness and total solids, noncorrosive, and non-scale-forming. To provide such water, chemists, biologists, and engineers must combine their efforts and talents. The chemist, through his knowledge of colloidal and physical chemistry, is especially helpful in solving problems related to the removal of color, turbidity, hardness, and harmful metal ions and to the control of corrosion and scaling. The biologist is often of great help in taste and odor problems that derive from aquatic growths.

As populations increase, the demand for water grows accordingly and at a much more rapid rate if the population growth is accompanied by improved living standards. The combination of these two factors is placing greater and greater stress upon water engineers to find adequate supplies. In many cases inferior-quality, and often polluted, water supplies must be developed to meet the demand. It is to be expected that this condition will continue and grow more complicated as long as population growth occurs. The ingenuity of scientists and engineers will be taxed to the limit to meet this need.

## 1-2. Sewage and Stream Pollution Control

The disposal of human wastes has always constituted a serious problem. With the development of urban areas, it became necessary, from public health and aesthetic considerations, to provide drainage or sewer systems to carry such wastes away from the area. The normal repository was usually the nearest watercourse. It soon became apparent that rivers and other receiving bodies of water have a limited ability to handle waste materials without creating nuisance conditions. This led to the development of purification or treatment facilities in which chemists, biologists, and engineers have played important roles. The chemist in particular has been responsible for the development of test methods for evaluating the effectiveness of treatment processes and providing a knowledge of the biochemical and physiochemical changes involved. Great strides have been made in the art and science of waste treatment in the past few decades. These have been made possible by the fundamental knowledge of sewage treatment established by scientists with a wide variety of training. It has been the responsibility of the engineers to synthesize this basic knowledge into practical systems of sewage treatment that are effective and economical.

It has long been known that all natural bodies of water have the ability to oxidize organic matter without the development of nuisance conditions, provided that the organic loading is kept within the limits of the oxygen resources of the water. It is also known that certain levels of dissolved oxygen must be maintained at all times if certain forms of aquatic life are to be preserved. A great deal of research has been conducted to establish these limits, and, undoubtedly, a great deal more is needed. Such surveys require the combined efforts of biologists, chemists, and engineers if their full value is to be realized. In general, streams are classified into four broad categories: (1) those to be used for the transportation of wastes without regard to aquatic growths but maintained to avoid the development of nuisance conditions, (2) those in which the pollutional load will be restricted to allow fish to flourish, (3) those to be used for recreational purposes, and (4) those which are used for water supplies.

The consensus at the present time in most areas of the United States is to allow maximum utilization of the purification capacity of streams commensurate with the highest order of use of the water downstream. If full use of the purification capacity is to be made, close supervision of treatment processes and stream conditions must be maintained at all times by personnel trained in biology and chemistry.

## 1-3. Industrial Wastes

Perhaps the most challenging field in sanitary engineering practice at the present time is the treatment and disposal of industrial wastes. Because of the great variety of wastes produced from established industries and the introduction of wastes from new processes, a knowledge of chemistry is essential to a solution of most of the problems. Some may be solved with a knowledge of inorganic chemistry; others may require a knowledge of organic, physical, or colloidal chemistry, biochemistry, or even radiochemistry. It is to be expected that, as further technological advances are made and industrial wastes of even greater variety appear, chemistry will serve as the basis for the development and selection of treatment methods.

## 1-4. Environmental Sanitation

Although the problems of water supply and liquid-waste disposal are of major importance to urban populations, their solution alone does not ensure a completely satisfactory environment.    Pollution of the atmosphere increases in almost direct ratio to the population density and is largely related to the products of combustion from heating plants, incinerators, and automobiles, plus gases, fumes, and smokes arising from industrial processes.    The intensity of most air pollution problems is usually related to the amount of particulate matter emitted into the atmosphere and to the atmospheric conditions that exist.    In general, visible particulate matter can be controlled by adequate regulations.    The most serious situations develop where local conditions favor atmospheric inversions and the products of combustion and of industrial processing are contained within an enclosed air mass.    A notable example is the situation at Los Angeles, where inversions occur frequently, and less often at a few other metropolitan areas.

In cases where atmospheric inversions occur over metropolitan areas under cloudless skies, a haze which is commonly called "smog" is produced in the atmosphere.    Under such conditions the atmosphere is usually highly irritating to the eyes and to the respiratory tract and is far more intense than can be accounted for by the materials emitted to the atmosphere from the separate sources.    Research on this problem has been extensive in the Los Angeles area.    Many theories have been advanced as to the cause but the consensus at present is that photochemical action between nitrogen dioxide and unsaturated hydrocarbons from automobile exhaust gases combine to form the irritating substance. The latter condenses on particulate matter in the atmosphere to form a fog.    A knowledge of chemistry has played an important role in finding the cause of this enigma.

Air pollution of quite another type is of growing interest to people everywhere.    This concerns the radioactive materials that gain entrance to the atmosphere through atomic and nuclear explosions.    The nuclides that are dispersed and settle as "fall-out" vary greatly in their effect upon living plants and animals.    Radio assays designed to differentiate and measure the most harmful nuclides, i.e., those with lowest tolerance levels, will be required to keep levels within safe limits.

## 1-5. Other Technological Developments

During the past few years, many new chemicals have been produced for agricultural purposes.    Some of them are used for weed control; others are for pest control.    Residues of these materials are often carried to watercourses during periods of heavy rainfall and have had serious effects upon the biota of streams.    A great deal of research by chemists and biologists is needed to obtain valid information on this new form of stream pollution.

## 1-6. Summary

From the discussions presented it should be apparent that the solution of many problems in sanitary engineering has required the concerted efforts of scientists and engineers and that chemists, in most instances, have played an indispensable role.  It is to be expected that problems arising in the future will be fully as complex as those of the past and that chemistry will continue to be an important factor.  Engineers with sound chemical training should find that their knowledge is a great aid and advantage in conquering unsolved problems and that liaison with scientists working on the same or allied problems will be facilitated.  The chapters following are dedicated to that purpose.

# 2. Basic Concepts from General Chemistry

The factual information and basic concepts that are taught in freshman chemistry vary considerably, depending upon the institution and the interests of the students. In many schools, engineers are given a considerably different course from that given to science majors. Because of these differences and because certain fundamental information is essential for sanitary engineers, a review of certain phases of general chemistry is indicated.

## 2-1. Elements, Symbols, Atomic Weights, Gram Atomic Weights

Remembering the names of the common elements poses no particular problem to the average student. However, the proper symbol does not always come to mind. This is mainly because many of the symbols are derived from Latin, Greek, or German names of the elements, and sometimes because of a similarity of names which makes a multiple choice of symbols possible. The latter is well illustrated by the symbols for magnesium, Mg, and manganese, Mn, which are commonly confused.

In the case of the symbols for magnesium, manganese, and those derived from Latin or other foreign names, one must rely entirely upon memory or association with the uncommon name. A list of the elements whose symbols are derived from Latin, Greek, or German names is given in Table 2-1.

Atomic weights of the elements refer to the relative weights of the atoms as compared with some standard. The standard chosen is oxygen which has a value of 16. It is not necessary to remember the atomic weights of the elements, as tables giving these values are readily available or can be made so. It will save time, however, to remember the weight of the more commonly used elements such as hydrogen, oxygen, carbon, calcium, magnesium, sodium, sulfur, aluminum, chlorine, and a few others. It is usually sufficient for all practical purposes to round off the atomic weights at three significant figures; thus aluminum is called 27.0, chlorine 35.5, gold 197, iodine 127, etc.

In general, elements do not have atomic weights that are whole numbers because they consist of a mixture of isotopes. Chlorine is a good example. Its atomic weight of 35.46 is due to the fact that it consists of two isotopes with atomic weights of 35 and 37. Cadmium contains eight isotopes whose atomic weights range from 110 to 116.

TABLE 2-1. LIST OF ELEMENTS WHOSE SYMBOLS ARE DERIVED FROM
LATIN, GREEK, OR GERMAN NAMES

| Element | Name from which symbol is derived | Symbol |
|---|---|---|
| Antimony | Stibium, L. | Sb |
| Copper | Cuprum, L. | Cu |
| Gold | Aurium, L. | Au |
| Iron | Ferrum, L. | Fe |
| Lead | Plumbum, L. | Pb |
| Mercury | Hydrargyrum, Gr. | Hg |
| Potassium | Kalium, L. | K |
| Silver | Argentum, L. | Ag |
| Sodium | Natrium, L. | Na |
| Tin | Stannum, L. | Sn |
| Tungsten | Wolfram, G. | W |

The *gram atomic weight* of an element refers to a quantity of the element in grams corresponding to the atomic weight. It has principal significance in the solution of problems involving weight relationships.

## 2-2. Compounds, Formulas, Molecular Weights, Gram Molecular Weights, Mole

Although the concept of chemical compounds is readily established, association of the proper and correct formula for each compound does not always follow. This difficulty is sometimes due to faulty use of symbols but much more often to a lack of knowledge regarding valence. The subject of valence will be discussed presently. If strict attention is paid to correct symbols and valences, errors in writing formulas will be eliminated.

Calculation of molecular weights poses no real problem except when rather complex formulas are involved. Most difficulties in this regard can be overcome by writing structural formulas and applying some effort in the form of practice. The importance of correct molecular weights as the basis for engineering calculations should be emphasized.

The term *gram molecular weight* (GMW) refers to the molecular weight in grams of any particular compound. It is also referred to as a *mole*. Its chief significance is in the preparation of *molar* or *molal* solutions.

A *molar* solution consists of one gram molecular weight dissolved in enough water to make one liter of solution, whereas a *molal* solution consists of one gram molecular weight dissolved in one liter of water, the resulting solution having a volume slightly in excess of one liter.

## 2-3. Polar Valence; Theory of Valency

A knowledge of valency serves as the key to ensure correct formulas. In general, the writing of formulas with elements and radicals that have a fixed valence is easy, if a knowledge of electrostatics is applied. The real difficulty stems from elements that can assume several valences, the variety of radicals that results, and a lack of knowledge concerning nomenclature, which is not always consistent.

The question is often asked: How is it possible to resort to the electron theory of valency to explain multiple valences? According to this theory, most atoms consist of neutrons, protons (+), and electrons (−). The neutrons and protons are contained within the nucleus, and a number of electrons, corresponding to the number of protons (atomic number) in the nucleus, are arranged in orderly rings outside. The outer ring contains the valence electrons. If electrons are lost, the atom becomes a positively charged ion, and if electrons are gained, the atom becomes a negatively charged ion. Except for inert elements (such as argon) that already have complete rings, atoms tend to gain or lose electrons so as to assume or approach complete rings. To do this, they must team up with another atom in some manner. When atoms of two elements react chemically, one gains electrons and the other loses electrons. In the exchange, the metal or metallike element loses electrons to gain or approach a stable condition with no electrons in its outer ring. The nonmetal steals electrons from the metal to complete its outer ring to eight electrons, a stable configuration. This exchange is normally accomplished by the release of a great deal of energy. This simple type of reaction is well illustrated by the one between sodium and chlorine, as shown in Fig. 2-1.

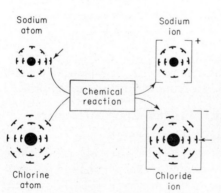

FIG. 2-1. Electron transfer during a chemical reaction, producing a sodium ion with a valence of + and a chloride ion with a valence of −.

The chlorine atom contains seven electrons in its outer ring. It can gain one electron to complete its outer octet, as in the case with sodium, or it may approach another stable configuration by the loss of one or more electrons. It is possible for it to lose all seven electrons but that is all. Chlorine does not combine directly with oxygen, but under special conditions it forms a variety of oxides, as illustrated in Fig. 2-2. It will

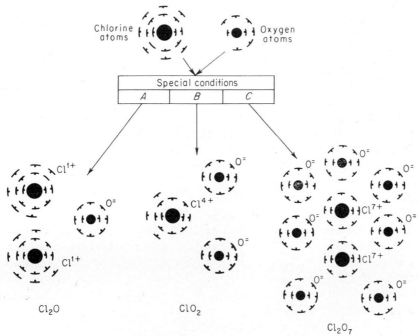

FIG. 2-2. Multiple valence states of chlorine due to loss of electrons. Chlorine forms similar compounds in all states of valence from $+$ to $7+$, except for $6+$.

yield one, three, four, five, or seven of its electrons, to form $Cl_2O$, $ClO_2^-$, $ClO_2$, $ClO_3^-$, and $Cl_2O_7$. The oxides from which $ClO_2^-$ and $ClO_3^-$ are derived have never been isolated. However, compounds of chlorine with valences of $+$, $3+$, $4+$, $5+$, and $7+$ are well defined. Sulfur, nitrogen, and the halogens are nonmetals that are capable of exhibiting a wide range of valences because of their ability to take on electrons to complete the outer shell to eight or to give up one or more electrons to reach a stable configuration. Manganese, chromium, copper, and iron are examples of metals that can obtain several valence states by yielding one or more electrons. Manganese is an extreme case in that it can yield two, three, four, six, or seven electrons.

## 2-4. Nomenclature

There are very few hard-and-fast rules concerning nomenclature of inorganic compounds. One concerns binary compounds; they all have the ending -*ide*. For example, anhydrous HCl is hydrogen chloride.

Most nomenclature problems arise from the acids containing oxygen.

In general, the nomenclature is related to the valence of the element that characterizes the acid. The acids having the highest valence state are usually called -*ic*, e.g., sulfuric, phosphoric, and chromic. They give rise to -*ate* salts. The acids that exist in the next lowest state of valence are called -*ous*, e.g., sulfurous, phosphorous, and chromous. They give rise to -*ite* salts. If acids of a lower valence state exist, they are called hypo · · · ous, e.g., hypochlorous or hypophosphorous, and their salts are called hypo · · · ites.

Occasionally, as with the oxy acids of the halogens, more than three acids are known. In such cases the acid in the highest valence is given the prefix per, e.g., perchloric or per-iodic, and their salts are called per · · · ates. The acid derived from manganese in a valence of 7 ($HMnO_4$) is known as permanganic acid, and its salts are the familiar permanganates. All per · · · acids contain an element that has a valence state of 7, which appears to be the reason why $HMnO_4$ is given a prefix per. The only other well-defined acid of manganese is manganic, in which the manganese has a valence of 6.

Acids are also named in terms of their degree of hydration: ortho, meta, and pyro. The ortho acids consist of the highest hydrated form of the acid anhydride, e.g., sulfuric ($H_2SO_4$), phosphoric ($H_3PO_4$), phosphorous ($H_3PO_3$), chromic ($H_2CrO_4$). The meta acids are derived from the ortho acids by removal of one molecule of water from each molecule of acid as follows:

$$H_3PO_4 \xrightarrow{\Delta} HPO_3 + H_2O\uparrow$$
$$\text{Ortho} \qquad \text{Meta}$$

where $\Delta$ = heat

$\uparrow$ indicates that water escapes

The ortho acids give rise to ortho salts and the meta acids to meta salts. The pyro acids may be derived, theoretically, from ortho acids by removal of one molecule of water from two molecules of acid, as follows:

$$2H_3PO_4 \xrightarrow{\Delta} H_4P_2O_7 + H_2O\uparrow$$
$$2H_2SO_4 \xrightarrow{\Delta} H_2S_2O_7 + H_2O\uparrow$$
$$2H_2CrO_4 \xrightarrow{\Delta} H_2Cr_2O_7 + H_2O\uparrow$$
$$\text{Ortho} \qquad \text{Pyro}$$

Free pyro acids are not known, but well-defined salts are common. The pyro salts of chromic acid are commonly called dichromates, another instance of deviation from the rule. A summary of nomenclature of the acids is given in Table 2-2.

## 2-5. Chemical Equations; Weight Relationships

A fundamental rule that must be observed at all times is that expressions of chemical reactions become equations only when they are balanced.   In order to balance a chemical equation it is essential that it represent a reaction in a true manner and all formulas used must be correct.   Unless these conditions are complied with, weight relationships are meaningless.   Weight relationships serve as the basis for the sizing of chemical feeding equipment, necessary storage space for chemicals, structural design, and cost estimates in engineering considerations. Their importance should not need further emphasis.

TABLE 2-2. NOMENCLATURE OF OXYGEN-BEARING ACIDS AND THEIR SALTS

On the basis of valence

| Name of acid | Formula | Name of salt |
|---|---|---|
| Sulfurous | $H_2SO_3$ | Sulfite |
| Sulfuric | $H_2SO_4$ | Sulfate |
| Hypochlorous | $HClO$ | Hypochlorite |
| Chlorous | $HClO_2$ | Chlorite |
| Chloric | $HClO_3$ | Chlorate |
| Perchloric | $HClO_4$ | Perchlorate |

On the basis of hydration

| | | |
|---|---|---|
| Orthosulfuric | $H_2SO_4$ | Orthosulfate |
| Orthophosphoric | $H_3PO_4$ | Orthophosphate |
| Orthophosphorous | $H_3PO_3$ | Orthophosphite |
| Metaphosphoric | $HPO_3$ | Metaphosphate |
| Metaphosphorous | $HPO_2$ | Metaphosphite |
| Pyrophosphoric | $H_4P_2O_7$ | Pyrophosphate |
| Pyrochromic | $H_2Cr_2O_7$ | Dichromate |
| Pyrosulfuric | $H_2S_2O_7$ | Pyrosulfate |

## 2-6. Oxidation-Reduction Equations

Modern concepts of oxidation and reduction are based upon the idea of atomic structure and electron transfer as described in Sec. 2-3.   The basic concept is derived from the action of oxygen (an oxidizing agent) with some other element or compound which, of course, must be a reducing agent.   The case is best illustrated by the reaction that occurs when hydrogen burns in oxygen.

$$H_2^\circ + O^\circ \rightarrow H^+ \!-\! O^= \!-\! H^+ \tag{2-1}$$

All elements initially have zero valence since each atom has an equal number of electrons and protons.   When hydrogen combines with oxygen, the hydrogen atom loses its one electron to the oxygen atom.   Since the oxygen atom needs two electrons to complete its outer orbit of eight electrons, it takes electrons from two atoms of hydrogen and assumes a negative valence of 2, as shown in Eq. (2-1). In this reaction, the hydrogen is considered to be oxidized and the oxygen is reduced. Thus oxidation may be defined as a loss of electrons, and reduction as a gain of electrons. With this concept of oxidation and reduction, general definitions of oxidizing agents and reducing agents can be derived.

An *oxidizing agent* is any substance that can add electrons, e.g.,

$$O°, \; Cl°, \; Fe^{3+}, \; Cr^{6+}, \; Mn^{4+}, \; Mn^{7+}, \; N^{5+}, \; N^{3+}, \; S°, \; S^{4+}, \; S^{6+}$$

A *reducing agent* is any substance that can give up electrons, e.g.,

$$H°, \; Fe°, \; Mg°, \; Fe^{2+}, \; Cr^{2+}, \; Mn^{4+}, \; N^{3+}, \; Cl^-, \; S°, \; S^{-2}, \; S^{4+}$$

It will be noted that $Mn^{4+}$, $N^{3+}$, $S°$, and $S^{4+}$ appear in both series above. Any element in an intermediate state of valence can serve as a reducing or as an oxidizing agent under proper conditions.

It is a fundamental rule that oxidation cannot occur without reduction, and the gain of electrons by the oxidizing agent must equal the loss of electrons by the reducing agent.

### Simple Oxidation-Reduction Reactions

$$H_2° + Cl_2° \rightarrow 2H^+Cl^- \tag{2-2}$$
$$4Fe° + 3O_2° \rightarrow 2Fe_2^{3+}O_3^= \tag{2-3}$$
$$Mg° + H_2^+SO_4^= \rightarrow Mg^{++}SO_4^= + H_2° \tag{2-4}$$
$$2Fe^{++} + Cl_2° \rightarrow 2Fe^{3+} + 2Cl^- \tag{2-5}$$
$$2I^- + Cl_2° \rightarrow I_2° + 2Cl^- \tag{2-6}$$

In each of the equations above, the oxidizing agent gains the same number of electrons as are lost by the reducing agent.

**Complex Oxidation-Reduction Reactions.**   Many oxidation-reduction reactions require the presence of a third compound, usually an acid or water, to progress. It is a rule that when the oxidizing agent is a compound containing oxygen, such as $KMnO_4$, $K_2Cr_2O_7$, etc., one of the products is water. The balancing of complex oxidation-reduction equations is simplified if the following three steps are followed:

1. Write the skeleton equation. This may be in either the molecular or ionic form but must be a *true* representation of the reaction that occurs.

2. Balance the equation with respect to valence change or electron transfer.

3. Complete the equation in the usual manner.

A few illustrations will serve to show how the scheme is applied.

*Example A:*

*Step* 1:

(a)   $KMnO_4 + FeSO_4 + H_2SO_4 \rightarrow Fe_2(SO_4)_3 + K_2SO_4 + MnSO_4 + H_2O$

or (b)        $MnO_4^- + Fe^{++} + H^+ \rightarrow Fe^{3+} + Mn^{++} + H_2O$

Equation (b) is the ionic form of Eq. (a), if one recognizes that the potassium and sulfate ions do not enter into the reaction. Note that neither equation is balanced at this stage of the example.

*Step 2:*

$$\overbrace{\hspace{5cm}}^{+5 \times 2 = 10e \text{ gain}}$$
$$2KMn^{7+}O_4 + 10Fe^{++}SO_4 + H_2SO_4 \to 5Fe_2^{3+}(SO_4)_3 + K_2SO_4 + 2Mn^{++}SO_4 + H_2O$$
$$\underbrace{\hspace{4cm}}_{-1 \times 10 = 10e \text{ loss}}$$

$$\overbrace{\hspace{4cm}}^{+5e \text{ gain}}$$
or $\qquad MnO_4^- + 5Fe^{++} + H^+ \to 5Fe^{3+} + Mn^{++} + H_2O$
$$\underbrace{\hspace{3cm}}_{-5e \text{ loss}}$$

In step 2 a total of 10 electrons are involved in the molecular equation because there are two atoms of iron in each molecule of ferric sulfate. The least common multiple of 2 and 5 is 10.

*Step 3:*

$2KMnO_4 + 10FeSO_4 + 8H_2SO_4$
$\qquad\qquad\qquad \to 5Fe_2(SO_4)_3 + K_2SO_4 + 2MnSO_4 + 8H_2O \qquad (2\text{-}7)$
or $\qquad MnO_4^- + 5Fe^{++} + 8H^+ \to 5Fe^{3+} + Mn^{++} + 4H_2O \qquad (2\text{-}8)$

*Example B:*

*Step 1:*

$\qquad K_2Cr_2O_7 + KI + H_2SO_4 \to Cr_2(SO_4)_3 + K_2SO_4 + I_2 + H_2O$
or $\qquad Cr_2O_7^= + I^- + H^+ \to Cr^{3+} + I_2 + H_2O$

*Step 2:*

$$\overbrace{\hspace{4cm}}^{+3 \times 2 = 6e \text{ gain}}$$
$$K_2Cr_2^{6+}O_7 + 6KI^- + H_2SO_4 \to Cr_2^{3+}(SO_4)_3 + K_2SO_4 + 3I_2^\circ + H_2O$$
$$\underbrace{\hspace{5cm}}_{-1 \times 6 = 6e \text{ loss}}$$

$$\overbrace{\hspace{4cm}}^{+3 \times 2 = 6e \text{ gain}}$$
$$Cr_2O_7^= + 6I^- + H^+ \to 2Cr^{3+} + 3I_2^\circ + H_2O$$
$$\underbrace{\hspace{4cm}}_{-1 \times 6 = 6e \text{ loss}}$$

*Step 3:*

$K_2Cr_2O_7 + 6KI + 7H_2SO_4 \to Cr_2(SO_4)_3 + 4K_2SO_4 + 3I_2 + 7H_2O \qquad (2\text{-}9)$
or $\qquad Cr_2O_7^= + 6I^- + 14H^+ \to 2Cr^{3+} + 3I_2 + 7H_2O \qquad (2\text{-}10)$

An even more complicated oxidation-reduction equation is involved when one element in a high state of positive valence oxidizes the same element in a lower state of valence, with all the particular element from both the oxidizing and reducing agent appearing in the same final state of valence. The action of potassium bi-iodate with potassium iodide is an excellent example since it is the basis of a reaction commonly used to release iodine for the standardization of sodium thiosulfate solutions.

*Step* 1:

$$KH(IO_3)_2 + KI + H_2SO_4 \rightarrow I_2 + I_2 + K_2SO_4 + H_2O$$

Since free iodine is formed from both the oxidizing and reducing agents, it is necessary to repeat $I_2$ in the equation.

*Step* 2:

$$\overbrace{+5 \times 2 = 10e \text{ gain}}$$
$$KH(\overset{5+}{I}O_3)_2 + 10KI^- + H_2SO_4 \rightarrow \overset{\circ}{I_2} + 5\overset{\circ}{I_2} + K_2SO_4 + H_2O$$
$$\underbrace{-1 \times 10 = 10e \text{ loss}}$$

*Step* 3:

$$2KH(IO_3)_2 + 20KI + 11H_2SO_4 \rightarrow 12I_2 + 11K_2SO_4 + 12H_2O \quad (2\text{-}11)$$

In order to balance the equation in step 3, it is necessary to multiply by 2 the parts that are balanced in step 2 because of the limitations imposed by potassium. Ionically this equation results in

$$IO_3^- + 5I^- + 6H^+ \rightarrow 3\overset{\circ}{I_2} + 3H_2O \tag{2-12}$$

## 2-7. Metals and Nonmetals

The division between metals and nonmetals is not as distinct as we often desire it to be. Two tests are commonly applied in making a decision: (1) Most metals form oxygen-bearing salts, such as nitrates and sulfates, and nonmetals do not and/or (2) metals form at least one oxide with reasonably strong basic characteristics. The latter is not of general application because of the limited solubility of some oxides and hydroxides.

## 2-8. The Gas Laws

The gas laws, particularly their influence on the solution or removal of gases from liquids, are of particular significance to the sanitary engineer.

At this point it may be well to state that many college graduates have not had proper instruction in how to adjust a common mercury barometer before making an observation of barometric pressure, and instructors should be prepared to correct this deficiency.

**Boyle's Law.** Boyle's law states: *The volume of a gas varies inversely with its pressure at constant temperature.* This law is so simple and usually so well understood that further elaboration seems unnecessary. Its principal application is in reducing observations of gas volumes from field conditions to some standard condition. This is particularly significant at high altitudes, such as at Denver, Salt Lake City, etc.

**Charles's Law.** Charles's law states: *The volume of a gas at constant pressure varies in direct proportion to the absolute temperature.* Interpretation of this law poses no problems provided that the absolute temperature scale is used. Charles's law finds its greatest use in the calculation of pressures in fixed-volume containers with variable temperature. In conjunction with Boyle's law, it serves as the basis for sizing gas holders.

**Dalton's Law of Partial Pressures.** This law has been presented in a number of ways but in essence it may be stated as follows: *In a mixture of gases, such as air, each gas exerts pressure independently of the others. The partial pressure of each gas is proportional to the amount (per cent by volume) of that gas in the mixture.* The basic concept of this law, in combination with Henry's law, serves in many engineering considerations and calculations.

**Henry's Law.** Henry's law states: *The weight of any gas that dissolves in a given volume of a liquid, at constant temperature, is directly proportional to the pressure that the gas exerts above the liquid.* This is, undoubtedly, the most important of all the gas laws in problems of sanitary engineering involving liquids. With a firm knowledge of Dalton's and Henry's laws, the sanitary engineer should be capable of coping with all problems involving gas transfer into and out of liquids.

In the sanitary engineering field, most of the problems related to the transfer of gases into liquids involve addition of oxygen by aeration to maintain aerobic conditions. The removal of gases from liquids is also accomplished by aeration devices of one sort or another. Usually, the processes involve gas transfer at or near atmospheric pressure from air bubbles passing through a liquid, liquid drops falling through air, or thin films of liquid flowing over surfaces exposed to the air. In aeration, to supply oxygen, the rate of transfer of gas to the liquid is a function of the area of air-water interface, the partial pressure of oxygen in the air or air bubbles, the partial pressure of oxygen dissolved in the liquid, and the rate transfer coefficient. On the basis of Henry's law, the rate of solution of oxygen is proportional to the difference in the partial pressure of oxygen in the gas and that in the liquid

$$\frac{dC}{dt} \propto (p_{gas} - p_{liquid})$$

These concepts serve as the basis for engineering calculations in aerobic methods of sewage treatment, such as the activated sludge process, and in the evaluation of the reaeration capacity of lakes and streams.

The removal of undesirable gases, such as carbon dioxide, hydrogen sulfide, and hydrogen cyanide, from liquids is commonly accomplished by some form of aeration. The general principles involved are Dalton's and Henry's laws. In these cases the normal partial pressure of the gas in air is very low, and the obnoxious gases pass from the liquid phase into the gaseous phase. The rate of transfer is proportional to the difference in partial pressures, as follows:

$$- \frac{dC}{dt} \propto (p_{liquid} - p_{gas})$$

The same principles apply to the removal of any volatile substance dissolved in water as long as it exerts a significant vapor pressure at the temperature involved. A knowledge of these fundamentals can often be used to good advantage in industrial waste treatment. In one instance, the biochemical oxygen demand (BOD) of a rather warm waste was reduced nearly 50 per cent through removal of ethyl alcohol by aeration. The operation also reduced the temperature of the waste to a more desirable level for subsequent treatment.

**Graham's Law.** Graham's law is concerned with the diffusion of gases, and it states: *The rates of diffusion of gases are inversely proportional to the square roots of their densities.* This law can be illustrated by a comparison of the rates of diffusion of hydrogen, oxygen, chlorine, and bromine, which have atomic weights of approximately 1, 16, 36, and 80, respectively. On the basis of Graham's law, oxygen diffuses about one-fourth, chlorine about one-sixth, and bromine about one-ninth as fast as hydrogen. This law finds its greatest application in the field of industrial hygiene and air pollution control.

**Gay-Lussac's Law of Combining Volumes.** Gay-Lussac's law is basic to an understanding of gas analysis as performed in sanitary engineering practice. The law states: *The volumes of all gases that react and that are produced during the course of a reaction are related, numerically, to one another as a group of small, whole numbers.* This law may be illustrated as follows:

$$C + O_2 \rightarrow CO_2 \qquad (2\text{-}13)$$
$$\square \qquad \square$$
$$1 \text{ vol} \quad 1 \text{ vol}$$

One volume of oxygen combines with carbon (a solid) to yield 1 volume of carbon dioxide, or

$$CH_4 + 2O_2 \rightarrow CO_2 + 2H_2O \qquad (2\text{-}14)$$
$$\square \qquad \square\square \qquad \square \qquad ?$$
$$1 \text{ vol} \quad 2 \text{ vol} \quad 1 \text{ vol} \quad 0 \text{ vol}$$

Two volumes of oxygen combines with 1 volume of methane to form 1 volume of carbon dioxide. If the temperature of the system is held above 100°C, 2 volumes of water vapor will result. Usually, the temperature of the system is brought back to room temperature, the water vapor condenses, and the volume of water is considered zero because it is segregated from the gaseous phase and does not interfere with measurement of the volume of gaseous products.

## 2-9. Solutions

The concepts of unsaturated, saturated, and supersaturated solutions are usually firmly entrenched in the minds of those who have studied general science or chemistry. The terms *molar* and *molal*, as described in Sec. 2-2, are not so well understood. Molar solutions are seldom used in sanitary engineering practice. They have been replaced largely by *normal* solutions, which are discussed in Sec. 4-4. Molal solutions are normally used when the physical properties of solutions, such as vapor pressure, freezing point, and boiling point, are involved.

**Vapor Pressure.** The presence of a nonvolatile solute in a liquid always lowers the vapor pressure of the solution. Thus when sugar, sodium chloride, or a similar substance is dissolved in water the vapor pressure is decreased. This phenomenon is believed to be due to a physical blocking effect at the surface of the liquid where particles (ions or molecules) of the solute happen to be.

**Raoult's Law.** *The extent of the physical blocking effect or depression of the vapor pressure is directly proportional to the concentration of the particles in solution.* For solutes that do not ionize, the effect is directly proportional to the molal concentration. For solutes that do ionize, the effect is proportional to the molal concentration times the number of ions formed per molecule of solute modified by the degree of ionization.

Sanitary engineers are mainly interested in the effect that solutes have upon the freezing and boiling points of water. Application of Raoult's law has shown that molal solutions of nonelectrolytes in water, such as sugar containing $6.02 \times 10^{23}$ (Avogadro's number) molecules or particles, have their vapor pressures decreased to the same degree, and the boiling point is raised 0.52°C while the freezing point is depressed 1.86°C. A molal solution of an electrolyte such as NaCl, which yields two ions, produces nearly twice as great an effect because, after solution and ionization occur, the molal solution contains nearly two times Avogadro's number of particles.

## 2-10. The Law of Mass Action, Le Chatelier's Principle

Practically all chemical reactions are reversible in some degree. Therefore, the concentration of the reactants and of the products is important in determining the final state of equilibrium.   For the classical equation

$$A + B \rightleftharpoons C + D \qquad (2\text{-}15)$$

an increase in either A or B will shift the equilibrium further to the right. Conversely, an increase of either C or D will shift the equilibrium to the left.   The shifting of an equilibrium in response to a change of concentration is an example of the well-known principle of Le Chatelier, which states: *A reaction, at equilibrium, will adjust itself in such a way as to relieve any force, or stress, that disturbs the equilibrium.*

A chemical reaction in true equilibrium can be expressed as

$$\frac{[C][D]}{[A][B]} = K \qquad (2\text{-}16)^*$$

In this form, commonly called the *mass action equation*, it is easily seen that a change in concentration of any of the four factors will change the concentrations of all the others.   This expression is widely used, and a clear understanding of its implications is necessary in all phases of science and applied sciences, such as sanitary engineering.

## 2-11. Ionization

The theory of ionization stems from a doctoral dissertation by Svante Arrhenius, in 1887.   In most respects this theory serves satisfactorily for most concepts of sanitary engineering that involve electrolytic dissociation.   In fact, it defines many situations more satisfactorily for analysis than some of the more modern concepts.

**Ionization Constants.**   According to the original theory of Arrhenius, all acids, bases, and salts dissociate into ions when placed in solution in water.   He noted that equivalent solutions[1] of different compounds often varied greatly in conductivity.   This phenomenon was attributed by Arrhenius to a difference in degree of dissociation or ionization and serves today to explain the variation in strength of acids and bases.   All strong acids and bases are considered to approach 100 per cent ionization in dilute solutions.   The weak acids and bases, however, are so poorly ionized that in most cases it is impractical to express the degree of ionization in terms of per cent.   Furthermore, it has been found that the degree of ionization of the weak electrolytes is quite independent of concentration. This observation has led to the use of ionization constants, which have many advantages from a mathematical viewpoint.   The constants are

---

* The designation [   ] signifies the concentration of the reacting substances in gram molecular weights, or moles, per liter.

[1] See Sec. 4-4 for definition.

derived by substituting experimentally determined values into the mass action equation, as illustrated below:

For a typical monobasic acid (acetic acid):

$$HAc \rightleftharpoons H^+ + Ac^-$$

$$\frac{[H^+][Ac^-]}{[HAc]} = K_A = 1.75 \times 10^{-5} \qquad at\ 25°C \qquad (2\text{-}17)$$

where $Ac^-$ is used to designate the acetate ion.

For a typical dibasic acid (carbonic acid):

$$H_2CO_3 \rightleftharpoons H^+ + HCO_3^-$$

$$\frac{[H^+][HCO_3^-]}{[H_2CO_3]} = K_1 = 4.45 \times 10^{-7} \qquad at\ 25°C \qquad (2\text{-}18)$$

$$HCO_3^- \rightleftharpoons H^+ + CO_3^=$$

$$\frac{[H^+][CO_3^=]}{[HCO_3^-]} = K_2 = 4.69 \times 10^{-11} \qquad at\ 25°C \qquad (2\text{-}19)$$

For a typical base (ammonium hydroxide):

$$NH_4OH \rightleftharpoons NH_4^+ + OH^-$$

$$\frac{[NH_4^+][OH^-]}{[NH_4OH]} = K_B = 1.75 \times 10^{-5} \qquad at\ 25°C \qquad (2\text{-}20)$$

For a poorly ionized salt (such as mercuric chloride):

$$HgCl_2 \rightleftharpoons Hg^{++} + 2Cl^-$$

$$\frac{[Hg^{++}][Cl^-]^2}{[HgCl_2]} = K = 2.6 \times 10^{-15} \qquad (2\text{-}21)$$

Tables giving ionization constants of weak acids, bases, and salts may be found in the usual handbooks and many textbooks of quantitative analysis or physical chemistry.

**Instability Constants.** All complex ions dissociate and exist in equilibrium with the parent ions and molecules. A few such ions are $NH_4^+$, $Ag(NH_3)_2^+$, $Zn(NH_3)_4^{++}$, and $Ag(S_2O_3)_2^{3-}$. For example,

$$Ag(NH_3)_2^+ \rightleftharpoons Ag^+ + 2NH_3$$

$$\frac{[Ag^+][NH_3]^2}{[Ag(NH_3)_2^+]} = K_{instab} = 6.8 \times 10^{-8} \qquad (2\text{-}22)$$

All such ions are readily destroyed by creating conditions, physically or chemically, that will remove one of the dissociation products.

The silver-ammonia complex ion can be destroyed by adding a source of hydrogen ions. In this case destruction is caused by the formation of a more stable complex ion, $NH_4^+$.

The ammonium ion ($NH_4^+$) exists in equilibrium as follows:

$$NH_4^+ \rightleftharpoons NH_3 + H^+ \tag{2·23}$$

Addition of a strong base such as sodium hydroxide will decrease the [$H^+$] concentration through the formation of poorly ionized water, and the equilibrium is shifted far to the right but not completely. The equilibrium may be completely destroyed by boiling the solution to expel ammonia. This is the basis of the separation and determination of ammonia nitrogen by the distillation technique.

### REFERENCES

Briscoe, H. T.: "College Chemistry," Houghton Mifflin Company, Boston, 1951.

Deming, H. G.: "General Chemistry," 6th ed., John Wiley & Sons, Inc., New York, 1952.

Holmes, H. N.: "General Chemistry," 5th ed., The Macmillan Company, New York, 1949.

Pauling, L.: "General Chemistry," 2d ed., W. H. Freeman & Company, San Francisco, 1953.

Sorum, C. H.: "Fundamentals of General Chemistry," Prentice-Hall, Inc., Englewood Cliffs, N.J., 1955.

Timm, J. A.: "General Chemistry," 3d ed., McGraw-Hill Book Company, Inc., New York, 1956.

# $3.$ Basic Concepts from Qualitative Chemistry

### 3-1. General

Very few modern-day civil engineering students have an opportunity to study qualitative analysis, for the trend in recent years has been to divorce the teaching of this subject from freshman courses in general chemistry. In many cases where qualitative analysis is retained in the first-year curriculum, the course is oriented toward presenting a scheme of analysis designed to obtain laboratory results, rather than to teach fundamental principles of chemistry.

A course in qualitative analysis is ideally suited to teach certain phases of chemistry, particularly applications of the mass action law, because the laboratory work is principally concerned with selective precipitation of ions and selective solution of precipitates, through the judicious choice of reagents to shift equilibria to accomplish the desired objective.

### 3-2. Homogeneous Chemical Equilibria

Homogeneous chemical equilibria are characterized by all reactants and products of the reaction occurring in the same physical state. The law of mass action as derived and applied in Sec. 2-10 was concerned with such equilibria. Since qualitative analysis deals largely with precipitation and solution of precipitates, our attention should be directed toward equilibria that occur when a given substance exists in two or more physical states.

### 3-3. Heterogeneous Chemical Equilibria

When an equilibrium exists between a substance in two or more physical states, it is termed a *heterogeneous equilibrium*. A fundamental concept involved is that all solids, no matter how insoluble, are soluble to some degree. For example, silver chloride and barium sulfate are considered to be very insoluble. However, in contact with water they do dissolve, slightly, and form the following equilibria:

$$AgCl \rightleftharpoons Ag^+ + Cl^- \tag{3-1}*$$
$$\underline{BaSO_4} \rightleftharpoons Ba^{++} + SO_4^= \tag{3-2}$$

According to modern concepts of crystal structure, crystals of compounds consist of ions arranged in an orderly manner. On this basis, when crystals of a compound are placed in water, the ions at the surface migrate into the water, and will continue to do so, until the salt is completely dissolved or a condition of saturation is attained. With so-called insoluble substances, the saturation value is very small and reached quickly.

In the case of silver chloride, barium sulfate, and other insoluble compounds the ionic concentrations that can exist in equilibrium with the solid or crystalline material are very small.

**Common Ion Effect.** The equilibrium that exists between crystals of a compound in the solid state and its ions in solution is amenable to consideration under the mass action law and can be treated mathematically in the same manner as though the equilibrium were homogeneous in nature. For example, consider the case of silver chloride at equilibrium, as shown in Eq. (3-1):

$$\frac{[Ag^+][Cl^-]}{[\underline{AgCl}]} = K \tag{3-3}$$

Now we are in a position to see that, if the concentration of chloride ion should be increased by addition from an outside source, such as HCl, the concentration of silver ion must decrease and the amount of precipitated AgCl must increase in order for $K$ to remain the same. Likewise, if the silver-ion concentration is increased from an outside source, such as $AgNO_3$, the chloride-ion concentration will decrease and the amount of solid AgCl will increase. This is an application of the *common ion effect* which is used extensively in qualitative and quantitative analysis to accomplish essentially complete precipitation of desired ions.

**Diverse Ion Effect.** The *diverse ion effect* describes the adverse effect that unrelated ions often have upon the solubility of some relatively insoluble substances. Such ions, theoretically, play no part in the chemical equilibrium involved but often increase the solubility of desired precipitates to such an extent that quantitative results cannot be obtained. Nitrate ion has such an effect on silver chloride. The classic example, described in many physical chemistry texts, concerns the influence of nitrate ion on the solubility of thallous chloride.

* The underscore represents solid or precipitated material, and the unbalanced arrows signify the slight solubility.

Because of the diverse ion effect, it is general practice to keep the concentration of extraneous ions as low as possible during qualitative and quantitative work. In some cases, a common ion may serve very well up to certain concentrations, but, when used at higher concentrations, it may have a diverse ion effect. Hydrochloric acid acts in such a manner when it is used as the agent to precipitate silver ion. Therefore, the amount used should be carefully controlled.

**Solubility-product Principle.** For any given set of conditions, the solubility of any relatively insoluble substance is a constant. These values have been so well established that they are published in critical tables and the ordinary handbooks. This information has led to the development of a statement of fact that is commonly referred to as the *solubility-product principle*. Briefly it is as follows: In a saturated solution of a poorly soluble substance at a given temperature, the product of the molar concentrations of the ions is a constant. This is a simplified expression of Eq. (3-3) and is derived through the following reasoning:

$$\frac{[Ag^+][Cl^-]}{[AgCl]} = K \tag{3-3}$$

but [AgCl] represents the silver chloride that exists in the solid state. The surface area of a solid is the only part that can be considered in equilibrium with the ions, and this area is considered to be more or less a constant value. Thus, for the sake of simplicity it is assumed equal to $K_S$; then

$$\frac{[Ag^+][Cl^-]}{[K_S]} = K \tag{3-4}$$

or $$[Ag^+][Cl^-] = KK_S = K_{sp} \tag{3-5}$$

For more complex substances, such as tricalcium phosphate, that ionize as follows,

$$Ca_3(PO_4)_2 \rightleftharpoons 3Ca^{++} + 2PO_4^{3-} \tag{3-6}$$

the solubility-product expression is

$$[Ca^{++}]^3[PO_4^{3-}]^2 = K_{sp} \tag{3-7}$$

Solubility products for nearly all insoluble substances may be obtained by reference to qualitative and quantitative textbooks or chemical handbooks.

A prediction of relative solubilities of compounds cannot be made by a simple comparison of solubility-product values because of the squares and cubes that enter into the calculation when more than two ions are derived from one molecule, as shown in Eqs. (3-6) and (3-7). The case of barium sulfate which yields two ions and calcium fluoride which yields three ions may be used to illustrate the point. The solubility of these compounds at 20°C is

$$BaSO_4 = 1.1 \times 10^{-5} \, M$$
$$CaF_2 = 2.05 \times 10^{-4} \, M$$

It will be noted that calcium fluoride is about twenty times more soluble than barium sulfate. In saturated solutions of poorly soluble substances, it is assumed that ionization of the dissolved material is complete. Therefore in a saturated solution of barium sulfate, both the $[Ba^{++}]$ and the $[SO_4^=]$ are equal to $1.1 \times 10^{-5}$, and, in a saturated solution of calcium fluoride, the $[Ca^{++}]$ is equal to $2.05 \times 10^{-4}$ and the $[F^-]$ is twice as great, or $4.1 \times 10^{-4}$. When these values are substituted into the solubility-product equation we obtain

$$[Ba^{++}][SO_4^=] = [1.1 \times 10^{-5}][1.1 \times 10^{-5}] = 1.2 \times 10^{-10}$$

and    $$[Ca^{++}][F^-]^2 = [2.05 \times 10^{-4}][4.1 \times 10^{-4}]^2 = 3.4 \times 10^{-11}$$

From this it is obvious that the most soluble material ($CaF_2$) has the smallest solubility product because of the squaring of the fluoride concentration. The case of compounds that yield more than three ions is even more exaggerated.

There are two corollary statements related to the solubility-product principle, an understanding of which is basic to explaining the phenomena of precipitation and solution of precipitates. They may be expressed as follows:

1. In an unsaturated solution, the product of the molar concentration of the ions is less than the solubility-product constant, or $[A^+][B^-] < K_{sp}$.

2. In a supersaturated solution, the product of the molar concentration of the ions is greater than the solubility-product constant, or

$$[A^+][B^-] > K_{sp}$$

In the former case, if undissolved AB is present, it will dissolve to the extent that $[A^+][B^-] = K_{sp}$, and a saturated solution results. In the second case, nothing will happen until such time as crystals of AB are introduced into the solution or internal forces allow formation of crystal nuclei; then precipitation will occur until the ionic concentrations are reduced equal to those of a saturated solution.

## 3-4. Ways of Shifting Chemical Equilibria

The sanitary engineer deals routinely with materials that are either in homogeneous equilibrium or heterogeneous equilibrium. He, like the analytical chemist, must be able to apply stresses to his system in accordance with Le Chatelier's principle to bring about desired changes. Many of the stresses that he applies are exactly the same in character as those

used by the chemist.    Therefore, it is important to consider the ways in
which equilibria can be shifted to bring about essentially complete reactions.    Five methods are commonly employed.

**Formation of Insoluble Substances.**    All precipitation reactions are
examples of this method of equilibrium shift.    In this case a knowledge
of the solubility-product principle, solubility-product constants, and the
common ion effect is brought into service.    The removal of metal ions
from industrial wastes, such as copper and brass wastes, by precipitation
with calcium hydroxide and the softening of hard waters by lime–soda
ash treatment are excellent examples of how the engineer applies this
method of shifting a chemical equilibrium to gain his objective.

**Formation of a Weakly Ionized Compound.**    Certain systems that are
in equilibrium can be destroyed by adding a reagent that will combine
with one of the ions to form a poorly ionized compound.    The neutralization of acid and of caustic wastes is based upon such formation, since
the reaction involved is between hydrogen ions and hydroxyl ions to
form poorly ionized water.    The sanitary engineer frequently uses this
reaction to bring the pH of industrial wastes into a favorable range for
subsequent biological treatment.

The analytical chemist uses this method of equilibrium shifting routinely to dissolve precipitates of the metallic hydroxides, such as ferric
and aluminum hydroxide.

**Formation of a Complex Ion.**    The chemist uses complex-ion formation
to dissolve insoluble salts and hydroxides.    Silver chloride, for example,
dissolves readily in ammonium hydroxide solution.    This is because silver
ion combines with molecular $NH_3$ contained in the ammonium hydroxide
to form $Ag \cdot 2NH_3^+$; as a result the solution becomes unsaturated with
respect to silver and chloride ions and solid silver chloride passes into
solution in an attempt to form a saturated solution.    If enough ammonium hydroxide is present, all silver chloride passes into solution.    Zinc
and copper hydroxides dissolve in ammonium hydroxide for the same
reason.    The complex ions formed are $Zn \cdot 4NH_3^{++}$ and $Cu \cdot 4NH_3^{++}$.    These
reactions illustrate why ammonium hydroxide would not be a good
reagent for precipitating copper and zinc ions from a brass-mill waste.

Industrial wastes containing sodium cyanide are particularly toxic to
fish, even though the concentration of cyanide ion may be reduced to
very low levels by dilution with river water.    The destruction or inactivation of cyanide ion may be accomplished by complex-ion formation.
Formerly, before development of more efficient methods, cyanide ion was
reduced to low levels by treatment with ferrous sulfate.    In the reaction,
$Fe^{++}$ combined with $CN^-$ to give the complex ion $Fe(CN)_6^{4-}$ which could
be precipitated as Prussian blue by subsequent oxidation of excess $Fe^{++}$
to $Fe^{3+}$.

**Formation of a Gaseous Product.** In reactions involving the formation of a gaseous product, the reactions go to practical completion because the gas escapes from the sphere of the reaction. The analytical chemist takes advantage of this method of forcing a reaction to completion when dissolving metallic sulfides, such as ferrous sulfide, in hydrochloric acid. This does not necessarily mean that all metallic sulfides are soluble in hydrochloric acid, for the sulfides of copper and mercury are not. This can be explained by considering that copper and mercury sulfides are so insoluble that the sulfide ion liberated by them at equilibrium is of such small concentration that not enough un-ionized hydrogen sulfide is formed, in the presence of concentrated hydrochloric acid, to be released as a gas. Consequently, the sulfides do not dissolve.

In industrial waste treatment, cyanides are sometimes removed from aqueous solution by treatment with sulfuric acid. The hydrogen cyanide released as a gas is diluted with large volumes of air and forced up through tall stacks to get proper dispersion and avoid serious atmospheric-pollution problems. A few such installations remain in operation in the United States. More modern methods accomplish destruction of cyanide ion by oxidation techniques.

**Oxidation and Reduction.** A very sure way of sending reactions to completion is by means of oxidation and reduction. In this way one or more of the ions involved in the equilibrium reaction can be destroyed, and the reaction will proceed to completion. A classic example, familiar to sanitary engineers, is the destruction of cyanide ion by chlorination according to the following equation:

$$2CN^- + 5Cl_2^0 + 8OH^- \rightarrow 10Cl^- + 2CO_2 + N_2\uparrow + 4H_2O \qquad (3\text{-}8)$$

From the discussion already presented, this reaction would go to completion for two reasons.

1. Cyanide ion is oxidized to carbon dioxide and nitrogen.
2. The nitrogen escapes as a gas.

Since formation of nitrogen is dependent upon oxidation of cyanide ion, the reaction is considered to be complete whether the nitrogen escapes or not.

## 3-5. Amphoteric Hydroxides

The oxides or hydroxides of metals are basic in character and react with acids to form salts. The insoluble metallic hydroxides, such as ferric hydroxide, dissolve readily in acids to form salts but are insoluble in solutions of bases. Likewise, the oxides of nonmetals are acidic in character, and insoluble forms are soluble in bases but not in acids. These characteristics serve as one basis of differentiating between metals and nonmetals.

The hydroxides of aluminum, zinc, chromium, and a few other elements are soluble in both acids and bases.  They are known as *amphoteric* hydroxides, and advantage is often taken of this fact to accomplish separations in qualitative analysis and in chemical processing.

An insoluble metallic hydroxide, of course, exists in equilibrium with its ions.  For example, ferric hydroxide dissolves to a limited extent to produce $Fe^{3+}$ and $OH^-$ ions

$$\underline{Fe(OH)_3 \rightleftharpoons Fe^{3+} + 3OH^-} \tag{3-9}$$

and at saturation

$$[Fe^{3+}][OH^-]^3 = K_{sp} \tag{3-10}$$

When a strong acid is added the $OH^-$ ions combine with the $H^+$ ions of the acid to form poorly ionized water and the $[OH^-]$ decreases so that

$$[Fe^{3+}][OH^-]^3 < K_{sp} \tag{3-11}$$

Therefore ferric hydroxide dissolves in an attempt to establish conditions represented in Eq. (3-10).  If enough acid is added, eventually all the ferric hydroxide will dissolve.  A similar situation holds for insoluble nonmetallic oxides that are soluble in bases, except that the insoluble oxide is in equilibrium with $H^+$ and some acid radical.

From the above considerations it may be concluded that an amphoteric hydroxide must ionize both as an acid and as a base.  Aluminum hydroxide will serve as an example.

$$Al^{3+} + 3(OH) \rightleftharpoons \underline{Al(OH)_3} \rightleftharpoons H^+ + AlO_2^- + H_2O \tag{3-12}$$

Insoluble aluminum hydroxide exists in equilibrium with $Al^{3+}$ and $OH^-$ on one hand and with $H^+$ and meta aluminate ion on the other, and at saturation

$$[Al^{3+}][OH^-]^3 = K_{sp} \text{ of } Al(OH)_3 \tag{3-13}$$
and $$[H^+][AlO_2^-] = K_{sp} \text{ of } HAlO_2 \cdot H_2O \tag{3-14}$$

Addition of a strong acid will provide sufficient $H^+$ ions to combine with the $OH^-$ ions and form water.  As a result,

$$[Al^{3+}][OH^-]^3 < K_{sp} \text{ of } Al(OH)_3 \tag{3-15}$$

and the $Al(OH)_3$ will dissolve.  If a strong base is added, the $OH^-$ ions it provides will combine with the $H^+$ ions to form water, and the $Al(OH)_3$ will dissolve, since

$$[H^+][AlO_2^-] < K_{sp} \text{ of } HAlO_2 \cdot H_2O \tag{3-16}$$

The amphoteric properties of aluminum hydroxide are a factor limiting its use as a coagulant in water purification and industrial waste treatment.  The amphoteric properties of zinc and chromium hydroxides are important considerations in treating industrial wastes containing $Zn^{++}$ and $Cr^{3+}$.

## REFERENCES

Curtman, L. J.: "Qualitative Chemical Analysis," 2d ed., The Macmillan Company, New York, 1938.
Engelder, C. J.: "Qualitative Analysis," John Wiley & Sons, Inc., New York, 1942.
Reedy, J. H.: "Theoretical Qualitative Analysis," McGraw-Hill Book Company, Inc., New York, 1938.

# 4. Basic Concepts from Quantitative Chemistry

## 4-1. General Operations

Quantitative chemistry may be considered as a keystone in the training of a sanitary engineer.  It serves as the basis for most research work and many field investigations.  Unfortunately, most collegiate courses in quantitative analysis, although they furnish excellent fundamental information, do not provide laboratory instruction and practice that are particularly valuable to sanitary engineers.  For this reason, specialized courses in quantitative analysis, often described as courses in "sanitary chemistry" or "water and sewage analysis," have been developed to meet the need.

At this writing, all the leading schools concerned with the training of sanitary engineers are using as a textbook "Standard Methods for the Examination of Water, Sewage and Industrial Wastes."[1]  This book is designed to be used by trained analysts and, therefore, presumes a certain background of information.  Since most sanitary engineers do not have such a background, the purpose of this chapter is an attempt to fill that need.  It is recommended that each sanitary engineer add a copy of a standard, up-to-date text on quantitative analysis to his library for reference purposes.  It is impossible and unnecessary in this chapter to cover in detail the many aspects of analytical chemistry that are adequately dealt with in all standard textbooks.

**Sampling.**  It is an axiom that the reliability of analytical results obtained in the laboratory can never be more reliable than the sample upon which the tests are performed.  It may be safely stated that more results are in error because of inadequate sampling than because of faulty laboratory techniques.  The subject of sample collection and care of samples is treated quite adequately in "Standard Methods," except for the subject of *grab* versus *composited* samples.

[1] Published jointly by the American Public Health Association, American Water Works Association, and Federation of Sewage and Industrial Wastes Associations.

Grab samples are those taken more or less instantaneously and analyzed separately. In general, most sampling in sanitary engineering practice is of the grab variety. The major problem confronting the engineer is the decision of frequency of sampling. In this decision he must always balance the issues of a sufficient number of samples for reliability versus costs. The number of samples may vary from one to over a hundred per day, depending upon the nature of the material to be sampled. At this point a good deal of engineering judgment is involved. A few examples will serve to illustrate.

1. Consider a deep well which has been in service for some time. The water quality will be uniform, and a single grab sample will give a true picture of conditions.

2. Oftentimes, changes occur slowly, such as in large rivers, and once-daily grab samples are adequate.

3. Where the character of a material changes considerably within a 24-hr period, the use of grab samples at frequent intervals is dictated. In sampling industrial wastes, it may be necessary to obtain such samples every 10 or 15 min. The individual samples may be analyzed for certain characteristics such as pH, acidity, alkalinity, etc., and then pooled into 2-, 4-, 8-, 12-, or 24-hr composites for more complete analysis.

Composited samples are used mainly in evaluating the efficiency of sewage or industrial waste treatment facilities, where average results are adequate. Such samples are collected at regular intervals, usually every hour or two, and pooled into one large sample over a 24-hr period. Under such conditions, detention times can be considered as self-canceling, and the only requirement that must be met is that each individual sample be taken in proportion to the flow existing at the time.

When composited samples are taken for shorter periods than 24 hr (8-hr composited samples have been quite common in sewage treatment practice), serious errors may be introduced by ignoring detention time. In conventional activated sludge plants, the theoretical detention time from influent to effluent is on the order of 8 hr; thus, samples of influent collected from 8 A.M. to 4 P.M. measure the strength of daytime sewage, but samples of effluent collected over the same period of time measure the treatment given to weak sewage that entered the plant prior to 8 A.M. In taking short-term composited samples, sampling at downstream locations should be adjusted to detention times in the treatment units involved. In the average conventional activated sludge treatment plant with a total of 8 hr of detention, sampling of the final effluent should not begin until 8 hr after sampling of the influent is started; thus, 16 hr are needed to collect a set of 8-hr composited samples.

**Laboratory Apparatus and Reagents.** A good grade of laboratory apparatus is adequate for all practical uses. Recalibrated or Bureau of

Standards graduated glassware is very expensive and not required for routine work.   Pyrex or a similar glassware of low solubility and low coefficient of expansion is highly recommended.   Reagents should be of analytical-reagent grade or known to meet the specifications of purity established by the American Chemical Society.   Lower grades of chemicals, even technical grade, may be used for some purposes, but the analyst must make sure that such grades do not contain undesirable amounts of certain impurities.   It is not practical to buy a reagent grade of sodium hydroxide for purposes where a high-purity sodium hydroxide is needed. The best grades obtainable are too impure.   It is just as easy to purify a cheaper grade in the laboratory, and it serves the purpose just as well, at a much lower cost.

**Precipitation.**   Some analytical methods depend upon precipitation of an ion to allow its separation and measurement by actual weighing of the precipitated material.   There are several requirements that must be met to make such procedures reliable.   The major ones are as follows:

1. The precipitated material must have a very low solubility in water; i.e., its $K_{sp}$ is a very small number.

2. It must precipitate in a high state of purity or be capable of reprecipitation for further purification.

3. It must be capable of drying or of ignition at temperatures above $100°C$ to a definite compound of fixed composition.

4. It should not be hydroscopic at room temperatures.

Precipitation may also be used as a method of purification.   Under such conditions, the desired ion is precipitated from solution, filtered, placed into solution again by the use of special reagents, and measured by other means than by weight analysis.

**Filtration.**   Filtration of precipitates or solids is accomplished by means of Gooch crucibles with asbestos filter mats or by means of paper filters.   Many materials that the sanitary engineer wishes to measure cannot be subjected to temperatures above $103°C$ without losing chemically bound water.   Gooch crucibles or similar filters are used for such measurements.   Filtration through filter paper (analytical, ashless grade) is commonly used where ignition at temperatures above $600°C$ is required or permissible.   At such temperatures the paper is destroyed and the desired residue remains.   An ashless paper or one whose ash weight is known should be used.

Filter papers vary greatly in their porosity.   It is essential to use one that is fine enough to retain all the precipitate but as coarse as possible to obtain rapid filtration rates.   Barium sulfate requires the use of a very fine paper.   Ferric hydroxide is retained on very coarse fast-filtering paper.

Separation of a precipitate can be accomplished by the use of a proper filter.   Quantitative results, however, depend upon two other important factors:

1. All the precipitate or solid material must be transferred from the original vessel to the filter.

2. The precipitate and filter must be washed with water or a suitable solvent to remove dissolved solids that remain in the precipitate and wetted filter.   Three washings with complete drainage between washings are considered to be sufficient.

**Drying or Ignition.**   The standard temperature for drying residues or solids is 103°C.   This is stipulated because many of the residues or solids involved in sanitary engineering practice are organic in nature and release water of composition in significant amounts at higher temperatures. Drying at 103°C ensures the removal of all free water, provided that the drying period is long enough, and minimizes the loss of other water.

Ignitions are commonly conducted at 600°C, unless specified otherwise, to ensure the destruction of all organic matter by oxidation to carbon dioxide and water while minimizing the loss of inorganic salts by volatilization or decomposition.   Calcium carbonate is a major component of many residues and is stable at 600°C.

From these considerations, it should be obvious that much of the analytical work with which the sanitary engineer is concerned involves measurement of organic materials; this is really the major reason why a conventional course in quantitative analysis falls short of supplying his needs.

**Desiccation.**   Following drying or ignition operations, the residues and their containers (crucibles or evaporating dishes) must be cooled to room temperature before weighing on the analytical balance.   If such cooling were allowed to take place in the open air, moisture would be picked up from the air by the residue and container.   The amount of moisture pickup would depend upon the time of exposure and the relative humidity. To overcome this difficulty, residues and their containers are cooled in *desiccators* where the relative humidity is kept near zero per cent by means of a *desiccant* such as anhydrous calcium chloride.

## 4-2. The Analytical Balance

The construction of analytical balances and the theory of weighing are adequately covered in standard texts on quantitative analysis.   The care of such instruments cannot be stressed too much, however, for engineers are accustomed to dealing in terms of pounds, tons, cast iron, concrete, and jackhammers.   It is important that they recognize that analytical balances fall into the realm of *delicate* instruments and that great care and scrupulous cleanliness must be maintained with respect to both the balance and the weights used.

Automatic single-pan balances, like the one shown in Fig. 4-1, are by all odds the most practical devices for modern laboratories.  They are about twice as expensive as other high-quality balances but, in commercial laboratories, will usually pay for themselves in time saved within a relatively short period.  Automatic balances are not very practical for

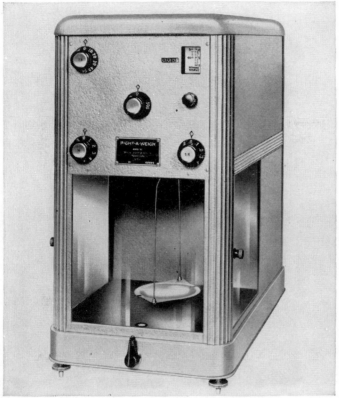

Fig. 4-1. A single-pan automatic balance.   (*Wm. Ainsworth & Sons, Inc.*)

laboratories concerned with teaching, however, as students trained on such balances are rather inept when they find themselves without similar facilities.

Balances of the chainomatic type, as shown in Fig. 4-2, are best suited for providing basic training for sanitary engineers.   Speedy weighing is a necessity in many cases in order to avoid unnecessary pickup of moisture. The chainomatic balance with a one-gram (g) beam rider and chain to eliminate all fractional gram weights allows weighings to be made very rapidly.   This is especially true if the balance is equipped with a magnetic damper.   The accuracy of such balances is normally within a $\pm 0.0001$ g and is satisfactory for all practical purposes.

The importance of having the objects to be weighed at room temperature cannot be overemphasized. The average student in quantitative analysis should not have difficulty in translating his knowledge of physics to explain why an object having a temperature above room temperature will weigh less than it should or why an object which is colder than room temperature will weigh more than it should.

FIG. 4-2. A chainomatic balance equipped with magnetic dampers. (*Wm. Ainsworth & Sons, Inc.*)

Chainomatic balances are easily put into *perfect balance*. For this reason, weighing by the method of equal swings is best when a magnetic damper is not used. Most balances may be considered in perfect balance when each swing is less than the previous swing. It is of considerable assistance in weighing to know the sensitivity of the balance. This is defined as the displacement from zero occasioned by a mass of one milligram (mg).

## 4-3. Gravimetric Analysis

Gravimetric analysis means analysis by weight and pertains to all determinations wherein the final results are obtained by means of the analytical balance. In the sanitary engineering field, determination of total solids (residue on evaporation), suspended solids, and volatile solids is made by gravimetric procedures because there is no better way of gaining the desired information.    In general, however, gravimetric procedures are avoided as much as possible because they are time-consuming. In other than solids determinations, the sanitary engineer has little occasion to use the analytical balance except to make up standard solutions, etc.    An outstanding exception is the determination of sulfates.    No other method, except possibly a newly developed turbidimetric method, approaches it in accuracy.

Because of the importance of solids determinations that must be done by gravimetric procedures, it is essential that the sanitary engineer know the fundamentals of gravimetric analysis.    Many of these have been discussed in Sec. 4-1; a few more follow.

**Constant Weight.**    All gravimetric measurements require some sort of crucible or dish to hold the residue or precipitate.    The weight of this container (tare) must be known and deducted from the gross weight to obtain the net weight of the material being measured.

Porcelain crucibles or dishes are commonly used for gravimetric work. Platinum ware has many advantages but is not ordinarily used, except for special determinations, because of its cost.    All objects exposed to the air for any length of time have a film of dust and adsorbed moisture. Porcelain ware is manufactured with some of its surface unglazed; consequently, it will also adsorb moisture into its interior.    To use such containers for gravimetric work without proper conditioning would lead to relatively large errors in the final results.    Oftentimes negative results are obtained when small quantities are involved.

The conditioning of crucibles and dishes for gravimetric work involves pretreatment to eliminate the dirt and moisture.    All containers should be thoroughly cleaned with water and then heat-treated under exactly the same conditions as those to which the container will be subjected in the actual determination.    If the container is to be used to measure residue on evaportion at 103°C, it should be conditioned at that temperature.    To heat the dish, particularly porcelain ware, at higher temperatures, such as at 600°C, will drive out more moisture than desired. The dishes should be heated or fired at the desired temperature, cooled in the desiccator and weighed, heated and fired, cooled and weighed, repeatedly, until the container reaches what is known as constant weight. For small dishes with a weight of less than 25 g, this is assumed to be $\pm 0.0002$ g.    For heavier dishes the allowance is greater but never over $\pm 0.0005$ g.    With a little experience, the beginner will learn that a preliminary heating or firing of less than 2 hr is seldom worthwhile.    This is particularly true of new dishes and of old dishes that have not been used for some time.    After dishes have been brought to constant weight they should be kept in a desiccator to avoid collection of dust or absorption of moisture prior to use.

Theoretically, the principles outlined above for getting the tare weight of containers should be applied to the dish plus the residue to be measured. This is true when inorganic residues are involved; however, when organic substances are concerned, it has been demonstrated that such materials will usually continue to yield moisture in small amounts for long periods of time. Since free water is given off rather rapidly, barring physical interference to its release, the drying time for such solids is usually specified, and the weight obtained at the end of that time is accepted as being constant. The drying time for total solids in water (following evaporation to practical dryness on a steam bath) and for suspended solids by Gooch crucibles is 1 hr. The drying time for total solids in sewage sludges and many industrial wastes (following evaporation to dryness) is considered to be 10 hr. Usually, drying overnight is more practical and is recommended for sludges and certain industrial wastes.

**Preparation of Gooch Crucibles.** Gooch crucibles require the use of a filter mat over the perforated bottom. Asbestos fibers are commonly used for this purpose. Asbestos fiber suitable for use in Gooch crucibles should be specified when purchasing. It should be of fairly long fiber length and should be acid-washed with hydrochloric acid. A "soup" of the fiber can be made by placing some in a bottle, adding water so that the bottle is about one-half full, and then shaking vigorously. The finely divided material may be decanted and the procedure repeated. Coarse particles that will not disperse can be shredded by placing them with some water in a blender and running the agitator for about 10 sec. The "soup" obtained should be thoroughly agitated by shaking, allowed to stand for 5 min, and then the fines that do not settle readily decanted to waste. The process should be repeated with addition of more water until a reasonably clear supernatant water is obtained following a 5-min settling period.

The Gooch crucible is prepared by adding asbestos "soup" so that it is about one-half full and then applying vacuum to withdraw the water. If all holes in the bottom are covered and the mat covers the bottom entirely, remove the crucible, hold it up to one eye, and look into a strong light. If none of the perforations in the crucible is discernible, the mat is of sufficient thickness. Replace the crucible in the suction filter, pour a small amount of the fines off the top of the unagitated "soup" into the crucible, and apply suction. This ensures a perfect filter mat. Filter about 250 milliliters (ml) of distilled water through the crucible. This will dislodge any fibers that may be in a vertical position in the perforations and give as nearly a perfect mat as possible. Remove any asbestos fibers that may be adhering to the rim or exterior of the crucible, place in the drying oven, and bring to constant weight. If the crucible is to be used for the determination of volatile solids as well as suspended solids, it should be dried at 103°C for a few minutes before placing in the furnace at 600°C to avoid disruption of the mat by explosions from steam formation.

Much of the dissatisfaction with the use of Gooch crucibles can be traced to improperly prepared filter mats.

## 4-4. Volumetric Analysis

Volumetric analysis is a phase of quantitative analysis that depends upon the measurement of liquid reagent volumes of *standard solutions* needed to complete particular reactions in samples submitted to test. A standard solution is defined as follows: *a solution whose strength or reacting value per unit volume is known.* The facilities needed for conducting a simple volumetric analysis are (1) equipment to measure the sample accurately, either an analytical balance or volumetric glassware such as pipets; (2) a standard solution of suitable strength, (3) an indicator to show when the stoichiometric end point has been reached, and (4) a carefully calibrated buret for measuring the volume of standard solution needed to reach the stoichiometric end point as shown by the indicator.

Analysis by volumetric methods is very popular, as compared with gravimetric methods, because of the time that usually can be saved by such procedures. Sanitary engineers use volumetric methods for many determinations such as dissolved oxygen, BOD, COD, and chlorides. There are a number of concepts and techniques involved in volumetric measurements that must be understood in order to obtain accurate results.

**Calibrated Glassware.** Calibrated glassware is of two types: (1) that which is calibrated to contain a definite volume, e.g., volumetric flasks and graduated cylinders; and (2) that which is calibrated to deliver prescribed volumes, e.g., pipets and burets. The former should never be used as a substitute for the latter because some liquid will always remain in the container and the delivered amount will be less than the calibrated amount. On the other hand, pipets are calibrated to deliver definite amounts under specified conditions and must always retain a small amount of the liquid after delivery.

Pipets are of two types, transfer and Mohr. Transfer or volumetric pipets have an enlarged section and only one graduation mark. They will deliver the specified amount provided that the pipet is clean, it is held in a near vertical position during delivery, contact is made between the tip of the pipet and the wall of the receiving vessel, and drainage is allowed to occur for 5 sec after the level of the liquid in the tip appears to have reached a static condition. Transfer pipets should be used where volumes must be measured with a high degree of accuracy. Mohr-style pipets are made from glass tubing of uniform bore and have multiple graduation marks. The small sizes of 5 ml or less capacity may be used to deliver small quantities of liquids quite accurately, but with 10-ml and larger sizes the bore and calibrations are of such a nature that delivery of accurate amounts cannot be expected.   The Mohr-type pipet is used largely for measuring fractional volumes of 1 ml or for measurement of volumes where accuracy is of little importance.

In general, it may be stated that transfer or volumetric pipets should be used for measurement of samples and of standard solutions.   Mohr pipets may be used for the addition of nonstandardized reagents.

Calibrated glassware should be kept thoroughly clean.   This is particularly true of transfer pipets and burets.   Cleaning may be accomplished by means of some of the modern detergents designed for such purposes or by the use of chromic acid cleaning solution ($K_2Cr_2O_7 + H_2SO_4$).

**Equivalent or Normal Solutions.**   By definition, *a standard solution is one whose strength or reacting value per unit volume is known.*   Volumetric analysis could be practiced solely with such solutions, but it is much more convenient to prepare and use solutions which are equivalent to one another in strength, so that 1.0 ml of reagent A will react with exactly 1.0 ml of reagent B, etc.

We can establish the basis for a system of equivalent solutions for the measurement of acids and bases (acidimetry and alkalimetry) from the fundamental equation which is involved.

$$\underset{1.008}{H^+} + \underset{17.008}{OH^-} \rightarrow H_2O \tag{4-1}$$

From this equation it is seen that 1 g atomic weight or 1.008 g of hydrogen ion reacts with 1 g ionic weight or 17.008 g of hydroxyl ion.   The figure 17 serves for all practical purposes in the latter case.   Solutions containing these amounts of hydrogen ion or hydroxyl ion can be considered equivalent.   When the volume of the solution is specified as 1 liter, the solutions are called *normal*.

A *normal* solution is defined as *one that contains one gram atom of available hydrogen ion or its chemical equivalent per liter of solution.*   For bases the chemical equivalent is 17 g of available hydroxyl ion.   Thus, for the preparation of 1 liter of a normal solution, all that is needed is enough of the compound that furnishes the ion to yield 1.008 g of $H^+$ or 17 g of $OH^-$ and enough distilled water to make a solution having a volume of 1 liter.   This amount is called the *equivalent weight*.   The preparation and standardization of normal solutions will be discussed in Part II.

Normal solutions are also used for volumetric measurements that do not involve acidimetry or alkalimetry.   For example, chlorides are measured by titration with a reagent such as silver nitrate.   The reaction involves precipitation of chloride ion as silver chloride as follows:

$$\underset{35.5}{Cl^-} + \underset{108}{Ag^+} \rightarrow \underline{AgCl} \tag{4-2}$$

In this reaction 1 mole of $Ag^+$ is equivalent to 1 mole of $Cl^-$. From the equation

$$HCl \rightleftharpoons H^+ + Cl^- \tag{4-3}$$

it can be reasoned that 1 mole of $Cl^-$ is equivalent to 1 mole of $H^+$. Since things equal to the same thing are equal to each other, it may be stated safely that 1 mole of $Ag^+$ is equivalent to 1 mole of $H^+$. Thus, a normal solution of $Ag^+$ is one that contains one mole of $Ag^+$ per liter. For all practical purposes, it may be stated that the equivalent weight of a compound used for precipitation purposes is equal to the molecular weight divided by the valence of the ion involved as the precipitating ion.

A third form of normal solutions involves those used for their oxidizing or reducing values. Examples are solutions of potassium dichromate, ferrous ammonium sulfate, and sodium thiosulfate. The equivalent weight or that weight of a compound needed to prepare 1 liter of a normal oxidizing or reducing solution is derived from the following equation:

$$\underset{23}{Na^\circ} + \underset{1.008}{H^+} \rightarrow Na^+ + H^\circ$$

In this reaction one $H^+$ steals one electron from one atom of sodium, or 1 mole of hydrogen ions can be considered as equivalent to "1 mole of electrons." Sodium undergoes a valence change of 1; therefore the equivalent weight of a compound to be used as an oxidizing or reducing agent is equal to the molecular weight divided by the valence change that the compound undergoes in the reaction involved. It is very important that this valence change be known. For example, potassium permanganate undergoes a valence change of 5 under acid conditions, and its equivalent weight for such use would be $MW/5$. Under alkaline conditions, it undergoes a valence change of 3, and its equivalent weight for such use is $MW/3$. Table 4-1 shows the equivalent weights of some common oxidizing and reducing agents.

**Primary Standards.** The standardization or measurement of the exact strength of a normal or other solution depends upon the use of some standard material whose purity is known. Primary standards are usually salts or acid salts of high purity that can be dried at some convenient temperature without decomposing and that can be weighed with a high degree of accuracy. Examples are sodium carbonate and potassium acid phthalate, which are used to standardize acid and base solutions, respectively; potassium bi-iodate and potassium dichromate for reducing solutions; potassium oxalate for oxidizing solutions; and sodium chloride for solutions of silver ion. Analytical-reagent-grade chemicals are usually satisfactory for most purposes. For some research purposes and possibly for referee work, analyzed primary standards may be obtained from the U.S. Bureau of Standards.

**Secondary Standards.** Any solution that has been standardized against a primary standard is considered a secondary standard and may be used as such. In the preparation and use of solutions of a base, standardization is often performed against a standard solution of an acid. This practice is particularly true and valuable as a time saver with solutions that are not stable and, therefore, have to be restandardized frequently.

TABLE 4-1. EQUIVALENT WEIGHTS OF SOME COMMON OXIDIZING AND REDUCING AGENTS

| Agent | Nature | Conditions | Valence change | Equivalent weight |
|---|---|---|---|---|
| $KMnO_4$ | Oxidizing | Acid | 5 | MW/5 |
| $KMnO_4$ | Oxidizing | Alkaline | 3 | MW/3 |
| $K_2Cr_2O_7$ | Oxidizing | Acid | $2 \times 3$ | MW/6 |
| I | Oxidizing | Acid | 1 | AW/1 |
| $KH(IO_3)_2$ | Oxidizing | Acid | $2 \times 5$ | ?* |
| $Na_2C_2O_4$ | Reducing | Acid | $2 \times 1$ | MW/2 |
| KI | Reducing | Acid | 1 | MW/1 |
| $As_2O_3$ | Reducing | Acid | $2 \times 2$ | MW/4 |
| $Na_2S_2O_3$ | Reducing | Acid | ? | MW/1† |

* In the case of $KH(IO_3)_2$, the reaction must be known in order to calculate the equivalent weight. For ordinary reactions it would be MW/10, but for the usual reaction with KI it is MW/12.

† The equivalent weight of $Na_2S_2O_3$ must be calculated indirectly because the valence change of sulfur is not known. In the reaction with iodine, one $Na_2S_2O_3$ is equivalent to one atom of iodine. Therefore, the equivalent weight is MW/1.

**Choice of Indicators.** Analysis by volumetric procedures requires that some method of indicating the stoichiometric end point be employed. Internal indicators are greatly preferred. In any event, they should herald the reaching of the completed reaction as closely as possible. Improper choice of indicators can introduce serious errors into volumetric work. Indicators in common use today are of several major types, viz., electrometric, acid-base, precipitation, adsorption, and oxidation-reduction. All types are used regularly in the practice of sanitary engineering. Because of the variety, it is ordinarily best to discuss indicators as to type. For sanitary engineers, however, it seems more appropriate to discuss applications to type reactions.

*Acidimetry and Alkalimetry.* Before proceeding with a discussion of the choice of indicators for measurements involved in acidimetry and alkalimetry, it is necessary to develop some of the theoretical aspects.

In the first place, the titrating agent used is always a strong acid or a strong base, meaning, of course, highly ionized; therefore, the combinations involved in titrations are strong plus strong, or weak plus strong. It is important that the pH changes occurring during acid and base titrations be understood, and several examples will be presented.

When a strong base is titrated with a strong acid, the initial pH of the base is very high, usually in the range of 12 to 13.   As acid is added the pH changes very little at first and then slowly declines to a pH of about 10.   From then on, the pH falls very rapidly until a pH of about 4 is reached; then changes become much more gradual.   A plot of such data, commonly called a *titration curve*, is shown in Fig. 4-3.   It may be noted

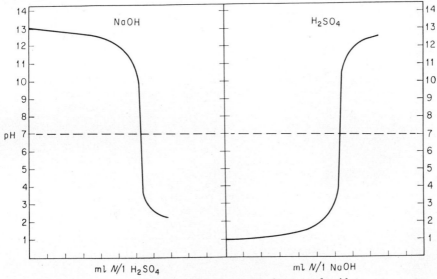

FIG. 4-3. Titration curves for strong bases and acids.

that the curve is essentially vertical between pH values of 10 and 4; therefore the stoichiometric end point lies between these values and, for all practical purposes, anywhere between them.   When a strong acid is titrated with a strong base a curve quite similar in character is produced but, of course, is a mirror image of the former, as shown also in Fig. 4-3.

When weak acids are titrated with strong bases the character of the titration curve depends upon whether the acid is monobasic or polybasic, i.e., whether it yields one or more hydrogen ions.   The initial pH of solutions of poorly ionized acids depends largely upon the degree of ionization, and the titration curves vary markedly, as shown in Fig. 4-4. Solutions of acetic acid normally have an initial pH of about 3.   During titration with a strong base, the pH increases slowly to about 7 and then rapidly until pH 10 is reached.   In the case of carbonic acid, the initial pH is determined by the first stage of ionization of the acid, and, because the ionization constant of $10^{-7}$ is much smaller than $10^{-5}$ for acetic acid, the initial pH is much higher. The nature of the titration curve for weak acids is quite similar, but that for carbonic acid does not begin to break sharply until a pH of 8 is approached. All weak acids with ionization constants greater than $10^{-7}$ show inflections in the curve or stoichiometric end points at a pH of about 8.5. The second hydrogen ion of carbonic acid is so poorly dissociated ($K_2 = 4.7 \times 10^{-11}$) that its

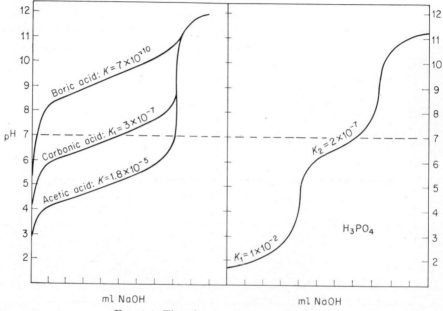

FIG. 4-4. Titration curves for weak acids.

presence cannot be detected in an ordinary titration. Theoretically, it begins to be released in significant amounts at pH levels above 10. The titration curve for boric acid shows that it is not completely neutralized until a pH of about 11 is reached.

The titration curve for phosphoric acid illustrates very well the behavior during titration of a weak acid that yields more than one measurable hydrogen ion. Reference to Fig. 4-4 will show that hydrogen ions resulting from the first step of ionization are neutralized by the time sufficient base has been added to reach a pH of about 4. The hydrogen ion resulting from the second step of ionization is neutralized by the time the pH has been raised to about 8.5. The third hydrogen ion of phosphoric acid ($K_3 = 4.8 \times 10^{-13}$), like the second of carbonic acid, is not measurable by ordinary titrations.

The titration curves for weak bases are related in some degree to those for weak acids. The initial pH of the solutions depends upon the ionization constant, and all with ionization constants greater than $10^{-7}$ show inflections in the curve or stoichiometric end points at a pH of about 4.5. Typical curves for weak bases are shown in Fig. 4-5.

Salts of strong bases and weak acids, such as sodium carbonate, are alkaline in character and behave like bases during titration (see Fig. 4-5). Sodium carbonate has characteristics of both a strong and a weak base. The initial pH of its solutions is rather high, and, during titration with a

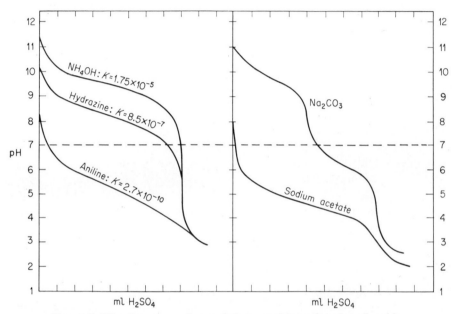

FIG. 4-5. Titration curves for weak bases and for salts of weak acids.

strong acid, neutralization occurs in two steps, corresponding to the ionization of carbonic acid. Addition of strong acid results in a gradual drop in pH, with a poorly defined inflection in the curve at a pH of about 8.5. This corresponds to the equivalence point for the conversion of all carbonate ion to bicarbonate ion, as follows:

$$CO_3^= + H^+ \rightarrow HCO_3^- \qquad (4\text{-}4)$$

Further addition of acid results in a gradual lowering of the pH until a value of about 5 is reached. The curve then passes through an inflection at a pH of about 4.5. This corresponds to the equivalence point for the conversion of bicarbonate ion to carbonic acid.

$$HCO_3^- + H^+ \rightarrow H_2CO_3 \qquad (4\text{-}5)$$

At this stage of the discussion, it should be obvious that the pH of equivalence points involved in acidimetry and alkalimetry vary, depending upon the ionization constants of the materials used.   For this reason, the use of an electrometric indicator (pH meter) is superior for measuring end points in acid or base titrations and will, undoubtedly, become standard practice in most laboratories.   Such titrations are commonly referred to as *electrometric titrations* and require the use of a standard pH meter.

*Color Indicators.*   From the titration curves that have been described, it will be noted that the concept of neutrality at pH 7 has little application in acidimetry and alkalimetry.   Only the curves for titration of strong versus strong can be said to have inflections at pH 7.   It will be noted that the titration curves for all acids with ionization constants greater than $10^{-7}$ show inflection points at or below pH 8.3.   Thus, the stoichiometric end point for all such measurements can be said to have been reached at pH 8.3, and any indicator that gives a well-defined color change at such a pH is satisfactory for measuring acids.   Phenolphthalein changes from colorless to pink in the pH range of 8.2 to 8.4 and is the color indicator commonly used in sanitary engineering practice.   Phenolphthalein is also of great value in that it may be used to indicate the end point when strong bases (caustic alkalinity) are being measured, because it changes from pink to colorless at a pH of about 8.3.   It is also used to measure carbonate ion (carbonate alkalinity) by indicating when the carbonate ion has been converted to bicarbonate ion.

The measurement of weakly basic substances requires the use of an indicator that will change color at pH levels of about 4.5.   The indicator commonly used for such purposes has been methyl orange.   It does not yield well-defined color changes that are easily detected by all people but is still considered the standard for most analysis that the sanitary engineer encounters.   In using methyl orange indicator it is good practice to use a "blank" for comparison.   Other indicators have been proposed as a substitute but most suffer from interference by carbon dioxide.   This is particularly true of methyl red.   The best substitute is electrometric measurement.   Methyl orange is also used as an indicator to measure strong acids, commonly referred to as *mineral acidity*.

In sanitary engineering practice, methyl orange and phenolphthalein are commonly used for all acid and base titrations.   The choice of which indicator to use is sometimes confusing to students, until they become acquainted with the chemistry involved.   Choice of methyl orange or phenolphthalein indicator can be simplified by applying the following steps:

1. Write chemical equations for the reactions that are expected.
2. Consider the products of the reaction or reactions and decide whether the resulting solution will be acidic, basic, or neutral.

3. If acidic, use methyl orange. If basic, use phenolphthalein. If neutral, either indicator may be used.

*Precipitation Methods.* The best example of a volumetric method involving formation of a precipitate in sanitary engineering practice is the determination of chloride (chloride ion) by titration with silver nitrate. The indicator commonly used is potassium chromate ($K_2CrO_4$). Like $Cl^-$, chromate ion ($CrO_4^=$) also forms a precipitate with $Ag^+$.

$$2Ag^+ + CrO_4^= \rightarrow \underline{Ag_2CrO_4} \tag{4-6}$$

Silver chromate is red in color, and its appearance is used to show completion of the precipitation of $Cl^-$.

In order for $CrO_4^=$ to serve in this capacity the solubility of $Ag_2CrO_4$ must be sufficiently greater than that of AgCl so that essentially all chloride ions are precipitated before detectable amounts of $Ag_2CrO_4$ are formed. This means that the *effective* solubility product ($K_{sp}$) of $Ag_2CrO_4$ must be slightly greater than that of AgCl. Since indicators of this kind require an excess of reagent to form enough colored precipitate for visual detection, determination of this excess, commonly referred to as *indicator error* or blank, must be made and applied to all titrations.

*Oxidation-Reduction Methods.* Two types of indicators are commonly used: adsorption and those that change with oxidation-reduction potential. The former is illustrated by the use of starch solution to indicate the end point when solutions of iodine are titrated with sodium thiosulfate. Titration is "by eye" until the iodine concentration is near extinction as shown by a pale yellow color. Upon the addition of a good starch indicator a blue solution results. This is due to adsorption of iodine upon the surface of the colloidal starch particles. As the titration proceeds, iodine is released from the starch, and disappearance of the blue color is taken as the end point. Other adsorption indicators show when an excess of titrant has been added. Starch acts in this manner when iodine solutions are used as the titrant.

The end point of an oxidation-reduction reaction can be determined electrometrically. A wide variety of electrode systems may be used. A rotating platinum electrode as employed in the Wallace & Tiernan amperometric titrator (Fig. 4-6) serves very well for many purposes.

Internal indicators that will change color with a change of oxidation-reduction potential (ORP) (see Sec. 6-14) are commonly used. An example familiar to sanitary engineers is Ferroin (ferrous 1, 10-phenanthroline sulfate) which is used to indicate when sufficient ferrous ammonium sulfate titrant has been added to measure excess dichromate ion in the chemical oxygen demand (COD) test. It should be mentioned that selection of an ORP indicator depends upon the ORP at the stoichiometric end point for the particular reaction involved, just as the selection of an indicator for acidimetry or alkalimetry depends upon the pH of the solution resulting at the equivalence point.

**Calculations.** The data obtained during a titration must be translated into terms of weight to be of practical value. Since the unit of volume

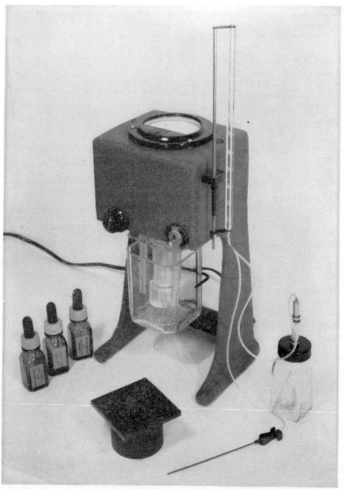

FIG. 4-6. A Wallace & Tiernan amperometric titrator. (*Wallace & Tiernan Incorporated.*)

commonly used for measuring the amount of titrant added to a sample is the milliliter, the weight of active material per milliliter is of importance. For the normal system of standard solutions, one equivalent weight of a substance, in grams, in a liter of solution is a 1.0 normal solution. Each milliliter of such a solution contains one one-thousandth of an equivalent weight or what is more commonly referred to as 1 milliequivalent (me).   Thus, when working with normal solutions,

$$\text{ml titrant} \times \text{me value in g} = \text{g active material in titrant used}$$

This result is of no direct value and must be interpreted in terms of the measured material.   Since all normal solutions are equivalent to each other, it is common practice to use the milliequivalent value for the measured substance in the expression above and obtain the weight of the desired material directly.

When solutions that are not exactly 1.0 normal are used, which is most often the case, the strength in terms of normality must be expressed in the equation

$$\text{ml} \times \text{normality} \times \text{me} = \text{wt in g}$$

This gives the weight of material in the sample tested, and from it the amount in the original sample can be calculated.

In sanitary analysis, the concentration of materials measured is usually so small that it is inconvenient to think in terms of grams.   Therefore, most of the thinking is done in terms of milligrams and results are expressed in terms of milligrams per liter (mg/l).   Samples are commonly measured by volume, and, to avoid unnecessary and repeated calculations, the sample size and the normality of titrant are often chosen so that the buret reading in milliliters times some whole number, such as 1, 10, 20, 50, or 100, gives the milligrams of material per liter.   This requires the use of solutions whose normality is some exact value.   The preparation, standardization, and use of such solutions will be discussed in Part II.

## 4-5. Colorimetry

Analytical chemists as well as others who use analytical procedures are constantly striving to find faster, more economical, and convenient ways of obtaining quantitative data.   To this end, colorimetric methods of analysis have been developed for many determinations of interest to the sanitary engineer.   Colorimetric methods are most applicable in the realm of dilute solutions.   This is most fortunate for the sanitary engineer because a large majority of materials with which he deals falls in this classification.

In order for a colorimetric method to be quantitative, it must form a compound with definite color characteristics and in amounts directly proportional to the concentration of the substance being measured. Solutions of the colored compound or complex must have properties that conform to Beer's law and to Lambert's law.

**Lambert's Law.**   Lambert's law, sometimes referred to as Bouguer's law, relates the absorption of light to the depth or thickness of the colored liquid.   If light intensity decreases inversely with depth or thickness, the colored solution behaves in conformity with the law.   There are no known exceptions to this law as long as homogeneous materials are involved.   The law is discussed solely because a knowledge of it is germane when the depth or thickness of colored samples is varied to decrease a color to a level in the range of a series of prepared standards or of spectrophotometric equipment.   Knowledge and application of this law can save much time and expense.

**Beer's Law.**   Beer's law is concerned with light absorption in relation to solution concentration.   If light is absorbed in direct proportion to concentration over a reasonable and practical range of concentration, the colored material is said to conform to Beer's law.   The best way to determine whether a colored compound or complex obeys Beer's law is to prepare a series of samples in the desired range of concentration and submit them to test on a photoelectric colorimeter or spectrophotometer.   If the observations of per cent light transmission plot along a straight line on a semilog graph, the material can be considered to obey Beer's law.   Many colored systems do not conform to Beer's law, and, therefore, development of any new colorimetric method should involve such a test procedure.

**Color-comparison Tubes.**   Colorimetric measurements may be made in a wide range of equipment.   The sanitary engineer uses standard color-comparison tubes, photoelectric colorimeters, or spectrophotometers.   Each has its place and particular application in sanitary analysis.

Color-comparison tubes, sometimes referred to as Nessler tubes, have been the standard equipment for making colorimetric measurements for many years.   Their use is being rapidly replaced, however, because of the convenience of photoelectric and spectrophotometric methods.   Precise work with color-comparison tubes requires that tubes of matched size or bore be used in order to comply with Lambert's law.   The chief difficulty with their use is that standard color solutions are seldom stable, and every time a determination has to be made it becomes necessary to prepare a series of fresh standards.   This adds greatly to the labor and time required.   Another objection is that all comparisons are made by eye, and the "human error" involved is often considerable because sensitivity to different colors varies.   Furthermore, the analyst is required to interpolate values between standards.   The method is principally used today for determination of fluorides, of color, and of ammonia and organic nitrogen.

**Photoelectric Colorimeters.**   Photoelectric colorimeters have been used quite extensively in colorimetric work and are very satisfactory within their limitations.   They make use of an electrometric device employing a photoelectric cell as the sensing element.   The current developed by the photoelectric cell is translated into per cent transmission or optical density through a suitable galvanometer.   The light source is an ordinary light bulb, and monochromatic light is obtained by allowing a beam of light to pass through a color filter.   The monochromatic light is directed through a cell containing the sample, and the light that penetrates hits the photoelectric cell.   The instrument is adjusted to yield a light transmission corresponding to 100 per cent with the cell containing a "blank sample."   The "blank sample" is a portion of distilled water that has been treated in the same manner as regular samples.   A schematic diagram of the basic essentials of a photoelectric colorimeter is shown in Fig. 4-7, and a typical instrument is shown in Fig. 4-8.

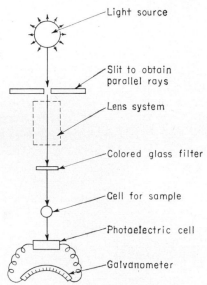

FIG. 4-7. Schematic diagram of a photoelectric colorimeter.

Photoelectric colorimeters require a separate color filter for each determination on which they are to be used; thus the investment may become considerable and the range of application is somewhat limited. They are not suitable for research purposes and should be considered for use principally where a very few well-established determinations are involved.

**Spectrophotometers.**   The modern spectrophotometer employing either a glass prism or a diffraction grating to produce monochromatic light is an extremely valuable instrument for colorimetric analyses in the sanitary engineering field.   It has a wide range of adaptability that allows selection of monochromatic light of any wavelength in the visible spectrum. In addition, all instruments provide light in the ultraviolet and near-infrared regions. One filter usually suffices for the entire visible range of wavelengths. Separate filters are needed for the ultraviolet and for the infrared regions. The principle upon which spectrophotometers is based is the same as that for photoelectric colorimeters, except for the manner in which the monochromatic light is obtained. Figure 4-9 shows a schematic diagram of a spectrophotometer, and Fig. 4-10 shows a typical instrument.

FIG. 4-8. A photoelectric colorimeter.    (*Klett Manufacturing Co.*)

A spectrophotometer is particularly recommended where a wide variety of determinations is made. Its versatility allows the best wavelength of light to be used at all times. The optimum wavelength can be determined at any time by establishing a spectral transmission curve. This is an essential part of research aimed at developing new methods of colorimetric analysis. The curve is established by making a series of observations of light transmission at several different wavelengths of light while using a typical colored solution in the cell. The results when plotted on linear coordinate paper yield a curve like that shown in Fig. 4-11 for nitrite. The wavelength that is absorbed to the greatest extent, in the case of nitrite 525 millimicrons (m$\mu$), is the optimum wavelength to use.

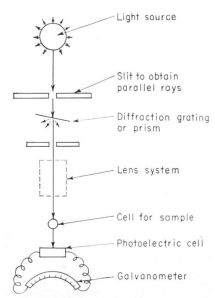

FIG. 4-9. Schematic diagram of a spectrophotometer.

FIG. 4-10. A spectrophotometer.    (*Coleman Instruments, Inc.*)

**Calibration and Use.**   Photoelectric colorimeters and spectrophotometers are calibrated for use in any particular determination by preparing a series of standards *in the same manner as regular tests are to be run* and by making observations on light transmission, using the wavelength specified for the determination.   When such data are plotted on semilog paper, the curve should be essentially a straight line.   The calibration

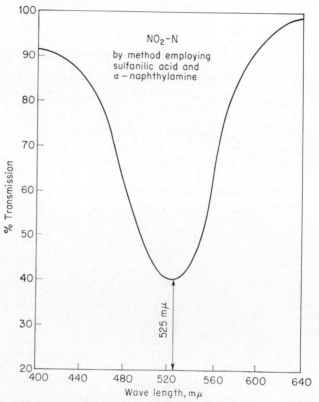

FIG. 4-11. Spectral transmission curve for nitrites or nitrite nitrogen, showing optimum wavelength of light for photometric determination.

curve, when carefully prepared, should serve for years and eliminate the need for the preparation of a series of standards.   A typical calibration curve is shown in Fig. 4-12.   It is usually good practice to include a standard in each set of samples, however, to make sure that unknown errors in reagents, etc., do not lead to faulty results.

It should be emphasized that instrumental analysis does not necessarily ensure accurate results.   The analyst must be constantly on guard to be sure that his instruments are in good working order, cells are kept scrupulously clean, and turbidity of samples is eliminated.

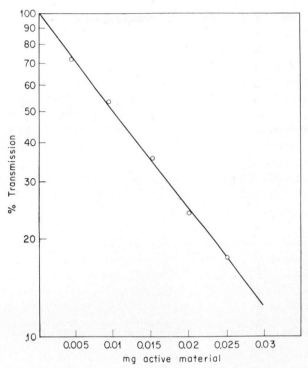

Fig. 4-12. A typical calibration curve for photoelectric or spectrophotometric analysis.

### 4-6. Physical Methods of Analysis

The sanitary engineer often has to employ other methods of analysis that are based upon physical measurements. Short discussions of each are in order.

**Turbidimetry.** The method in which ordinary white light transmitted through a finely divided suspension is compared with that transmitted by a standard suspension is known as *turbidimetry*. The sanitary engineer employs turbidimetric analysis when he employs the Jackson candle turbidimeter or standard bottles for the measurement of turbidity. Some of the patented devices used for this purpose employ the same principle. Sulfates may also be determined in this manner.

**Nephelometry.** Nephelometric methods are also employed to measure turbidity. In this method light is allowed to strike a suspension at right angles to the eye of the observer or photoelectric cell of the instrument. The light reflected by the dispersed particles (Tyndall effect) is recorded. This principle is employed in measuring very low turbidities in filtered water when using the Baylis or St. Louis type of turbidimeter. Bacteriologists often use nephelometry in following bacterial-growth rates.

**Refractive Index.** This is not commonly used.

**Optical Rotation.**    This method is not commonly used.

**Infrared and Ultraviolet Spectroanalysis.**    The use of infrared and ultraviolet spectroanalysis is increasing in the sanitary engineering profession.    Infrared analysis is being used more and more to identify and determine amounts of biologically resistant compounds that gain entrance to public water supplies.    A notable example is the measurement of the alkyl benzene sulfonate type of synthetic detergent.

**X-ray Analysis.**    X-ray analysis is used largely in identification of unknown crystalline materials.    Its greatest use is in research and in the area of air pollution.

**Polarography.**    The determination of minute amounts of metallic ions is made by a modification of electroanalysis commonly referred to as *polarography*.    It is used in research on special problems in relation to corrosion or to industrial hygiene.

**Coulometry.**    Coulometry is a special phase of electroanalysis in which measurement of the quantity of a constituent is determined by the amount of electricity required to react, directly or indirectly, with that constituent.    Its application in the field of sanitary engineering has not been established.

## 4-7. Precision, Accuracy, and Statistical Treatment of Data

Every analyst should have a clear understanding of the difference between precision and accuracy in so far as analytical results are concerned.    A knowledge of statistics is of considerable importance as an aid to establishing sampling programs so that data obtained may be subjected to statistical treatment, when necessary.    These subjects are treated quite adequately in "Standard Methods."

REFERENCES

Diehl, H. C., and G. F. Smith: "Quantitative Analysis," John Wiley & Sons, Inc., New York, 1952.
Pierce, W. C., E. L. Haenisch, and D. T. Sawyer: "Quantitative Analysis," 4th ed., John Wiley & Sons, Inc., New York, 1958.
Rieman, W., J. D. Neuss, and B. Naiman: "Quantitative Analysis," 3d ed., McGraw-Hill Book Company, Inc., New York, 1951.

# 5. Basic Concepts from Organic Chemistry

## 5-1. Introduction

The fundamental information that a sanitary engineer needs concerning organic chemistry differs considerably from that which the organic chemist requires. This difference is due to the fact that chemists are concerned principally with the synthesis of compounds whereas the sanitary engineer is concerned, in the main, with how the organic compounds in liquid and gaseous wastes can be destroyed. Another major difference lies in the fact that the organic chemist is usually concerned with the product of the reaction; the by-products of a reaction are of little interest to him. Since few organic reactions give better than 85 per cent yields, the amount of by-products and unreacted raw materials that represent processing wastes is of considerable magnitude. In addition, many raw materials contain impurities that do not enter the desired reaction and, of course, add to the organic load in waste streams. A classic example is formaldehyde, which normally contains about 5 per cent of methanol unless special precautions are taken in its manufacture.

The sanitary engineer, like the biochemist, must have a fundamental knowledge of organic chemistry. It is not important for either to know a multiplicity of ways of preparing a given organic compound and the yields to be expected from each. Rather, the important consideration concerns how the compounds react in the realm of dilute solutions or when serving as a source of energy for living organisms. It is from this viewpoint that organic chemistry will be treated in this chapter, and considerations will be from the viewpoint of classes rather than individual compounds. Unfortunately, organic chemists have presented very little information on the nature of the by-products of reactions to aid sanitary engineers in solving industrial waste problems.

**History.** Organic chemistry deals with the compounds of carbon. The science of organic chemistry is considered to have originated in 1685 with the publication by Lémery[1] of a chemistry book which classified substances according to their origin as mineral, vegetable, or animal. Compounds derived from plants and animals became known as *organic* and those derived from nonliving sources were inorganic.

Until 1828 it was believed that organic compounds could not be formed except by living plants and animals. This was known as the *vital-force theory*, and belief in it severely limited the development of organic chemistry. Wöhler,[2] in 1828, by accident, found that application of heat to ammonium cyanate, an inorganic compound, caused it to change to urea, a compound considered to be organic in nature. This discovery dealt a deathblow to the vital-force theory, and by 1850 modern organic chemistry is considered to have become well established. Today about a half million organic compounds are known. Many of these are products of synthetic chemistry, and similar compounds are not known in nature.

**Elements.** All organic compounds contain carbon in combination with one or more elements. The hydrocarbons contain only carbon and hydrogen. A great many compounds contain carbon, hydrogen, and oxygen, and they are considered to be the major elements. Minor elements in naturally occurring compounds are nitrogen, phosphorus, and sulfur. Compounds produced by synthesis may contain, in addition, halogens, certain metals, and a wide variety of other elements.

**Properties.** Organic compounds, in general, differ greatly from inorganic compounds in seven respects:

1. Organic compounds are usually combustible.

2. Organic compounds, in general, have lower melting and boiling points.

3. Organic compounds are usually less soluble in water.

4. Several organic compounds may exist for a given formula. This is known as *isomerism.*

5. Reactions of organic compounds are usually molecular rather than ionic. As a result, they are often quite slow.

6. The molecular weights of organic compounds may be very high, often well over 1,000.

7. Most organic compounds can serve as a source of food for bacteria.

**Sources.** Organic compounds are derived from three sources:

1. Nature: fibers, vegetable oils, animal oils and fats, alkaloids, cellulose, starch, sugars, etc.

2. Synthesis: A wide variety of compounds and materials are prepared by manufacturing processes.

3. Fermentation: Alcohols, acetone, glycerol, antibiotics, acids, etc., are derived by the action of microorganisms upon organic matter.

The wastes produced in the processing of natural organic materials and

---

[1] Nicholas Lémery (1645–1715), French physician and chemist.

[2] Friedrich Wöhler (1800–1882), German chemist.

from the synthetic organic and fermentation industries constitute a major part of the industrial waste problems that the sanitary engineer is called upon to solve.

**The Carbon Atom.** A question commonly asked is: How is it possible to have so many compounds of carbon? There are two reasons. In the first place, the normal valence of carbon is 4. This factor alone allows many possibilities, but the most important reason is concerned with the ability of carbon atoms to link together in a wide variety of ways. They may be in a continuous open chain,

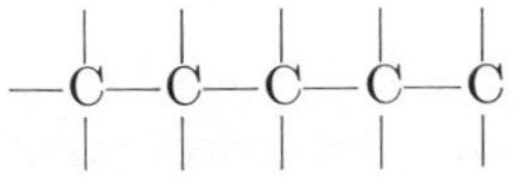

$$
\begin{array}{ccccc}
 & | & | & | & | & | \\
-C & -C & -C & -C & -C \\
 & | & | & | & | & |
\end{array}
$$

or a chain with branches,

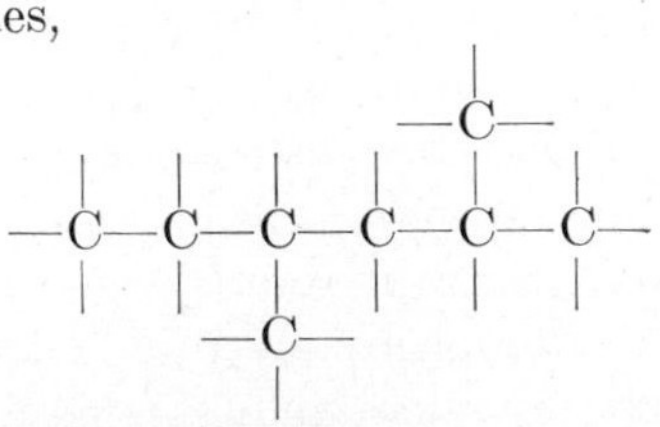

$$
\begin{array}{ccccccc}
 & & & & -C- & & \\
 & & & & | & & \\
-C-C-C-C-C-C- \\
 & | & | & | & | & | & | \\
 & & & -C- & & & \\
 & & & | & & &
\end{array}
$$

or in a ring,

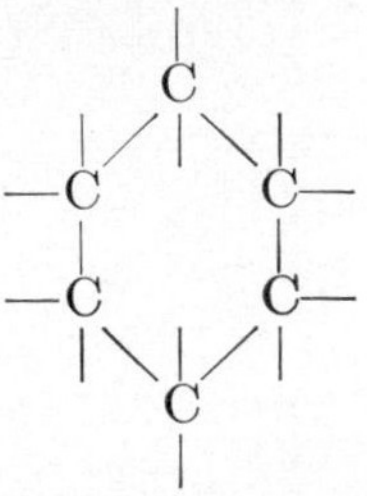

or in chains or rings containing other elements,

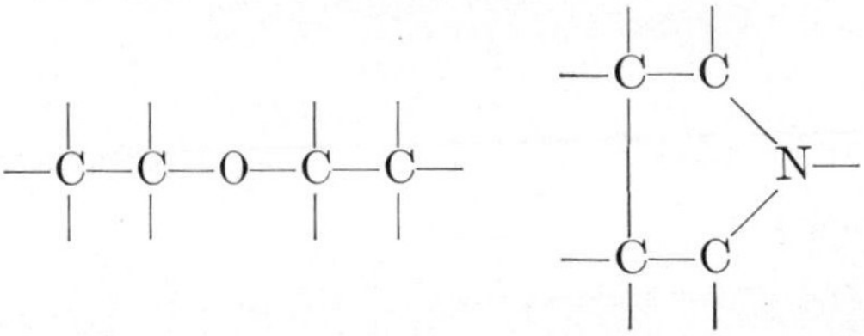

These examples will serve to show the tremendous number of possibilities that exist.

**Isomerism.** In inorganic chemistry, a molecular formula is specific for one compound. In organic chemistry, most molecular formulas do not represent any particular compound. For example, the molecular formula $C_3H_6O_3$ represents at least four separate compounds and, therefore, is of little value in imparting information other than that the compound contains carbon, hydrogen, and oxygen. Four compounds having the formula $C_3H_6O_3$ are

$$H-\underset{\underset{\displaystyle H}{|}}{\overset{\overset{\displaystyle H}{|}}{C}}-\underset{\underset{\displaystyle H}{|}}{\overset{\overset{\displaystyle O}{|}}{C}}-\overset{\overset{\displaystyle O}{\|}}{C}-O-H \qquad H-O-\underset{\underset{\displaystyle H}{|}}{\overset{\overset{\displaystyle H}{|}}{C}}-\underset{\underset{\displaystyle H}{|}}{\overset{\overset{\displaystyle H}{|}}{C}}-\overset{\overset{\displaystyle O}{\|}}{C}-O-H$$

$$H-O-\underset{\underset{\displaystyle H}{|}}{\overset{\overset{\displaystyle H}{|}}{C}}-\overset{\overset{\displaystyle O}{\|}}{C}-O-\underset{\underset{\displaystyle H}{|}}{\overset{\overset{\displaystyle H}{|}}{C}}-H \qquad H-\underset{\underset{\displaystyle H}{|}}{\overset{\overset{\displaystyle H}{|}}{C}}-O-\underset{\underset{\displaystyle H}{|}}{\overset{\overset{\displaystyle H}{|}}{C}}-\overset{\overset{\displaystyle O}{\|}}{C}-OH$$

Compounds having the same molecular formula are known as *isomers*. In the case cited above, the first two isomers are hydroxy acids, the third is an ester of a hydroxy acid, and the fourth is a methoxy acid.   To the organic chemist, each of the formulas represents a chemical compound with definite physical and chemical properties.   The term *graphic* formulas is applied to molecular representations as given above.   They are as useful to a chemist as blueprints are to an engineer.

In many cases graphic formulas may be condensed so as to use only one line.   Thus, the formula

$$H-\underset{\underset{\displaystyle H}{|}}{\overset{\overset{\displaystyle H}{|}}{C}}-\underset{\underset{\displaystyle H}{|}}{\overset{\overset{\displaystyle H}{|}}{C}}-\underset{\underset{\displaystyle H}{|}}{\overset{\overset{\displaystyle H}{|}}{C}}-O-H$$

may be written as

$$CH_3-CH_2-CH_2OH \qquad \text{or} \qquad CH_3CH_2CH_2OH$$

thereby saving a great deal of space.   Such condensed formulas are known as *structural* formulas.

## ALIPHATIC COMPOUNDS

### 5-2. Hydrocarbons

The hydrocarbons are compounds of carbon and hydrogen.   There are two types, *saturated* and *unsaturated*.   Saturated hydrocarbons are those in which adjacent carbon atoms are joined by a single valence bond and all other valances are satisfied by hydrogen.

$$H-\underset{\underset{\displaystyle H}{|}}{\overset{\overset{\displaystyle H}{|}}{C}}-\underset{\underset{\displaystyle H}{|}}{\overset{\overset{\displaystyle H}{|}}{C}}-\underset{\underset{\displaystyle H}{|}}{\overset{\overset{\displaystyle H}{|}}{C}}-H$$

A saturated compound

Unsaturated hydrocarbons have at least two carbon atoms that are joined by more than one valence bond and all remaining valences are satisfied by hydrogen.

$$\begin{array}{ccc} & \text{H} & \text{H} & \text{H} \\ & | & | & | \\ \text{H}-&\text{C}-&\text{C}=&\text{C}-\text{H} \\ & | \\ & \text{H} \end{array} \qquad \text{or} \qquad \text{HC} \equiv \text{CH}$$

Unsaturated compounds

**Saturated Hydrocarbons.** The saturated hydrocarbons form a whole series of compounds starting with one carbon atom and increasing one carbon atom, stepwise. These compounds are also known as the *paraffin* series, the *methane* series, and as *alkanes*. The principal source is petroleum. Gasoline is a mixture containing several of them; diesel fuel is another such mixture.

The hydrocarbons are known as parent compounds by organic chemists because they may be used to prepare a wide variety of organic chemicals. This knowledge serves as the basis of the great petrochemical industry within the petroleum industry. Saturated hydrocarbons are quite inert toward most chemical reagents. For this reason they were termed "paraffins" by early chemists (from the Latin *parum affinis*, meaning little affinity).

*Methane* ($CH_4$) is the simplest hydrocarbon. It is a gas of considerable importance to sanitary engineers since it is a major end product of the anaerobic digestion process as applied to sewage sludge and other organic waste materials. It is a component of marsh gas and of natural gas and, in a mixture with air containing from 5 to 15 per cent methane, it is highly explosive. This property allows its use as fuel for gas engines. Methane is commonly called "firedamp" by miners and makes their work particularly hazardous.

*Ethane* ($CH_3$—$CH_3$) is the second member of the series.

*Propane* ($CH_3$—$CH_2$—$CH_3$) is the third member of the series.

*Butane* ($C_4H_{10}$) is the fourth member of the series and is of interest because it occurs in two isomeric forms:

$$\begin{array}{cccc} \text{H} & \text{H} & \text{H} & \text{H} \\ | & | & | & | \\ \text{H}-\text{C}-&\text{C}-&\text{C}-&\text{C}-\text{H} \\ | & | & | & | \\ \text{H} & \text{H} & \text{H} & \text{H} \end{array} \qquad \begin{array}{ccc} \text{H} & \text{H} & \text{H} \\ | & | & | \\ \text{H}-\text{C}-&\text{C}-&\text{C}-\text{H} \\ | & | & | \\ \text{H} & \text{HCH} & \text{H} \\ & \text{H} \end{array}$$

n-Butane                    Isobutane

*Pentane* ($C_5H_{12}$) is the fifth member of the series and exists in three isomeric forms:

```
                                                                H
                                                                HCH
  H  H  H  H  H          H  H  H  H            H    |    H
  HC—C—C—C—CH          HC—C—C—CH            HC—C—CH
  H  H  H  H  H          H  |  H  H            H    |    H
                           HCH                      HCH
                            H                        H
     n-Pentane             Isopentane             Neopentane
     bp, 36.2°C            bp, 28°C               bp, 9.5°C
```

The third isomer of pentane might also be called tetramethylmethane or dimethyl propane, as the reader will shortly recognize.

As the number of carbon atoms increases in the molecule, the number of possible isomers increases accordingly. There are five possible isomers of *hexane* ($C_6H_{12}$) and 75 possible isomers of *decane* ($C_{10}H_{22}$).

*Physical Properties.* Table 5-1 lists the names and physical constants of the *normal* saturated hydrocarbons of 1 to 10 carbon atoms per mole-

TABLE 5-1. PHYSICAL CONSTANTS OF SOME NORMAL PARAFFINS*

| Name | Formula | Mp, °C | Bp, °C | Sp. gr., 20°/4° | Calcd. no. of isomers |
|------|---------|--------|--------|-----------------|-----------------------|
| Methane | $CH_4$ | $-183$ | $-161.5$ | $0.554^{0°}$ | 1 |
| Ethane | $C_2H_6$ | $-172$ | $-88.3$ | $0.56^{-100°}$ | 1 |
| Propane | $C_3H_8$ | $-187.1$ | $-42.2$ | $0.585^{-44.5°}$ | 1 |
| Butane | $C_4H_{10}$ | $-135$ | $-0.6$ | $0.6^{0°}$ | 2 |
| Pentane | $C_5H_{12}$ | $-130$ | $36.2$ | $0.626$ | 3 |
| Hexane | $C_6H_{14}$ | $-94.3$ | $69.0$ | $0.660$ | 5 |
| Heptane | $C_7H_{16}$ | $-90.5$ | $98.5$ | $0.684$ | 9 |
| Octane | $C_8H_{18}$ | $-56.5$ | $125.8$ | $0.704$ | 18 |
| Nonane | $C_9H_{20}$ | $-53.7$ | $150.7$ | $0.718$ | 35 |
| Decane | $C_{10}H_{22}$ | $-30$ | $174$ | $0.730$ | 75 |

* From E. Wertheim and H. Jeskey, "Introductory Organic Chemistry," 3d ed., McGraw-Hill Book Company, Inc., New York, 1956. Table reproduced by permission of the authors.

cule. The term "normal" applies to the isomer that has all its carbon atoms linked in a *straight chain*. The others are referred to as *branched-chain* compounds. The branched form of butane and the simplest branched form of pentane are commonly given the prefix *iso-*.

The saturated hydrocarbons are colorless, practically odorless, and quite insoluble in water, particularly those with five or more carbon atoms. They dissolve readily in many organic solvents. At room temperature, all members through $C_5$ are gases, those from $C_6$ to $C_{17}$ are liquids, and those above $C_{17}$ are solids.

*Homologous Series.* It will be noted from Table 5-1 that each successive member of the series differs from the previous member by $CH_2$. When the formulas of a series of compounds differ by a common increment, such as $CH_2$, the series is referred to as being a *homologous series*. Such compounds can be expressed by a general formula. That for the methane series is $C_nH_{2n+2}$.

*Radicals.* The inert character of the paraffin hydrocarbons has been mentioned; however, they may be made to react under the proper conditions, and a wide variety of compounds results. It becomes necessary, therefore, to establish some form of nomenclature to identify the products formed. When one hydrogen is replaced from a molecule of a methane-series hydrocarbon, the *-ane* ending is dropped and a *-yl* is added. The names of some are as shown in Table 5-2. The system serves quite well for the normal compounds but is of little value in naming derivatives of the isomers.

TABLE 5-2. NAMES OF METHANE-SERIES RADICALS (ALKYL GROUPS)

| Parent compound | Radical | Formula |
| --- | --- | --- |
| Methane | Methyl | $CH_3-$ |
| Ethane | Ethyl | $C_2H_5-$ |
| Propane | *n*-Propyl | $C_3H_7-$ |
| Propane | Isopropyl | $(CH_3)_2CH-$ |
| *n*-Butane | *n*-Butyl | $C_4H_9-$ |

*Nomenclature.* The methane series of hydrocarbons is characterized by names ending in *-ane*. The straight-chain compounds are termed *normal* compounds. The branched-chain compounds and the derivatives of both straight- and branched-chain compounds are difficult to name with any degree of specificity. The IUC system, as proposed by the International Union of Chemistry, is commonly used. In this system the compounds are named in terms of the longest continuous chain of carbon atoms in the molecule. A few examples will illustrate the method.

$$
\begin{array}{ccccc}
H & H & H & H & H \\
HC & —C & —C & —C & —CH \\
H & H & H & H & H
\end{array}
$$

*n*-Pentane

$$
\begin{array}{cccccc}
H & H & H & H & H & H \\
HC & —C & —C & —C & —C & —CH \\
H & H & H & H & H & H
\end{array}
$$

*n*-Hexane

$$
\begin{array}{ccccccc}
\text{H} & \text{H} & \text{H} & \text{H} & \text{H} & \text{H} \\
\text{HC} & \text{C} & \text{C} & \text{C} & \text{C} & \text{CH} \\
\text{H} & \text{H} & | & \text{H} & \text{H} & \text{H} \\
& & \text{HCH} \\
& & \text{H}
\end{array}
$$

3-Methylhexane
(one of the group
of heptanes)

$$
\begin{array}{ccccccccc}
\text{H} & \text{H} & \text{H} & \text{H} & \text{H} & \text{H} & \text{H} & \text{H} & \text{H} \\
\text{HC} & \text{C} & \text{C} & \text{C} & \text{C} & \text{C} & \text{C} & \text{C} & \text{CH} \\
\text{H} & \text{H} & \text{H} & | & \text{H} & \text{H} & \text{H} & \text{H} & \text{H} \\
& & & \text{H} \\
& & \text{HC} & \text{CH} \\
& & \text{H} & \text{H}
\end{array}
$$

4-Ethylnonane
(a member of
the undecane
group)

$$
\begin{array}{cccccc}
\text{H} & \text{H} & \text{H} & \text{H} & \text{H} & \text{H} \\
\text{HC} & \text{C} & \text{C} & \text{C} & \text{C} & \text{CH} \\
\text{H} & | & \text{H} & | & \text{H} & \text{H} \\
& & & & \\
\text{HCH} & & \text{HCH} \\
\text{H} & & \text{H}
\end{array}
$$

2,4-Dimethyl
hexane (one of the
isomeric octanes)

It will be noted that a chain is numbered from the end nearest the attached radical. The rule is to make the numbers as small as possible. The IUC system is applied to other compounds as well as to hydrocarbons.

*Chemical Reactions.* Strong bases, acids, or aqueous solutions of oxidizing agents do not react with saturated hydrocarbons at room temperature. At elevated temperatures, strong oxidizing agents, such as concentrated sulfuric acid, oxidize the compounds to carbon dioxide and water. This reaction is of importance to sanitary engineers in the determination of organic nitrogen. Other reactions of importance are as follows:

1. Oxidation with oxygen or air:

$$CH_4 + 2O_2 \xrightarrow{\Delta} CO_2 + 2H_2O \tag{5-1}$$

2. Substitution of hydrogen by halogens:

$$CH_4 + Cl_2 \rightarrow HCl + CH_3Cl \tag{5-2}$$

This reaction does not ordinarily occur in aqueous solutions and, therefore, is of little significance to sanitary engineers.

3. Pyrolysis or cracking: High-molecular-weight hydrocarbons may be broken into smaller molecules by heat treatment. The process is used

in the petroleum industry to increase the yield of light boiling fractions, suitable for sale as gasoline or for chemical synthesis.   Heat treatment results in disruption of the large molecules as follows:

$$\left.\begin{array}{l}\text{High mol. wt} \\ \text{paraffin compound}\end{array}\right\} \xrightarrow[\text{pressure}]{\text{heat}} \left\{\begin{array}{l}\text{paraffin compounds of lower mol. wt} \\ \quad + \text{ olefin compounds} \\ \quad + \text{ hydrogen } + \text{ naphthenes} \\ \quad + \text{ carbon}\end{array}\right. \tag{5-3}$$

4.  Biological oxidation: Hydrocarbons are oxidized by certain bacteria under aerobic conditions.   The oxidation proceeds through several steps. The first step involves conversion to alcohols with attack occurring on terminal carbon atoms, i.e., omega oxidation.

$$\underset{\text{Hydrocarbon}}{2CH_3CH_2CH_3} + O_2 \xrightarrow[\text{bact.}]{} \underset{\text{Alcohol}}{2CH_3CH_2CH_2OH} \tag{5-4}$$

The bacteria derive energy from this oxidation and, through additional oxidative steps which will be developed later, convert the hydrocarbon to carbon dioxide and water.

$$CH_3CH_2CH_3 + 5O_2 \xrightarrow[\text{bact.}]{} 3CO_2 + 4H_2O \tag{5-5}$$

This reaction, particularly the intermediate steps, is of great interest to sanitary engineers.

**Unsaturated Hydrocarbons.**   The unsaturated hydrocarbons are usually separated into four classes.

*Ethylene Series.*   The *ethylene* series corresponds to the methane series of hydrocarbons.   Each member of the latter except methane can lose hydrogen to form unsaturated compounds.   Because ethane is the first member capable of doing this, the series takes its name from it.   The ethylene series of compounds all contain one double valence bond between two adjacent carbon atoms,

Ethylene
or
Ethene

Butylene
or
2-Butene

and their names all end in -*ene*.   The ethylene series of compounds are also called *olefins* and *alkenes*.   Olefin compounds, particularly ethylene, propylene, and butylenes, are formed in great quantities during the cracking or pyrolysis of petroleum.

The names, formulas, and physical constants of a number of important alkenes are given in Table 5-3.   In naming specific alkenes, the IUC system must be employed on all compounds with over three carbon atoms. The nomenclature becomes quite complicated with branched-chain isomers.   Fortunately, there is little reason to differentiate between normal and branched-chain compounds in this series.

TABLE 5-3. PHYSICAL CONSTANTS OF SELECTED ALKENES*

| IUC name | Formula | Mp, °C | Bp, °C | Sp. gr., 20°/4° | Calcd. no. of isomers |
|----------|---------|--------|--------|-----------------|------------------------|
| Ethene    | $C_2H_4$                  | −169.4  | −103.9 | $0.566^{-102°}$ | 1   |
| Propene   | $CH_2{=}CHCH_3$           | −185.2  | − 47   | $0.610^{-47°}$  | 1   |
| 1-Butene  | $CH_2{=}CHCH_2CH_3$       | −130    | − 5    | $0.668^{0°}$    | 3   |
| 1-Pentene | $CH_2{=}CH(CH_2)_2CH_3$   | −138    | 30     | $0.645^{25°}$   | 5   |
| 1-Hexene  | $CH_2{=}CH(CH_2)_3CH_3$   | − 98.5  | 64.1   | 0.673           | 13  |
| 1-Heptene | $CH_2{=}CH(CH_2)_4CH_3$   | −120    | 95     | 0.699           | 27  |
| 1-Octene  | $CH_2{=}CH(CH_2)_5CH_3$   | −102.1  | 126    | 0.722           | 66  |
| 1-Nonene  | $CH_2{=}CH(CH_2)_6CH_3$   |         | 149.9  | 0.730           | 153 |
| 1-Decene  | $CH_2{=}CH(CH_2)_7CH_3$   | − 80    | 172    | 0.763           | 377 |

* From E. Wertheim and H. Jeskey, "Introductory Organic Chemistry," 3d ed., McGraw-Hill Book Company, Inc., New York, 1956.   Table reproduced by permission of the authors.

*Diolefins.*   When aliphatic compounds contain two double bonds in the molecule they are called *diolefins.*

*Polyenes.*   Some organic compounds contain more than two double bonds per molecule.   Such compounds are called polyenes.   The red coloring matter of tomatoes, lycopene, and the yellow coloring matter of carrots are examples.

Lycopene ($C_{40}H_{56}$)

These compounds are of interest to sanitary engineers because of their occurrence in industrial wastes produced in preparation of vegetables for canning.   The chlorine demand of such wastes is extremely high.

*Acetylene Series.*   The acetylene series of unsaturated compounds have a triple bond between adjacent carbon atoms.

$$H—C{\equiv}C—H$$

These compounds are found to some extent in industrial wastes from certain industries, particularly those from the manufacture of certain types of synthetic rubber.

*Chemical Reactions.* Unsaturated hydrocarbons seldom create problems in sanitary engineering. However, unsaturated linkages occur in many types of organic compounds and exhibit many properties in common, regardless of the type of compound in which they exist. For this reason, the sanitary engineer should be acquainted with the chemistry of the double bond.

Unsaturated compounds undergo several reactions with relative ease.

1. Oxidation: The compounds are easily oxidized in aqueous solution by oxidizing agents such as potassium permanganate. A glycol is the normal product.

2. Reduction: Under special conditions of temperature, pressure, and catalysis, hydrogen may be caused to add at double or triple bonds. This reaction is of considerable importance commercially in the conversion of vegetable oils to more acceptable solid fats. Crisco, Spry, and many other vegetable shortenings are made by this process.

3. Addition: Halogen acids, hypochlorous acid, and halogens will add across unsaturated linkages.

$$
\begin{array}{ccc}
\text{H} \quad \text{H} & & \text{H} \quad \text{H} \\
| \quad\; | & & | \quad\; | \\
\text{H--C=C--H} + \text{Cl}_2 \rightarrow & & \text{H--C--C--H} \\
& & | \quad\; | \\
& & \text{Cl} \quad \text{Cl}
\end{array}
\qquad (5\text{-}6)
$$

The reaction with halogens is of most importance to sanitary engineers. Industrial wastes containing appreciable amounts of unsaturated compounds exhibit high chlorine-demand values because of such reactions.

4. Polymerization: Molecules of certain compounds having unsaturated linkages are prone to combine with each other to form polymers of higher molecular weight. This reaction serves as the basis for many industrial products, e.g., synthetic resins, synthetic fibers, synthetic rubber, synthetic detergents, polyethylene, etc. Industrial wastes from such industries can be expected to contain a wide variety of polymers and usually exhibit a high chlorine demand.

5. Bacterial oxidation: It is generally considered that organic compounds possessing unsaturated linkages are more prone to bacterial oxidation than corresponding saturated compounds because of the ease of oxidation at the double bonds.

## 5-3. Alcohols

Alcohols are considered to be the primary oxidation product of hydrocarbons.

$$CH_4 \; + \tfrac{1}{2}O_2 \to \quad CH_3OH \qquad\qquad (5\text{-}7)$$
Methane         Methyl alcohol

$$CH_3—CH_2—CH_3 + \tfrac{1}{2}O_2 \to CH_3—CH_2—CH_2OH \qquad (5\text{-}8)$$
Propane           n-Propyl alcohol

They cannot be prepared in this manner, however, because the reaction cannot be stopped with alcohols as the end product. Therefore, the reaction is of theoretical interest only but is often used to illustrate the steps in biological degradation of hydrocarbons under aerobic conditions.

Alcohols may be considered as *hydroxy alkyl* compounds. For convenience, the alkyl group in alcohols and other organic compounds is often represented by R—, and the general formula for alcohols is R—OH. The OH group does not ionize; consequently, alcohols are neutral in reaction. The chemistry of alcohols is related entirely to the OH group.

**Classification.** Alcohols are classified into three groups: primary, secondary, and tertiary, depending upon where the OH group is attached to the molecule. If the OH group is on a terminal (primary) carbon atom, it is a *primary* alcohol.

H  H         H  H  H  H<br>
HC—C—OH    HC—C—C—C—OH     R—OH<br>
H  H         H  H  H  H<br>
Primary alcohols

If the OH group is attached to a carbon atom that is joined to two other carbon atoms, it is a *secondary* alcohol, and the carbon atom to which it is attached is a *secondary carbon atom*.

H  H  H      H  H  H  H     R<br>
HC—C—CH    HC—C—C—CH     \\<br>
H  |  H       H  H  |  H        CHOH<br>
O            O      /<br>
H            H     R′<br>
Secondary alcohols

If the OH group is attached to a carbon atom that is joined to three other carbon atoms it is a *tertiary* alcohol, and the carbon atom to which it is attached is a *tertiary carbon atom*.

                C<br>
H             |<br>
HCH          C<br>
H  |  H        |        R<br>
HC—C—CH    C—C—C—C    R′—C—OH<br>
H  |  H        |        |<br>
O          O     R″<br>
H          H<br>
Tertiary alcohols

The chemistry of the primary, secondary, and tertiary alcohols differs considerably; therefore it is important to know how to differentiate among them.

**Common Alcohols.** The alcohols of greatest commercial importance are methyl, ethyl, isopropyl, and $n$-butyl. In addition, hexadecanol is of some importance in sanitary engineering practice.

*Methyl Alcohol* ($CH_3OH$). Methyl alcohol is used to a considerable extent for synthesis of organic compounds. It has been used as an antifreeze for automobiles. It is prepared mainly by synthesis from carbon monoxide and hydrogen.

$$CO + 2H_2 \xrightarrow[\text{atm pressure; catalyst}]{\text{about 300°, about 200}} CH_3OH \qquad (5\text{-}9)$$

*Ethyl Alcohol* ($CH_3CH_2OH$). Ethyl alcohol is used for the synthesis of organic compounds, the production of beverages, and the manufacture of medicines. It is prepared largely by fermentation processes. Alcohol intended for beverage purposes is manufactured by fermentation of starch derived from a variety of materials, such as corn, wheat, rye, rice, and potatoes. The reactions involved are as follows:

$$\text{Starch} + \text{water} \xrightarrow[\text{of malt}]{\text{enzyme}} \text{maltose} \qquad (5\text{-}10)$$

$$\underset{\text{Maltose}}{C_{12}H_{22}O_{11}} + H_2O \xrightarrow[\text{of yeast}]{\text{enzyme}} 2 \text{ glucose} \qquad (5\text{-}11)$$

Fermentation of the glucose yields carbon dioxide and alcohol:

$$\underset{\text{Glucose}}{C_6H_{12}O_6} \xrightarrow{\text{fermentation}} 2CO_2 + 2C_2H_5OH \qquad (5\text{-}12)$$

Industrial alcohol is produced largely from the fermentation of solutions containing sugars which are difficult to reclaim, such as molasses and, in Europe, spent sulfite liquor.

$$C_{12}H_{22}O_{11} + H_2O \xrightarrow{\text{invertase}} \underset{\text{Glucose}}{C_6H_{12}O_6} + \underset{\text{Fructose}}{C_6H_{12}O_6} \qquad (5\text{-}13)$$

$$\underset{\substack{\text{Glucose}\\\text{Fructose}}}{C_6H_{12}O_6} \xrightarrow{\text{zymase}} 2CO_2 + 2C_2H_5OH$$

The residues remaining after distillation of the desired product, ethyl alcohol, constitute some of the most potent industrial wastes with which the sanitary engineer has to deal.

*Isopropyl Alcohol* ($CH_3CHOHCH_3$). Isopropyl alcohol is widely used in organic synthesis, and considerable amounts are sold as "dry gas" to prevent separation of water in the fuel tanks of automobiles.    It is prepared by hydration of propylene derived from the cracking of petroleum.

$n$-Butyl Alcohol $(CH_3CH_2CH_2CH_2OH)$.   Normal butyl alcohol is used to prepare butyl acetate, an excellent solvent.   It is often referred to as "synthetic banana oil" because of its odor which resembles natural banana oil, amyl acetate.   Normal butyl alcohol is prepared from cornstarch by a fermentation process utilizing a particular microorganism, *Clostridium acetobutylicum.*   Considerable amounts of acetone and some ethyl alcohol and hydrogen are produced during the fermentation.   The liquid wastes remaining after distillation of the desired products are classed as industrial wastes, and their treatment and ultimate disposal usually fall to the lot of the sanitary engineer.   They are similar in character to the residues from the production of ethyl alcohol but offer less promise of by-product recovery.

TABLE 5-4. PHYSICAL CONSTANTS OF NORMAL PRIMARY ALCOHOLS*

| Name of radical | IUC name of alcohol | Formula | Mp, °C | Bp, °C | Sp. gr., 20°/4° | Calcd. no. of isomers |
|---|---|---|---|---|---|---|
| Methyl | Methanol | $CH_3OH$ | − 97.8 | 64.7 | 0.793 | 1 |
| Ethyl | Ethanol | $C_2H_5OH$ | −117.3 | 78.4 | 0.789 | 1 |
| Propyl | 1-Propanol | $C_3H_7OH$ | −127 | 97.2 | 0.804 | 2 |
| Butyl | 1-Butanol | $C_4H_9OH$ | − 89.2 | 117.7 | 0.810 | 4 |
| Amyl | 1-Pentanol | $C_5H_{11}OH$ | − 78.5 | 138 | 0.814 | 8 |
| Hexyl | 1-Hexanol | $C_6H_{13}OH$ | − 51.6 | 157.2 | 0.819 | 17 |
| Heptyl | 1-Heptanol | $C_7H_{15}OH$ | − 34.6 | 176 | 0.822 | 39 |
| Octyl | 1-Octanol | $C_8H_{17}OH$ | − 16.3 | 195 | 0.825 | 89 |
| Nonyl | 1-Nonanol | $C_9H_{19}OH$ | − 5 | 213 | 0.827 | 211† |
| Decyl | 1-Decanol | $C_{10}H_{21}OH$ | 7 | 231 | 0.829 | 507 |

* From E. Wertheim and H. Jeskey, "Introductory Organic Chemistry," 3d ed., McGraw-Hill Book Company, Inc., New York, 1956.   Table reproduced by permission of the authors.

† These numbers are for all the isomers of a given carbon content.

*Hexadecanol* $[CH_3(CH_2)_{14}CH_2OH]$.   Hexadecanol is a 16-carbon-atom alcohol that is used to reduce evaporation in water reservoirs.   It is quite insoluble in water but, owing to the polar nature of its molecules, does form a monomolecular layer over the surface of the water which retards evaporation.   The film must be renewed continuously as microorganisms in the water gradually consume the hexadecanol for food.

**Physical Properties of Alcohols.**   The short-chain alcohols are completely soluble in water.   Those with more than 12 carbon atoms are colorless waxy solids and very poorly soluble in water.   The physical constants of several alcohols are given in Table 5-4.

**Nomenclature.** The alcohols of commercial significance are usually called by their common names. The IUC system must be employed, however, to differentiate among isomers and to name the higher members, such as hexadecanol. In IUC terminology, the names of all alcohols end in *-ol*. The formulas, common names, and IUC names of several alcohols are given in Tables 5-4 and 5-5. In the IUC system, the longest carbon chain determines the name. The location of alkyl groups and the hydroxyl group are described by number; e.g., isobutyl alcohol is described as 2-methyl-1-propanol.

TABLE 5-5. NOMENCLATURE OF ALCOHOLS*

| Formula | Common name | IUC name |
|---|---|---|
| $CH_3OH$ | Methyl alcohol | Methanol |
| $C_2H_5OH$ | Ethyl alcohol | Ethanol |
| $CH_3CH_2CH_2OH$ | *n*-Propyl alcohol | 1-Propanol |
| $CH_3$<br>$\quad$CHOH<br>$CH_3$ | Isopropyl alcohol | 2-Propanol |
| $CH_3CH_2CH_2CH_2OH$ | *n*-Butyl alcohol | 1-Butanol |
| $CH_3$<br>$\quad$CHCH$_2$OH<br>$CH_3$ | Isobutyl alcohol | 2-Methyl-1-propanol |
| $CH_3$<br>$\quad$CHOH<br>$C_2H_5$ | *sec*-Butyl alcohol | 2-Butanol |
| $(CH_3)_3COH$ | *tert*-Butyl alcohol | 2-Methyl-2-propanol |

* From E. Wertheim and H. Jeskey, "Introductory Organic Chemistry," 3d ed., McGraw-Hill Book Company, Inc., New York, 1956. Table reproduced by permission of the authors.

**Polyhydroxy Alcohols.** Those alcohols having two hydroxyl groups per molecule are known as *glycols*. The principal glycol of commercial significance is *ethylene glycol*, which is prepared from ethylene. Ethylene adds hypochlorous acid to form ethylene chlorohydrin,

$$
\begin{array}{ccc}
H \;\; H & & H \;\; H \\
HC{=}CH + HOCl \rightarrow & & HC{-}CH \\
& & | \quad\; | \\
& & Cl \;\; OH
\end{array}
\qquad (5\text{-}14)
$$

Ethylene chlorohydrin

and treatment of the chlorohydrin with sodium bicarbonate produces ethylene glycol.

$$\underset{\substack{| \quad | \\ \text{Cl} \quad \text{OH}}}{H_2C-CH_2} + NaHCO_3 \rightarrow NaCl + CO_2 + \underset{\substack{| \quad | \\ \text{OH} \quad \text{OH} \\ \text{Ethylene glycol}}}{H_2C-\!-\!-\!-CH_2} \qquad (5\text{-}15)$$

It is used extensively as a nonevaporative, radiator antifreeze compound, formerly sold exclusively under the trade name Prestone but now sold under a wide variety of names.

*Glycerol* or glycerine is a trihydroxy alcohol.

$$\underset{\substack{| \quad | \quad | \\ \text{OH} \ \text{OH} \ \text{OH}}}{\overset{H_2 \ H \ H_2}{C-C-C}}$$

It was formerly produced in large quantities in the soap industry through saponification of fats and oils. Presently, considerable amounts are produced by synthesis. Glycerol is used in a wide variety of commercial products: foods, cosmetics, medicines, tobaccos, etc. It is used for the manufacture of nitroglycerine, an important component of dynamite.

**Chemical Reactions of Alcohols.** Alcohols undergo two types of reactions that are of interest to sanitary engineers.

*Ester Formation.* Alcohols react with acids, both inorganic and organic, to form esters. Inorganic hydroxy acids yield "inorganic" esters:

$$ROH + H_2SO_4 \rightleftharpoons H_2O + ROSO_3H \qquad (5\text{-}16)$$

Organic acids yield organic esters:

$$ROH + R_1CO_2H \rightleftharpoons H_2O + R_1CO_2R \qquad (5\text{-}17)$$

Organic esters are discussed in Sec. 5-6.

*Oxidation.* Most alcohols are readily oxidized by strong oxidizing agents and by many microorganisms under aerobic conditions. The product of the oxidation depends upon the class of alcohol involved.

Primary alcohols are oxidized to aldehydes. The general equation is

$$\underset{\substack{\text{Primary} \\ \text{alcohol}}}{RCH_2OH} + \tfrac{1}{2}O_2 \rightarrow H_2O + \underset{\text{An aldehyde}}{\overset{H}{RC}\!=\!O} \qquad (5\text{-}18)$$

Care must be used in selecting the oxidizing agent or the aldehyde may be oxidized still further to an acid.

Secondary alcohols are oxidized to ketones.

$$\underset{\substack{\text{Isopropyl alcohol}}}{H_3C{-}\underset{\underset{H}{|}}{\overset{\overset{OH}{|}}{C}}{-}CH_3} + \tfrac{1}{2}O_2 \rightarrow H_3C{-}\underset{\underset{OH}{|}}{\overset{\overset{O|H}{|}}{C}}{-}CH_3 \rightarrow H_2O + \underset{\substack{\text{Acetone,}\\\text{a ketone}}}{H_3C{-}\overset{\overset{O}{\|}}{C}{-}CH_3}$$

$$(5\text{-}19)$$

The ketones are not easily oxidized and can usually be recovered completely.

Tertiary alcohols are not oxidized by ordinary agents in aqueous solution. When attacked by very strong oxidizing agents they are converted to carbon dioxide and water.

Microorganisms oxidize primary and secondary alcohols readily under aerobic conditions. The end products are carbon dioxide and water, but aldehydes and ketones are believed to exist as intermediates. Present evidence indicates that microorganisms cannot attack tertiary alcohols, except through terminal methyl groups, as with the hydrocarbons.

## 5-4. Aldehydes and Ketones

*Aldehydes* are the oxidation products of primary alcohols (ROH). *Ketones* are the oxidation products of secondary alcohols

$$(R{-}CH_2OH{-}R')$$

**Aldehydes.** Oxidation of primary alcohols is considered to go through the following steps:

$$R{-}\underset{\underset{H}{|}}{\overset{\overset{H}{|}}{C}}{-}OH + \tfrac{1}{2}O_2 \rightarrow R{-}\underset{\underset{\underset{H}{|}}{O}}{\overset{\overset{H}{|}}{C}}{-}OH \rightarrow R{-}\overset{\overset{H}{|}}{C}{=}O + H_2O \quad (5\text{-}20)$$

The first step involves oxidation to produce a compound with two hydroxyl groups on the same carbon atom. Such compounds are unstable and water is eliminated, leaving an aldehyde with the characteristic *carbonyl* group, $-\overset{\overset{H}{|}}{C}{=}O$. The general structural formula for an aldehyde is R—CHO, where R represents any alkyl group, $CH_3-$, $C_2H_5-$, etc.

All primary alcohols are capable of forming aldehydes. Only a few, however, are of commercial importance.

*Formaldehyde.* Formaldehyde is formed by the oxidation of methyl alcohol.

$$\begin{matrix} H \\ HC-OH \\ H \end{matrix} + \tfrac{1}{2}O_2 \rightarrow \begin{matrix} H \\ HC=O \\ \text{Formaldehyde} \end{matrix} + H_2O \qquad (5\text{-}21)$$

It is used extensively in organic synthesis. It is very toxic to micro-organisms, and, because of this property, it is used in embalming fluids and fluids used for the preservation of biological specimens. Industrial wastes containing formaldehyde were considered, at one time, to be too toxic for treatment by biological methods. Through dilution of such wastes to reduce the concentration of formaldehyde below 1,500 mg/l, it was found that microorganisms could use the formaldehyde as food and oxidize it to carbon dioxide and water. This experience has led to the concept of *toxicity thresholds* in industrial waste treatment practice. It means that below certain concentrations all materials are nontoxic.

TABLE 5-6. COMMON ALDEHYDES

| Common name | IUC name | Formula |
|---|---|---|
| Formaldehyde | Methanal | $HCHO$ |
| Acetaldehyde | Ethanal | $CH_3CHO$ |
| Propionaldehyde | Propanal | $C_2H_5CHO$ |
| Butyraldehyde | Butanal | $C_3H_7CHO$ |
| Valeraldehyde | Pentanal | $C_4H_9CHO$ |
| Caproaldehyde | Hexanal | $C_5H_{11}CHO$ |
| Heptaldehyde | Heptanal | $C_6H_{13}CHO$ |
| Acrolein | | $CH_2=CHCHO$ |
| Citral | | $C_9H_{15}CHO$ |
| Citronellal | | $C_9H_{17}CHO$ |

*Acetaldehyde.* Acetaldehyde is formed by oxidation of ethyl alcohol.

$$CH_3CH_2OH + \tfrac{1}{2}O_2 \rightarrow \begin{matrix} H \\ CH_3-C=O \\ \text{Acetaldehyde} \end{matrix} + H_2O \qquad (5\text{-}22)$$

It is used extensively in organic synthesis. A major industrial use involves its condensation with formaldehyde to produce pentaerythritol $[C(CH_2OH)_4]$, an important intermediate for the production of a wide variety of products, including aldehyde resin paints. Development of a biological treatment process for the formaldehyde-bearing industrial wastes from the manufacture of pentaerythritol led to the concept of toxicity threshold mentioned above.

A wide variety of aldehydes are of commercial interest. The names and formulas of several of them are given in Table 5-6. The IUC name of all aldehydes ends in -al.

**Ketones.** Ketones are prepared by the oxidation of secondary alcohols. The steps in the reaction are

$$R\overset{\underset{\displaystyle H}{|}}{\underset{\underset{\displaystyle H}{|}}{C}}R' + \tfrac{1}{2}O_2 \rightarrow R\overset{\underset{\displaystyle H}{|}}{\underset{\underset{\displaystyle H}{|}}{C}}R' \rightarrow R\overset{O}{\underset{}{C}}R' + H_2O \quad (5\text{-}23)$$

$$\text{Ketone}$$

Ketones have two alkyl groups attached to the carbonyl group, $-\overset{O}{\underset{}{C}}-$, while aldehydes have one R group and a hydrogen atom. The R groups in ketones may be the same or different.

TABLE 5-7. COMMON KETONES

| Common name | IUC name |
|---|---|
| Acetone | Propanone |
| Ethyl methyl ketone | Butanone |
| Diethyl ketone | 3-Pentanone |
| Methyl propyl ketone | 2-Pentanone |
| Methyl isopropyl ketone | 3-Methyl-2-butanone |
| n-Butyl methyl ketone | 2-Hexanone |
| Ethyl propyl ketone | 3-Hexanone |
| Dipropyl ketone | 4-Heptanone |
| Dibutyl ketone | 5-Nonanone |

*Acetone.* Acetone (dimethyl ketone) is the simplest ketone and is produced by oxidation of isopropyl alcohol (2-propanol).

$$CH_3\overset{\underset{\displaystyle H}{|}}{\underset{\underset{\displaystyle H}{|}}{C}}CH_3 + \tfrac{1}{2}O_2 \rightarrow CH_3\overset{O}{\underset{}{C}}CH_3 + H_2O \quad (5\text{-}24)$$

$$\text{Acetone}$$

*Ethyl Methyl Ketone.* Ethyl methyl ketone is prepared by the oxidation of 2-butanol.

$$CH_3\overset{\underset{\displaystyle H}{|}}{\underset{\underset{\displaystyle H}{|}}{C}}CH_2\overset{}{}CH_3 + \tfrac{1}{2}O_2 \rightarrow CH_3\overset{O}{\underset{}{C}}C_2H_5 + H_2O \quad (5\text{-}25)$$

$$\text{Ethyl methyl ketone}$$

Ketones are used as solvents in industry and for the synthesis of a wide variety of products. The names of a few ketones are given in Table 5-7.

*Chemical Properties of Aldehydes and Ketones.* Aldehydes and ketones differ in ease of oxidation.

1. Aldehydes are easily oxidized to the corresponding acids.

$$R—C\overset{H}{=}O + \tfrac{1}{2}O_2 \rightarrow R—\overset{O}{\underset{}{C}}—OH \qquad (5\text{-}26)$$

2. Ketones are difficult to oxidize.  This is because there is no hydrogen attached to the carbonyl group.  As a result, further oxidation must initiate in one of the alkyl groups, the molecule is cleaved, and two or more acids are produced.

$$CH_3\overset{O}{\underset{}{C}}CH_3 + 2O_2 \rightarrow CO_2 + H_2O + CH_3COOH \qquad (5\text{-}27)$$

Acetone                                        Acetic acid

In the case of acetone, carbon dioxide and acetic acid are formed.  Theoretically, formic acid should be formed but it is so easily oxidized that it is converted under the prevailing conditions to carbon dioxide and water.  Higher ketones such as diethyl ketone (3-pentanone) are oxidized as follows:

$$R—\overset{H}{\underset{H}{C}}—\overset{O}{\underset{}{C}}—R' + O_2 \rightarrow R—\overset{H}{\underset{O\ H}{C}}—\overset{O}{\underset{}{C}}—R' \qquad (5\text{-}28)$$

Compounds with two hydroxyl groups on the same carbon atom are unstable and decompose with further oxidation to produce two acids.

$$R—\overset{H\ O}{\underset{O\ H}{C}}—\overset{O}{\underset{}{C}}—R' + \tfrac{1}{2}O_2 \rightarrow R—\overset{O}{\underset{}{C}}—OH + R'—\overset{O}{\underset{}{C}}—OH \qquad (5\text{-}29)$$

Oxidation of both aldehydes and ketones is accomplished readily by many microorganisms under aerobic conditions.  However, since organic acids also serve as a good food supply, the end products are carbon dioxide and water.

## 5-5. Acids

Acids represent the highest oxidation state that an organic compound can attain.  Further oxidation results in the formation of carbon dioxide and water, which are classed as inorganic compounds, and the organic compound is considered as being completely destroyed.

Oxidation sequence

$$CH_4 \rightarrow CH_3OH \rightarrow H_2C{=}O \rightarrow HCOOH \rightarrow H_2O + CO_2 \quad (5\text{-}30)$$

| Hydro-carbon | Alcohol | Aldehyde | Acid | Products of complete oxidation |

All organic acids contain the $-\overset{\text{O}}{\underset{\|}{C}}-OH$ group. This is called the *carboxyl* group and is commonly written —COOH. Acids with one carboxyl group are known as *monocarboxylic* acids and those with more than one are *polycarboxylic* acids. The acids may be saturated or unsaturated. Some contain hydroxy groups within the molecule.

**Saturated Monocarboxylic Acids.** A wide variety of saturated monocarboxylic acids occur in nature as constituents of fats, oils, and waxes. Unsaturated acids are also found in these materials, and, as a result, both types are commonly known as *fatty* acids. The majority of the fatty acids derived from natural products have an even number of carbon atoms and usually have straight-chain or normal structure.

*Physical Properties.* The first nine members, $C_1$ to $C_9$, are liquids. All the others are greasy solids. Formic, acetic, and propionic acid have sharp penetrating odors; the remaining liquid acids have disgusting odors, particularly butyric and valeric. Butyric acid gives rancid butter its characteristic odor. Industrial wastes from the dairy industry must be treated with considerable care to prevent formation of butyric acid and consequent odor problems.

The names, formulas, and physical constants of the important saturated acids are given in Table 5-8. All the acids are considered weak acids from the viewpoint of ionization. Formic acid is the strongest of all.

*Nomenclature.* The common names are usually used for most of the acids, except for those with 7, 8, 9, and 10 carbon atoms. The IUC names are given in Table 5-8. In naming derivatives of acids, the IUC system is frequently abandoned for a system using Greek letters to identify the carbon atoms. In this system the carboxyl group is the reference point, and carbon atoms are numbered from it as follows:

$$\overset{5}{C}H_3\overset{4}{C}H_2\overset{3}{C}H_2\overset{2}{C}H_2\overset{1}{C}OOH$$
$$\underset{\delta}{\phantom{x}}\underset{\gamma}{\phantom{x}}\underset{\beta}{\phantom{x}}\underset{\alpha}{\phantom{x}}$$

The carbon atom next to the carboxyl group is *alpha*, the next *beta*, then *gamma, delta,* etc. The terminal carbon atom is also referred to as being in the *omega* position. The $\alpha$-amino acids are particularly important compounds and are discussed in Sec. 5-22.

**Unsaturated Monocarboxylic Acids.** The principal unsaturated monocarboxylic acids are as follows:

*Acrylic Acid* ($CH_2{=}CHCOOH$). Acrylic acid is used extensively because of its ability to polymerize, a characteristic of many compounds with unsaturated linkages.    Derivatives of the acid are used to form colorless plastics such as Lucite and Plexiglas.

*Oleic Acid* [$CH_3(CH_2)_7CH{=}CH(CH_2)_7COOH$]
*Linoleic Acid* [$CH_3(CH_2)_4CH{=}CHCH_2CH{=}CH(CH_2)_7COOH$]
*Linolenic Acid* [$CH_3(CH_2CH{=}CH)_3CH_2(CH_2)_6COOH$]

Oleic, linoleic, and linolenic acids are normal constituents of the glycerides of most fats and oils.    Oleic acid is considered to be an essential acid in the diet of man and animals.    Linoleic and linolenic acids as glycerides are important constituents of linseed and other drying oils.

TABLE 5-8. PHYSICAL CONSTANTS OF SOME NORMAL MONOCARBOXYLIC ACIDS*

| Common name | IUC name | Formula | Mp, °C | Bp, °C | Sp. gr., 20°/4° | $K_a$ at 25° |
|---|---|---|---|---|---|---|
| Formic | Methanoic | HCOOH | 8.4 | 100.7 | $1.226^{16°}$ | $2.14 \times 10^{-4}$ |
| Acetic | Ethanoic | $CH_3COOH$ | 16.6 | 118.1 | 1.049 | $1.75 \times 10^{-5}$ |
| Propionic | Propanoic | $C_2H_5COOH$ | −22 | 141.1 | 0.992 | $1.4 \ \times 10^{-5}$ |
| Butyric | Butanoic | $C_3H_7COOH$ | − 4.7 | 163.5 | 0.959 | $1.48 \times 10^{-5}$ |
| Valeric | Pentanoic | $C_4H_9COOH$ | −34.5 | 187 | 0.942 | $1.6 \ \times 10^{-5}$ |
| Caproic | Hexanoic | $C_5H_{11}COOH$ | − 2 | 205 | $0.945^{0°}$ | |
| Enanthic | Heptanoic | $C_6H_{13}COOH$ | −10 | 223.5 | $0.913^{25°}$ | |
| Caprylic | Octanoic | $C_7H_{15}COOH$ | 16 | 237.5 | 0.910 | |
| Pelargonic | Nonanoic | $C_8H_{17}COOH$ | 12 | 254 | 0.906 | |
| Capric | Decanoic | $C_9H_{19}COOH$ | 31.5 | 268–70 | $0.886^{40°}$ | |
| Palmitic | Hexadecanoic | $C_{15}H_{31}COOH$ | 64 | 339–56 (dec.) | $0.853^{62°}$ | |
| Stearic | Octadecanoic | $C_{17}H_{35}COOH$ | 69.4 | 383 | $0.847^{69°}$ | |

* From E. Wertheim and H. Jeskey, "Introductory Organic Chemistry," 3d ed., McGraw-Hill Book Company, Inc., New York, 1956.    Table reproduced by permission of the authors.

Their value for this purpose is dependent upon the multiple double bonds which they possess.

*Chemical Properties of Acids.*    The chemical properties of acids are determined largely by the carboxyl group.    All form metallic salts that have a wide range of commercial use.    In addition, the unsaturated acids have chemical properties characterized by the double bond, as described under unsaturated hydrocarbons in Sec. 5-2.    The unsaturated acids may be reduced with hydrogen to give corresponding saturated acids.

Organic acids serve as food for many microorganisms and are oxidized to carbon dioxide and water.    Ease and rate of oxidation are believed to be enhanced by the presence of unsaturated linkages.    The rate of biological attack on high-molecular-weight fatty acids is often limited by their solubility in water. This is a particular problem in sludge digesters where fatty materials tend to float in a scum layer.

**Polycarboxylic Acids.** The most important of the polycarboxylic acids are those that have two carboxyl groups, one on each end of a normal chain of carbon atoms. The most important acids are listed in Table 5-9.

TABLE 5-9. DICARBOXYLIC ACIDS

| Name | Formula |
|------|---------|
| Oxalic | $(COOH)_2$ |
| Malonic | $CH_2(COOH)_2$ |
| Succinic | $(CH_2)_2(COOH)_2$ |
| Glutaric | $(CH_2)_3(COOH)_2$ |
| Adipic | $(CH_2)_4(COOH)_2$ |
| Pimelic | $(CH_2)_5(COOH)_2$ |
| Suberic | $(CH_2)_6(COOH)_2$ |

Adipic acid is of some interest to sanitary engineers because it is used in the manufacture of nylon fiber and may be expected to occur in the industrial wastes of that industry.

**Hydroxy Acids.** Hydroxy acids have OH groups attached to the molecule other than in the carboxyl group. Thus they act chemically as acids and as alcohols. A number of the hydroxy acids have special names. Some examples are

| | |
|---|---|
| $HOCH_2COOH$ | Hydroxyacetic acid, glycolic acid |
| $CH_3CHOHCOOH$ | $\alpha$-Hydroxypropionic acid, lactic acid |
| $HOCH_2CH_2COOH$ | $\beta$-Hydroxypropionic acid, hydracrylic acid |
| $HOCH_2CH_2CH_2COOH$ | $\gamma$-Hydroxybutyric acid |

Lactic acid, $\alpha$-hydroxypropionic acid, is of special interest to sanitary engineers since it is formed during bacterial fermentation of milk and, therefore, is a normal constituent of industrial wastes from the dairy industry. Whey from cheese making contains considerable amounts of lactic acid. It is the principal acid in *sauerkraut* juice and prevents spoilage of the sauerkraut.

Lactic acid is also of interest because it is the first organic compound, to come to our attention, that possesses the property of *optical activity*. The common form of lactic acid is levorotatory and turns polarized light to the left. An uncommon form is dextrorotatory and turns polarized light to the right.

Many organic compounds are optically active. In order to be optically active, a compound must possess at least one *asymmetric* carbon atom. An asymmetric carbon atom is one having four dissimilar groups attached to it, as follows:

$$
\begin{array}{c}
\text{a} \\
| \\
\text{d}\!-\!\mathbf{C}\!-\!\text{b} \\
| \\
\text{c}
\end{array}
$$

Lactic acid has one asymmetric carbon atom, and two optical isomers are possible.

$$
\begin{array}{ccc}
\text{COOH} & & \text{COOH} \\
| & & | \\
\text{H}\!-\!\mathbf{C}\!-\!\text{OH} & \quad & \text{HO}\!-\!\mathbf{C}\!-\!\text{H} \\
| & & | \\
\text{CH}_3 & & \text{CH}_3
\end{array}
$$

D- and L-Lactic acids

**Hydroxy Polycarboxylic Acids.**    There are several hydroxy polycarboxylic acids.    Citric and tartaric are of interest to sanitary engineers.

$$
\left[
\begin{array}{c}
\text{H}_2\text{CCOOH} \\
| \\
\text{HOCCOOH} \\
| \\
\text{H}_2\text{CCOOH}
\end{array}
\right]\!\cdot\!\text{H}_2\text{O}
\qquad
\begin{array}{c}
\text{COOH} \\
| \\
\text{HCOH} \\
| \\
\text{HOCH} \\
| \\
\text{COOH}
\end{array}
$$

Citric acid            L(+)-Tartaric acid

Tartaric acid occurs in many fruits, especially grapes, and is present in canning and winery wastes.    Citric acid is the major acid of all citrus fruits: oranges, lemons, limes, and grapefruit.    It is, of course, a major component of the liquid wastes of the citrus industry.

## 5-6. Esters

Esters are compounds formed by the reaction of acids and alcohols. In organic chemistry, they correspond to salts in inorganic chemistry. The reaction between low-molecular-weight organic acids and alcohols is never complete.    Hydrolysis occurs and a reversible reaction results. The reaction may be represented by the general equation

$$
\text{RCOO}\!-\!\boxed{\text{H} + \text{HO}}\!-\!\text{R}_1 \rightleftharpoons \text{H}_2\text{O} + \text{RCOOR}_1
$$

$$(5\text{-}31)$$

or as        $\text{RCO}\!-\!\boxed{\text{OH} + \text{H}}\!-\!\text{OR}_1 \rightleftharpoons \text{H}_2\text{O} + \text{RCOOR}_1$

The general formula of an ester is

$$
\begin{array}{c}
\text{O} \\
\|\\
\text{R}\!-\!\text{C}\!-\!\text{O}\!-\!\text{R}'
\end{array}
$$

A wide variety of esters are used in chemical manufacturing.    Most esters have highly pleasing odors.    Butyl acetate smells like banana oil (amyl acetate) and is used for solvent purposes.    Many esters are used in flavoring extracts and perfumes.

Esters have been used to some extent as immiscible solvents in the separation and purification of antibiotics.    Considerable quantities often reach the sewer system and become an industrial waste problem. Enzymes liberated by many microorganisms hydrolyze esters to yield the corresponding acid and alcohol.

$$\begin{matrix} \text{O} \\ \| \\ \text{R--C--OR}' + \text{HOH} \end{matrix} \xrightarrow[\text{enzyme}]{} \text{RCOOH} + \text{R}'\text{--OH} \qquad (5\text{-}32)$$

The acid and alcohol serve as bacterial food and are oxidized to carbon dioxide and water, as discussed in Secs. 5-3 and 5-5.

## 5-7. Ethers

Ethers are formed by treatment of alcohols with strong dehydrating agents.    In the reaction, one molecule of water is removed from two molecules of alcohol.

$$\text{RO}[\text{H} + \text{HO}]\text{R} \xrightarrow[\substack{\text{dehydrating} \\ \text{agent}}]{\Delta} \text{R--O--R} + \text{H}_2\text{O} \qquad (5\text{-}33)$$
$$\hspace{7cm} \text{Ether}$$

The two fragments of the alcohol join to form an ether.    The alkyl groups are joined through an oxygen atom; thus, a carbon-to-oxygen-to-carbon bond, $-\overset{|}{\underset{|}{\text{C}}}-\text{O}-\overset{|}{\underset{|}{\text{C}}}-$, is established.

Ethers are used widely as solvents.    The low-molecular-weight ethers are highly flammable.    When left exposed to air, they are prone to form peroxides that are extremely explosive, particularly when recovery by distillation is practiced and the distillation is allowed to go to dryness. Diethyl ether has been used widely as an anesthetic.

Ethers are extremely resistant to biological oxidation.    Fortunately, they are relatively insoluble in water and can be separated from industrial wastes by flotation or decantation procedures.

## 5-8. Alkyl Halides

The *alkyl halides* are used extensively in organic synthesis, and a few of them have important industrial uses.

**Simple Alkyl Halides.**    The simple alkyl halides (R—X) may be prepared by treatment of an alcohol with $PCl_3$.

$$\begin{aligned} 3\text{ROH} + \text{PCl}_3 &\rightarrow \text{P(OH)}_3 + 3\text{RCl} \\ 3\text{CH}_3\text{CH}_2\text{CH}_2\text{OH} + \text{PCl}_3 &\rightarrow \text{P(OH)}_3 + 3\text{C}_3\text{H}_7\text{Cl} \end{aligned} \qquad (5\text{-}34)$$
$$\hspace{5cm} \textit{n}\text{-Propyl chloride}$$

Phosphorus bromide may also be employed:

$$3ROH + PBr_3 \rightarrow P(OH)_3 + 3RBr \qquad (5\text{-}35)$$

The alkyl halides are of great value in organic synthesis because they react with potassium cyanide to form compounds with an additional carbon atom.

$$R \cdot \overline{[I + K]} \cdot CN \longrightarrow KI + R \cdot CN \qquad (5\text{-}36)$$
$$\text{A nitrile}$$
$$\text{(alkyl}$$
$$\text{cyanide)}$$

The nitrile formed can be hydrolyzed to an acid and then reduced to an alcohol, if desired. The alcohol can be converted to an alkyl halide and the process repeated. In this manner the organic chemist can increase the length of carbon-chain compounds one atom at a time.

Methyl chloride ($CH_3Cl$) and ethyl chloride ($C_2H_5Cl$) were used extensively as refrigerants in the past. Ethyl chloride is used in the manufacture of tetraethyl lead, great quantities of which are used in the production of high-octane, antiknock, gasolines.

$$4C_2H_5Cl + 4NaPb \text{ (alloy)} \xrightarrow{40\text{-}60°} 4NaCl + 3Pb + (C_2H_5)_4Pb \qquad (5\text{-}37)$$
$$\text{Tetraethyl lead}$$

**Polyhalogen Compounds.** A wide variety of *polyhalogen* compounds are used for industrial purposes.

*Ethylene Bromide.* Ethylene bromide is formed from ethylene by addition of bromine. It has many industrial uses.

$$\begin{array}{ccc} H & H & \qquad\qquad H \ \ H \\ HC{=}CH + Br_2 \rightarrow & HC{-}CH \\ & Br \ \ Br \end{array} \qquad (5\text{-}38)$$
$$\text{Ethylene bromide}$$

*Chloroform* ($CHCl_3$). Chloroform (trichloromethane) was one of our first anesthetics (1847) and was widely used until about 1920. It is used in industry as a solvent for oils, waxes, etc. It is nonflammable and relatively nontoxic.

*Carbon Tetrachloride* ($CCl_4$). Carbon tetrachloride (tetrachloromethane) is widely used as a fire extinguisher in small units (Pyrene) and as a solvent. It is considered a toxic compound, and its use should be restricted to well-ventilated areas. Its use as a fire extinguisher is fraught with some danger. In contact with hot iron and oxygen it is converted to phosgene ($COCl_2$), a highly toxic gas. For this reason, trained fire fighters use other types of fire-fighting equipment.

*Freon* ($CCl_2F_2$). Freon is dichlorodifluoromethane. It is the preferred refrigerant in household appliances because of its nonflammable and nontoxic properties.

## 5-9. Simple Compounds Containing Nitrogen

The simple aliphatic compounds containing nitrogen are of three types: amines, amides, and nitriles (cyanides).

**Amines.** The amines are alkyl derivatives of ammonia. They are of three types: primary, secondary, and tertiary.

$$
\begin{array}{ccc}
& R & R \\
& \diagdown & \diagdown \\
R-NH_2 & NH & N-R'' \\
\text{Primary} & \diagup & \diagup \\
\text{amine} & R' & R' \\
& \text{Secondary}[1] & \text{Tertiary}[1] \\
& \text{amine} & \text{amine}
\end{array}
$$

In *primary amines*, one hydrogen atom of ammonia has been replaced by an alkyl group such as $CH_3-$, $C_2H_5-$, etc. In *secondary amines*, two hydrogen atoms of ammonia have been replaced by alkyl groups, and in *tertiary amines*, all three hydrogens have been replaced. The amines, like ammonia, are all basic in reaction. The basicity increases from primary to tertiary.

The amines are found in certain industrial wastes, particularly those from the fish and beet-sugar industries. Very little is known about their susceptibility to biological oxidation.

Tertiary amines combine with alkyl halides to form *quaternary ammonium salts* as follows:

$$
\begin{array}{c}
R \\
| \\
R-N \\
| \\
R
\end{array}
+ RCl \xrightarrow{\Delta}
\left[
\begin{array}{c}
R \\
| \\
R-N-R \\
| \\
R
\end{array}
\right]^+
+ Cl^- \qquad (5\text{-}39)
$$

The compounds formed are actually chloride salts and ionize to form a quaternary ammonium ion and a chloride ion. The quaternary ammonium salts have bactericidal properties which can be enhanced by the proper choice of the R groups. They are, therefore, of interest to public health engineers who find them useful as disinfecting agents in food- and beverage-dispensing establishments. They are also used as disinfectants in the laundering of babies' diapers to control infections of bacteria responsible for the rapid hydrolysis of urea. Solutions of the quaternary ammonium salts are sold for disinfecting purposes under a variety of trade names.

**Amides.** The amides may be considered as being derived from organic acids and ammonia under special conditions. The ordinary reaction between ammonia and an organic acid, of course, produces an **ammonium salt.**

[1] R, R', and R'' represent alkyl groups. All may be different or alike.

$$RCOOH + NH_3 \rightarrow RCOO^- + NH_4^+ \qquad (5\text{-}40)$$

Under special conditions, an amide results.

$$R-\overset{\overset{\textstyle O}{\|}}{C}\!-\!\overline{OH + H}\!-\!NH_2 \longrightarrow R-\overset{\overset{\textstyle O}{\|}}{C}\!-\!NH_2 + H_2O \quad (5\text{-}41)$$
Amide

Amides are of considerable significance to organic chemists in synthetic work. When they are caused to react with a halogen (Hofmann reaction) an atom of carbon is lost from the amide, and an amine with one less carbon atom is formed.

$$CH_3CONH_2 + Br_2 + 4NaOH \rightarrow$$
$$2NaBr + Na_2CO_3 + 2H_2O + CH_3NH_2 \quad (5\text{-}42)$$

This constitutes a method of reducing the length of a carbon chain by one atom.

Amides are of little importance to the sanitary engineer except that the *amide group* $\left(\overset{\overset{\textstyle O}{\|}}{-C}\!-\!NH_2\right)$ is related to the *peptide linkage* $\left(\overset{\overset{\textstyle O}{\|}}{-C}\!-\!\overset{\textstyle H}{N}\!-\right)$, as discussed in Sec. 5-22.

*Urea,*

$$\begin{array}{c} NH_2 \\ | \\ C\!=\!O \\ | \\ NH_2 \end{array}$$

is an amide of considerable importance because of its many commercial uses and because it is a normal constituent of urine. It is a constituent of many agricultural fertilizers and is used in the manufacture of synthetic resins.

Although urea was originally considered to be an organic compound and its accidental production from ammonium cyanate by Wöhler is considered to have initiated the modern age of organic chemistry, it is, in effect, an inorganic compound since it cannot be used by saprophytic bacteria as a source of energy. In aqueous solutions containing soil bacteria, urea is hydrolyzed to carbon dioxide and ammonia. These combine to form ammonium bicarbonate and ammonium hydroxide in the presence of water.

$$\begin{array}{c} NH_2 \\ \diagup \\ C\!=\!O + H_2O \xrightarrow[\text{enzymes}]{\text{bact.}} CO_2 + 2NH_3 \\ \diagdown \\ NH_2 \end{array} \qquad (5\text{-}43)$$

and $\qquad CO_2 + 2NH_3 + 2H_2O \rightarrow NH_4HCO_3 + NH_4OH \qquad (5\text{-}44)$

The penetrating odor of latrines, privies, and some urinals is due to bacterial infections and their action on urea with subsequent release of free ammonia to the atmosphere. The use of disinfectants will control the decomposition of urea and, thereby, control odors.

**Nitriles.** *Nitriles*, or organic cyanides, are important compounds of industry. They have the general formula R—CN, and the R group may be saturated or unsaturated. The names and formulas of a few nitriles of industrial importance are given in Table 5-10.

TABLE 5-10. IMPORTANT NITRILES

| Name as nitrile | Name as cyanide | Formula |
|---|---|---|
| Acetonitrile | Methyl cyanide | $CH_3$—CN |
| Propionitrile | Ethyl cyanide | $CH_3$—$CH_2$—CN |
| Acrylonitrile | Vinyl cyanide | $CH_2$=CH—CN |

The nitriles are used extensively in the manufacture of synthetic fibers and can be expected to be present in industrial wastes of that industry. Some are quite toxic to microorganisms.

## 5-10. Cyclic Aliphatic Compounds

A number of *cyclic aliphatic* hydrocarbons are known. Many of these occur in petroleum and are known as naphthenes.

Cyclopropane    Cyclopentane    Cyclohexane

They are characterized by having two atoms of hydrogen attached to each carbon in the ring; i.e., they are saturated.

A wide variety of cyclic alcohols and ketones are known. Examples are cyclohexanol and cyclohexanone.

Cyclohexanol    Cyclohexanone

## 5-11. Mercaptans or Thioalcohols

*Mercaptans* or *thioalcohols* are aliphatic compounds that contain sulfur. They have a structure similar to alcohols except that oxygen is replaced by sulfur.

$$\text{ROH} \qquad \text{RSH}$$

Alcohol      Mercaptan

Mercaptans are noted for their disagreeable odor and are found in certain industrial wastes, particularly those from the pulping of wood by the Kraft or sulfate process.   They are considered to be quite toxic to fish. The odor of skunks is largely due to butyl mercaptan.

## AROMATIC COMPOUNDS

## 5-12. Introduction

The *aromatic* organic compounds are all ring compounds or have cyclic groups of aromatic nature in their structure.   The carbon atoms in these ring compounds have only one free valence bond, in contrast to those in aliphatic compounds with two.

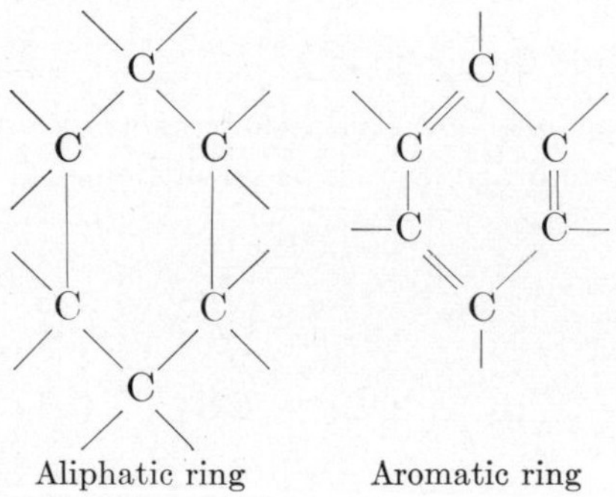

Aliphatic ring          Aromatic ring

The simplest aromatic ring is made up of six carbon atoms and is known as the benzene ring.   *Benzene* ($C_6H_6$) is known as the *parent compound* of the aromatic series.   The benzene ring is usually represented by the Kekule formula.

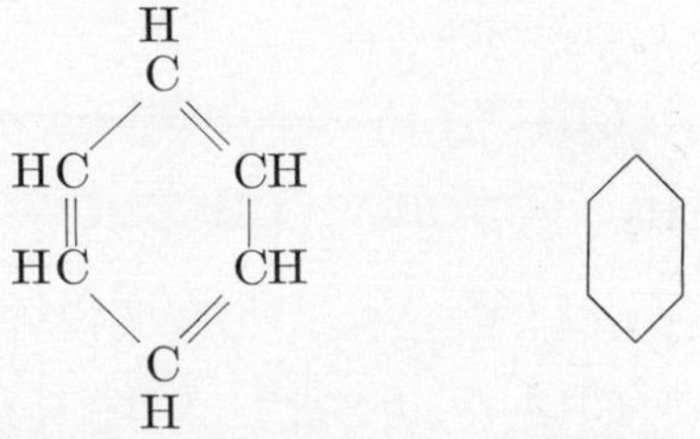

Kekule benzene formula      Simplified formula

This formula shows double bonds between alternate carbon atoms in the ring. The double bonds, however, are not like those in the aliphatic series. For example, halogens will not add to such bonds. In order to avoid confusion and for purposes of simplicity, most chemists represent the benzene ring without double bonds, as in the simplified formula above.

**Nomenclature.** It is important to note that carbon atoms are not shown in the simplified benzene formula. Also, each carbon atom in a ring is like all others, and, therefore, when substitution occurs on one carbon atom, the same compound is formed as though substitution had occurred on any of the other five carbon atoms. Thus, for monochlorobenzene ($C_6H_5Cl$) there is only one compound, no matter how the structural formula is written.

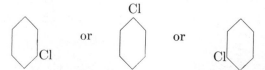

When substitution occurs on two or more carbon atoms of a benzene ring, it becomes necessary to establish some system of nomenclature. Two systems are in vogue.

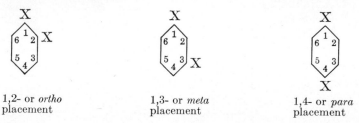

1,2- or *ortho* placement

1,3- or *meta* placement

1,4- or *para* placement

Di-substituted compounds, such as dichlorobenzene, are commonly referred to as *ortho, meta,* or *para,* depending upon the point of substitution. If substitution is on adjacent carbon atoms, the term ortho is used; if on carbon atoms once removed, the term meta is used; and if on carbon atoms opposite each other, the term para is used. Tri- and other poly-substituted compounds must be named by the other system. In this system, the carbon atoms of the benzene ring are numbered in a clockwise manner. Examples are

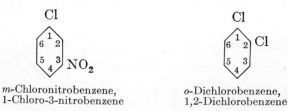

*m*-Chloronitrobenzene, 1-Chloro-3-nitrobenzene

*o*-Dichlorobenzene, 1,2-Dichlorobenzene

p-Bromotoluene,
1-Bromo-4-methylbenzene

2,5-Dichloro-1-nitrobenzene

When the benzene ring is attached to aliphatic compounds, the products are also called *phenyl* derivatives, the phenyl group being $C_6H_5$—. Thus, ethyl benzene is also phenyl ethane.

## 5-13. Hydrocarbons

Two series of homologous aromatic hydrocarbons are known: the benzene and the polyring series.

**Benzene Series.** The benzene series of homologous compounds is made up of alkyl substitution products of benzene. They are found along with benzene in coal tar and in many crude petroleums. Table 5-11

TABLE 5-11. BENZENE-SERIES HYDROCARBONS*

| Name | Formula | Mp, °C | Bp, °C | Sp. gr., 20°/4° |
|---|---|---|---|---|
| Benzene | $C_6H_6$ | 5.51 | 80.09 | 0.879 |
| Toluene | $C_6H_5 \cdot CH_3$ | −95 | 110.8 | 0.866 |
| o-Xylene | $C_6H_4(CH_3)_2$ | −29 | 144 | 0.875 |
| m-Xylene | | −53.6 | 138.8 | 0.864 |
| p-Xylene | | 13.2 | 138.5 | 0.861 |
| Ethylbenzene | $C_6H_5 \cdot C_2H_5$ | −93.9 | 136.15 | 0.867 |

* From E. Wertheim and H. Jeskey, "Introductory Organic Chemistry," 3d ed., McGraw-Hill Book Company, Inc., New York, 1956. Table reproduced by permission of the authors.

lists the benzene-series hydrocarbons of commercial importance. *Toluene*, or methyl benzene, is the simplest alkyl derivative of benzene. *Xylene* is a dimethyl derivative of benzene.

Toluene    Ethylbenzene    o-Xylene    m-Xylene    p-Xylene

It exists in three isomeric forms: ortho-xylene, meta-xylene, and para-xylene. All are isomeric with ethyl benzene in that they have the same general formula, $C_8H_{10}$.

The benzene-series hydrocarbons are used extensively as solvents and in chemical synthesis. Because of their relative insolubility in water, they are normally not a problem in industrial wastes.

**Polyring Hydrocarbons.** A wide variety of polyring aromatic hydrocarbons are known. A few examples will illustrate the possibilities.

*Naphthalene* $(C_{10}H_8)$. *Naphthalene* is a white crystalline compound derived from coal tar and was formerly used to produce moth balls.

It has been displaced largely from this market by paradichlorobenzene. A new system of nomenclature is applied to this type of compound. Carbon atoms adjacent to those shared in common by the two rings are known as $\alpha$-carbon atoms and the others are known as $\beta$-carbon atoms. The carbon atoms shared by the two rings do not have hydrogen attached to them and so are given no designation. The specific name, naphthalene, should not be confused with naphthene (Sec. 5-10).

*Anthracene* $(C_{14}H_{10})$ *and Phenanthrene* $(C_{14}H_{10})$. *Anthracene* and *phenanthrene* are isomers.

Anthracene                    Phenanthrene

Their formulas illustrate the possible ways in which polyring aromatic hydrocarbons may occur. Many other more complex compounds, such as *chrysene* and *picene*, are known.

Chrysene                    Picene

It should be remembered that hydrogen atoms occur on all carbon atoms of these compounds that are not common to two rings.

Napthalene and anthracene are widely used in the manufacture of dyestuffs. The phenanthrene nucleus is found in important alkaloids, such as morphine, vitamin D, sex hormones, and other compounds of great biological significance.

### 5-14. Phenols

The phenols are among the most important of the aromatic compounds.

**Monohydric Phenols.**　There are several monohydric phenols of interest to sanitary engineers.

*Phenol* ($C_6H_5OH$).　The monohydroxy derivative of benzene is known as *phenol*.

H
O

Its formula and name indicate that it might correspond in the aromatic series to alcohols in the aliphatic series. This is not the case, however. Phenol is known to the layman as carbolic acid. It ionizes to yield $H^+$ to a limited extent ($K_a = 1.2 \times 10^{-10}$) and in concentrated solution is quite toxic to bacteria. It has been used widely as a germicide, and disinfectants have been rated in terms of "phenol coefficients," i.e., relative disinfecting power with respect to phenol. The system is considered archaic at the present time.

Phenol is recovered from coal tar, and considerable amounts are manufactured synthetically. It is used extensively in the synthesis of organic products, particularly phenolic-type resins. It occurs as a natural component in industrial wastes from the coal-gas, coal-coking, and petroleum industries as well as in a wide variety of industrial wastes from processes involving the use of phenol as a raw material.

Biological treatment of wastes containing more than 25 mg/l of phenol was considered impossible until relatively recent times. Research at the Dow Chemical Co. plant in Midland, Michigan, and elsewhere[1] has shown that phenol will serve as a bacterial food without serious toxic effects at levels as high as 500 mg/l. Studies with it and with formaldehyde have established the concept of toxicity thresholds. At levels below the threshold, bacteria use the material as food, but above the threshold they find it too toxic for use as food and reproduction of the organisms.

[1] R. E. McKinney, H. D. Tomlinson, and R. L. Wilcox, *Sewage and Ind. Wastes*, **28**, 547–557 (1956).

*Cresols.* The next higher homologues of phenol are cresols.

o-Cresol      m-Cresol      p-Cresol

They are found in coal tar and have a higher germicidal action than phenol. They are less toxic to man. *Lysol* is a mixture of cresols which is sold as a household and sickroom disinfectant. Cresols are the major constituents of "creosote" which is used extensively for the preservation of wood.

Industrial wastes containing cresols are difficult to treat by biological methods. Research[1] has shown the pure cresols to be relatively nontoxic at concentrations of 250 mg/l. The toxicity of crude cresols is believed, therefore, to be due to other compounds.

**Polyhydric Phenols.** Three isomeric dihydric phenols are known. All have been shown[1] to be readily oxidized by properly acclimated activated sludges.

Benzene-1,2-diol,    Benzene-1,3-diol,    Benzene-1,4-diol,
Pyrocatechol,        Resorcinol         Hydroquinone
Catechol

*Pyrogallol.* *Pyrogallol*, 1,2,3-trihydroxybenzene, is known as *pyrogallic acid*.

It is easily oxidized and serves as a photographic developer. Sanitary engineers often use alkaline solutions of it to remove oxygen from gases. It may be used in gas analysis to absorb oxygen and allow its measurement. Pyrogallol is a minor constituent of spent tan liquors. When they are discharged to streams containing iron, inky black ferric pyrogallate is formed.

[1] *Ibid.*

## 5-15. Alcohols, Aldehydes, Ketones, and Acids

The aromatic alcohols, aldehydes, ketones, and acids are all formed from alkyl derivatives of benzene or one of its homologues. The active group is always in the alkyl group, and, therefore, the chemistry of the aromatic alcohols, aldehydes, ketones, and acids is very similar to that of the corresponding aliphatic compounds. Common names are usually employed with these compounds, but they may be more properly named as phenyl derivatives of aliphatic compounds.

**Alcohols.** The aromatic alcohols compose a homologous series. They are phenyl methyl, phenyl ethyl, phenyl n-propyl, phenyl isopropyl, etc.

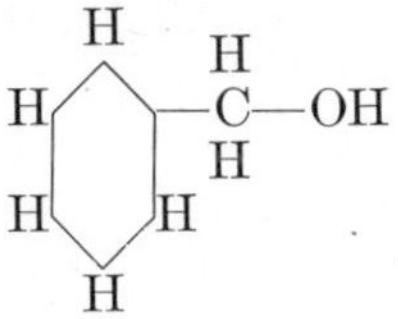

Benzyl alcohol
Phenyl methyl alcohol

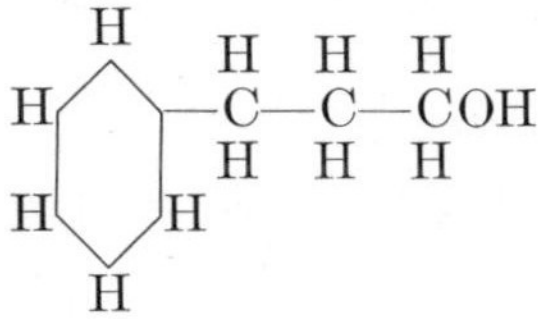

Phenyl, n-propyl alcohol

The aromatic alcohols are subject to chemical and biological oxidation. Oxidation of primary alcohols produces aldehydes and of secondary alcohols produces ketones.

**Aldehydes.** The aromatic aldehydes are important compounds in chemical synthesis.

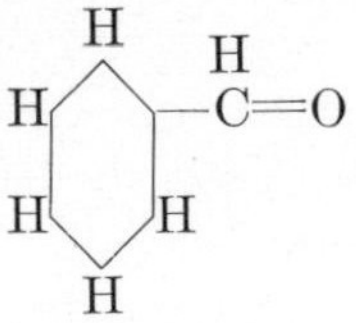

Benzaldehyde

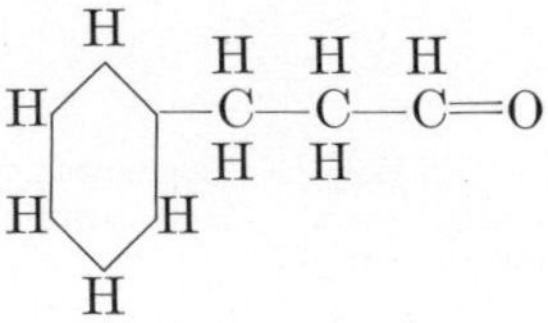

Phenyl propyl aldehyde

They are easily oxidized to the corresponding acids. Many of the more complex aldehydes have fragrant odors: coumarin, anisaldehyde, vanillin, etc.

**Ketones.** The aromatic ketones are of two types: those that have one phenyl group attached to the carbonyl group and those that have two.

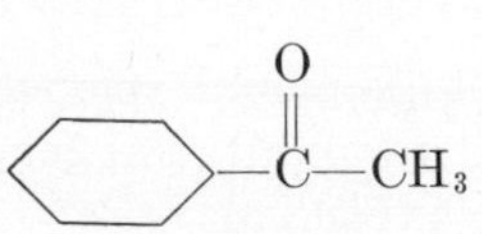

Acetophenone

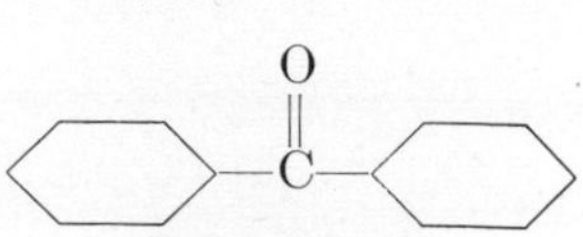

Benzophenone

Chemical and biological oxidation results in disruption of the molecule with the formation of lower-molecular-weight acids and, possibly, carbon dioxide.

**Acids.**   A wide variety of aromatic, monocarboxylic acids are known. Oxidation of benzaldehyde produces benzoic acid.   Sodium benzoate is used as a food preservative.   Salicylic acid is used to prepare aspirin.

Benzoic acid          Salicylic acid

Oxidation of naphthalene produces an important dicarboxylic acid, phthalic acid.

Phthalic acid          Phthalic
                       anhydride

It and its anhydride are important in the manufacture of a variety of organic compounds.   Phenolphthalein,

Phenolphthalein

used as an indicator in the laboratory, is an example.

The aromatic acids are subject to biological oxidation.   The normal end products are carbon dioxide and water.

## 5-16. Simple Compounds Containing Nitrogen

The aromatic compounds containing nitrogen are either derivatives of ammonia or of nitric acid.   The former are called *amines*, and the latter are called *nitro* compounds.   In addition, many complex nitrogen compounds exist which are outside the scope of this book.

**Amines.**   The aromatic amines are of two types: those in which the phenyl or other aromatic group is attached directly to nitrogen and those in which the nitrogen occurs in an attached alkyl group.   There are three phenyl derivatives of ammonia: primary, secondary, and tertiary amines.

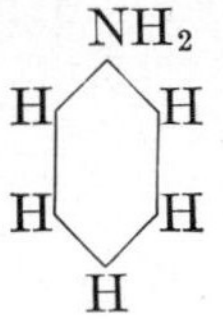

Aniline

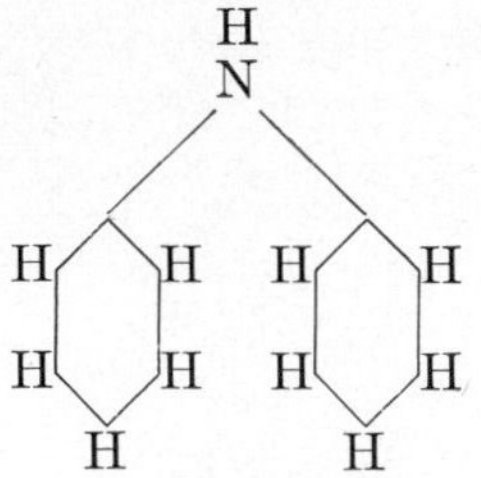

Diphenylamine

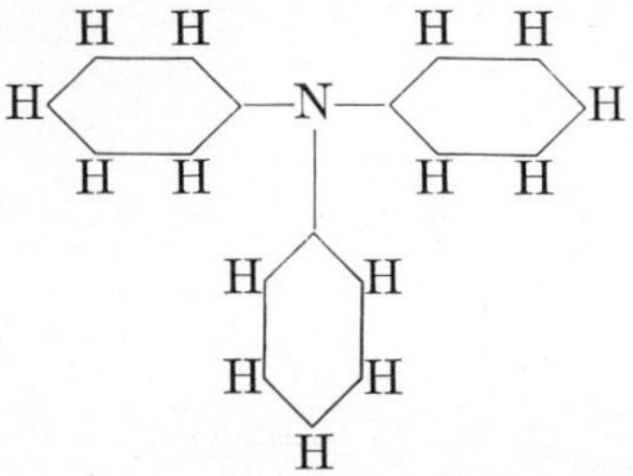

Triphenylamine

The primary form is called aniline and the secondary form is diphenyl-amine. They are both basic in character, react with strong acids to form salts, and are important compounds in organic synthesis. Aniline dyes are derived from aniline. Sulfanilic acid, used in the colorimetric determination of nitrites, is made from aniline.

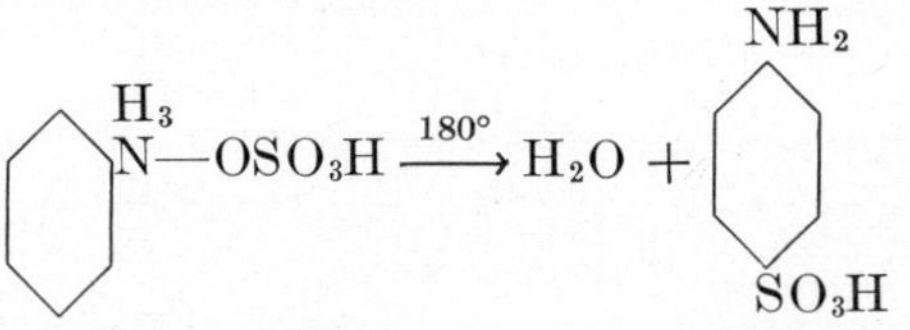

$$\text{Aniline hydrogen sulfate} \xrightarrow{180°} H_2O + \text{Sulfanilic acid} \qquad (5\text{-}46)$$

*α-Naphthylamine* is an important compound in sanitary analysis.

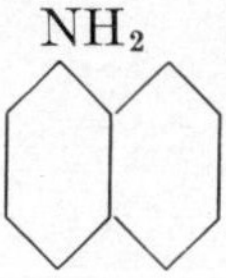

It is used in conjunction with sulfanilic acid in the determination of nitrites or nitrite nitrogen.

*Benzylamine* ($C_6H_5CH_2NH_2$) is an example of an aromatic amine that has the —$NH_2$ group attached to the aliphatic part of the molecule. They are not important commercially.

**Nitro Compounds.** Nitric acid reacts with benzene and other aromatic compounds to form *nitro* compounds. The reaction is as follows:

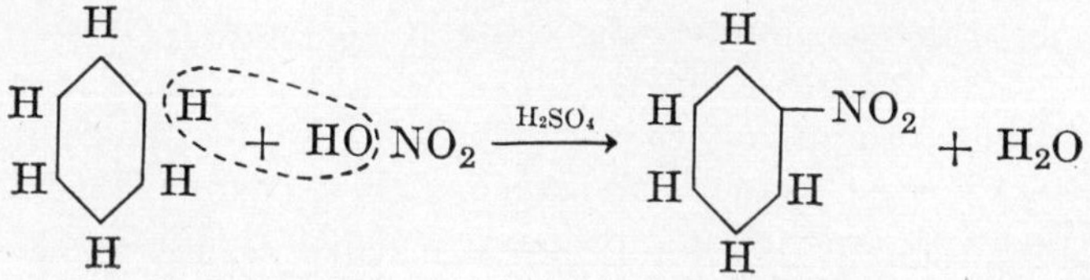

$$\text{benzene} + HO\text{-}NO_2 \xrightarrow{H_2SO_4} \text{Nitrobenzene} + H_2O \qquad (5\text{-}47)$$

A dehydrating agent, usually sulfuric acid, must be present to remove the water that is formed.   One additional nitro group may be added under proper conditions.   The principal product is *m*-dinitrobenzene,

m-Dinitrobenzene          Trinitrotoluene (TNT)

as the presence of the first nitro group directs the second into the meta position.   Trinitrobenzene is very difficult to prepare.

Nitration of toluene results in the formation of trinitrotoluene, or TNT. The first nitro group is directed into the ortho position by the methyl group, and additional nitro groups attach in meta positions with respect to the first nitro group.   TNT is widely used as an ingredient of military explosives.

## HETEROCYCLIC COMPOUNDS

### 5-17. Heterocyclic Compounds

Heterocyclic compounds have one other element in the ring in addition to carbon.   A wide variety of compounds exists; some are aliphatic in character, and some are aromatic.   Several are of importance to sanitary engineers.

*Furaldehyde*, or *furfural*, is an example of an aliphatic heterocyclic compound having a five-membered ring containing oxygen.   It is produced from pentose sugars by dehydration.   Commercially it is made from oat hulls and corn cobs, waste products of the cereal industry.

Furaldehyde

Both were formerly disposed of by burning.   Manufacture of furfural yields some liquid wastes of concern to sanitary engineers.

*Pyrrole* and *pyrrolidine* are examples of heterocyclic compounds having five-membered rings containing nitrogen.

Pyrrole                              Pyrrolidine

The pyrrole or pyrrolidine ring occurs in the structure of many important natural compounds, e.g., nicotine, cocaine, chlorophyll, hemoglobin.

*Pyridine* is an example of a six-membered aromatic heterocyclic compound with nitrogen contained in the ring.

It is an especially vile-smelling liquid. It is used as a denaturant in ethyl alcohol, to make it unpalatable, and in chemical synthesis. It is weakly basic in character and forms salts with strong acids.

*Indole* and *skatole* are examples of heterocyclic compounds that possess a benzene nucleus condensed with a pyrrole nucleus.

Indole          Skatole

Both possess unpleasant odors and are produced during the putrefaction of protein matter. Under controlled conditions, such as exist in well-operated digesters for sewage sludge, very little indole or skatole is formed.

### 5-18. Dyes

The subject of *dyes* is of such magnitude and complexity that a discussion of various types will not be presented here. The sanitary engineer concerned with the treatment of textile wastes, and possibly a few others, will be confronted with the need to learn more about the materials. Recourse for information should be made to standard organic chemistry texts or treatises on dyes. The sulfur dyes are noted for their toxic properties.

### THE COMMON FOODS AND RELATED COMPOUNDS

### 5-19. General

The term *food* applies to a wide variety of organic materials that can serve as a source of energy for living organisms. In the case of bacteria, these compounds range from hydrocarbons through various oxidation products, including organic acids. In the case of higher animals and humans, the principal or common foods are restricted to *carbohydrates*, *fats*, and *proteins*. Other organic compounds such as ethyl alcohol, certain aldehydes, and many acids serve as food or energy sources also. The latter are sometimes referred to as exotic foods, as they are not considered part of an essential diet but are added to increase palatability or for other reasons.

## 5-20. Carbohydrates

The term *carbohydrate* is applied to all compounds of carbon, hydrogen, and oxygen in which the hydrogen and oxygen are in the same ratio as in water, i.e., two atoms of hydrogen for each atom of oxygen. The processing of carbohydrate materials occurs in the lumber, paper, and textile industries as well as in the food industry. Wastes from these industries are major problems and tax the ingenuity of sanitary engineers to find satisfactory solutions.

Carbohydrates may be grouped into three general classifications, depending upon the complexity of their structure: (1) simple sugars, or *monosaccharides;* (2) complex sugars, or *disaccharides;* (3) *polysaccharides.* In general, the *-ose* ending is used to name carbohydrates.

**Simple Sugars, or Monosaccharides.** The simple sugars, or *monosaccharides*, all contain a carbonyl group in the form of an aldehyde or a keto group. Those with aldehyde groups are known as *aldoses* and those with keto groups are known as *ketoses.* They are also glycols as they possess several OH groups. Two series of simple sugars are of importance commercially: The *pentoses* are five-carbon-atom sugars and the hexoses are six-carbon-atom sugars.

*Pentoses.* Pentoses have the general formula $C_5H_{10}O_5$. Two pentoses are of commercial importance and both are *aldopentoses*. *Xylose* is formed by the hydrolysis of pentosans which are commonly found in waste organic materials such as oat hulls, corn cobs, and cottonseed hulls. Considerable amounts of xylose are formed in the pulping of wood through hydrolysis of hemicellulose. *Arabinose* is produced by the hydrolysis of gum arabic or wheat bran.

D(−)-Xylose[1]          D(−)-Arabinose[1]

---

[1] All sugars are optically active. The nomenclature is a bit confusing, however, and details should be obtained from a standard text on organic chemistry.

Both xylose and arabinose are used in bacteriological work in media used to differentiate among various bacteria. Certain bacteria can ferment one but not the other, and vice versa. Mixed cultures of bacteria, such as those derived from the soil or sewage, convert both sugars to carbon dioxide and water. The pentose sugars are not fermented by yeast under anaerobic conditions; therefore, they cannot be used to produce ethyl alcohol. They do serve as an energy source for yeast under aerobic conditions, however, and advantage is taken of this fact in one method of treating spent sulfite liquors from the pulping of wood.

*Hexoses.* There are four hexose sugars with the general formula $C_6H_{12}O_6$. *Glucose, galactose,* and *mannose* are all *aldoses,* and *fructose* is a *ketose.*

GLUCOSE. Glucose is the most common of the aldohexose sugars. It is found naturally in fruit juices and in honey. It is manufactured in great quantity by the hydrolysis of corn starch. It is the principal component of corn syrup. Both corn syrup and glucose are used extensively in candy manufacture. Glucose is much less sweet than ordinary sugar and replaces it for many purposes.

$$
\begin{array}{c}
H \\
C{=}O \\
| \\
H{-}C{-}OH \\
| \\
HO{-}C{-}H \\
| \\
H{-}C{-}OH \\
| \\
H{-}C{-}OH \\
| \\
CH_2OH
\end{array}
$$

D-Glucose

Glucose is the only hexose sugar that can be prepared in relatively pure form by hydrolysis of disaccharides or polysaccharides. All the other hexose sugars occur in combination with glucose.

FRUCTOSE. Fructose is the only ketohexose and occurs naturally in honey. When cane or beet sugar is hydrolyzed, one molecule of fructose and one molecule of glucose are formed from each molecule of sucrose.

GALACTOSE AND MANNOSE. Galactose and mannose do not occur in free form in nature. Galactose is produced by hydrolysis of lactose, more commonly called milk sugar. Glucose is formed simultaneously. Mannose is produced by the hydrolysis of ivory nut, and glucose is formed at the same time.

$$\begin{array}{ccc}
\text{CH}_2\text{OH} & \text{H} & \text{H} \\
| & \text{C}=\text{O} & \text{C}=\text{O} \\
\text{C}=\text{O} & \text{H}-\text{C}-\text{OH} & \text{HO}-\text{C}-\text{H} \\
\text{HO}-\text{C}-\text{H} & \text{HO}-\text{C}-\text{H} & \text{HO}-\text{C}-\text{H} \\
\text{H}-\text{C}-\text{OH} & \text{HO}-\text{C}-\text{H} & \text{H}-\text{C}-\text{OH} \\
\text{H}-\text{C}-\text{OH} & \text{H}-\text{C}-\text{OH} & \text{H}-\text{C}-\text{OH} \\
\text{CH}_2\text{OH} & \text{CH}_2\text{OH} & \text{CH}_2\text{OH} \\
\text{D}(-)\text{-Fructose} & \text{D-Galactose} & \text{D-Mannose}
\end{array}$$

Glucose and galactose are of particular interest to sanitary engineers. Glucose is always one of the products and may be the sole product when di- or polysaccharides are hydrolyzed. It, therefore, is found in a wide variety of industrial wastes. Galactose is formed from the hydrolysis of lactose, or milk sugar, and is found in wastes from the dairy industry. Both sugars are readily oxidized by aerobic bacteria to form acids, and the oxidation may stop at that point because of the unfavorable pH conditions produced by the acids unless precautions are taken to control the pH by means of buffers or alkaline materials. Lactic acid is an important intermediate in the oxidation of galactose. Both sugars are fermented rapidly under anaerobic conditions, with acid formation.

**Complex Sugars, or Disaccharides.** There are three important sugars with the general formula $C_{12}H_{22}O_{11}$: *sucrose, maltose,* and *lactose.* All disaccharides may be considered as consisting of two hexose sugars hooked together in one molecule. Hydrolysis results in cleavage of the molecule and formation of the hexoses.

*Sucrose.* Sucrose is the common sugar of commerce. It is derived largely from sugar cane and sugar beets. The sap of such trees as the sugar maple contains considerable sucrose. Hydrolysis of the sucrose molecule results in the formation of one molecule of glucose and one molecule of fructose.

Sucrose ($C_{12}H_{22}O_{11}$)

*Maltose.* Maltose does not occur in nature. It is made by hydrolysis of starch, induced by *diastase*, an enzyme present in barley malt. The starch may be derived from a wide variety of sources, and its hydrolysis by diastase results in commercial maltose which is used in infant foods and in malted milk.

$$
\begin{array}{ll}
\text{H—C}{=}\text{O} & \text{H—C} \\
\text{H—C—OH} \quad \text{O} & \text{H—C—OH} \\
\text{HO—C—H} & \text{HO—O—H} \quad \text{O} \\
\text{H—C} & \text{H—C—OH} \\
\text{H—C—OH} & \text{H—C} \\
\text{CH}_2\text{OH} & \text{CH}_2\text{OH}
\end{array}
$$

Maltose $(C_{12}H_{22}O_{11})$

Maltose is readily hydrolyzed to yield two molecules of glucose.

Alcohol production by fermentation processes uses starch from a wide variety of sources. The starch is converted to maltose by the enzyme from barley malt. Enzymes from the yeast hydrolyze maltose to glucose and convert the glucose to alcohol and carbon dioxide. See Sec. 5-3.

*Lactose.* Lactose, or milk sugar, occurs in the milk of all mammals. Upon hydrolysis, the molecule is split to yield a molecule of glucose and a molecule of galactose.

$$
\begin{array}{lll}
& \text{H—C}{=}\text{O} & \text{H} \\
& & \text{C} \\
& \text{H—C—OH} & \text{H—C—OH} \\
& \quad \text{O} & \\
& \text{HO—C—H} & \text{HO—C—H} \quad \text{O} \\
\text{Glucose} & \text{H—C} & \text{HO—C—H} \quad \text{Galactose} \\
\text{part} & & \text{part} \\
& \text{H—C—OH} & \text{H—C} \\
& \text{CH}_2\text{OH} & \text{CH}_2\text{OH}
\end{array}
$$

Lactose $(C_{12}H_{22}O_{11})$

Lactose is used in infant foods and in candy making. Dried skimmed-milk solids contain about 60 per cent lactose.

**Polysaccharides.** The polysaccharides are all condensation products of hexoses or other monosaccharides. Glucose and xylose are the most common units involved. Three polysaccharides are of interest to sanitary engineers: *starch, cellulose,* and *hemicellulose.* None of them have the characteristic sweet taste of sugars because of their insolubility and complex molecular structure.

*Starch.* Starch has the general formula $(C_6H_{10}O_5)_x$. It occurs in a wide variety of products grown for food purposes (corn, wheat, potatoes, rice, etc.). It is the cheapest foodstuff and serves mainly in human nutrition as a source of energy. Starch is used in fermentation industries to produce a wide variety of products. The structure of the starch molecule is not known definitely. Its molecular weight is on the order of 4,000. Hydrolysis of starch yields glucose only. About 22 to 28 molecules of glucose are produced from each molecule of starch; thus, its general formula may be written $(C_6H_{10}O_5)_{22-28}$.

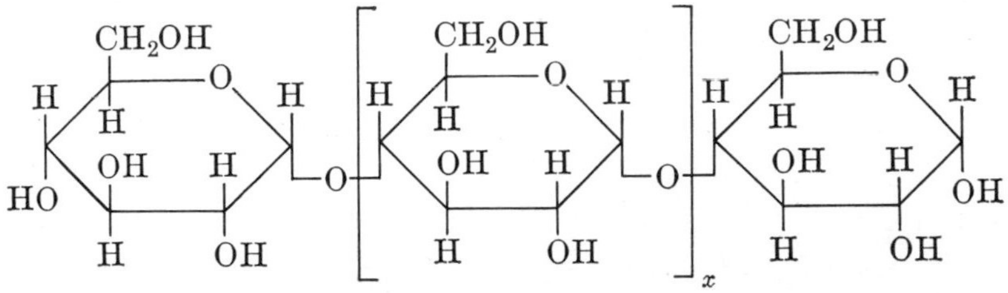

Starch ($x$ = about 20 to 26)

The industrial wastes produced from the manufacture of starch, from the processing of carbohydrate foods, and from the industrial uses of starch are among the most difficult ones sanitary engineers have had to treat.

*Cellulose.* Cellulose forms the structural fiber of many plants. Its general formula is $(C_6H_{10}O_5)_x$, where $x$ varies from 100 to about 200. Cotton is essentially pure cellulose. High-grade cellulose can be produced from wood through the sulfite pulping process. Hydrolysis of cellulose produces glucose but it is impractical to produce it by such procedures. Biological degradation presumably involves hydrolysis to glucose as the first step.

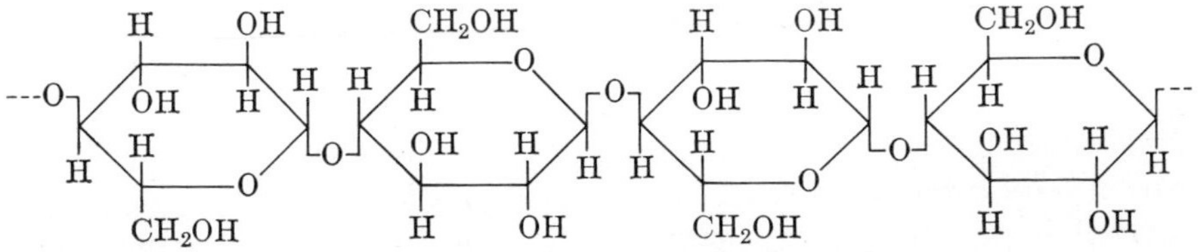

Portion of cellulose molecule

Cellulose is used for the manufacture of a wide variety of products. In various combinations with other materials it serves as the basic substance in all paper products. It is used as a raw material for the manufacture of gun cotton, pyroxylin lacquers, cellulose acetate, cellophane, and acetate and viscose rayons.

Industrial wastes from the paper industry usually contain considerable amounts of cellulose in suspension. This is particularly true of the wastes from the manufacture of low-grade papers involving the reuse of waste paper. Most of the wastes from other industries processing cellulose contain very little cellulose. The principal contaminants are inorganic compounds, derivatives of cellulose, and other organic compounds.

*Hemicelluloses.* The hemicelluloses are compounds which have characteristics somewhat like cellulose. They are composed of a mixture of hexose and pentose units, however, and upon hydrolysis yield glucose and a pentose, usually xylose. Most natural woods contain cellulose,

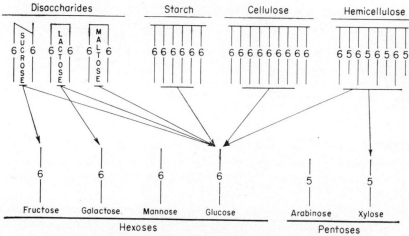

Fig. 5-1. Summary of hydrolytic behavior of carbohydrates.

hemicelluloses, and lignin along with resins, pitch, etc. In the pulping process, the lignin, hemicellulose, resins, etc., are dissolved, leaving cellulose as the product. As a result, spent pulping liquors contain considerable amounts of glucose and xylose as well as other organic substances, principally derivatives of lignin. The lignin derivatives are very resistant to biological degradation. Glucose, xylose, and other organic substances are converted to carbon dioxide and water by yeast or bacteria under aerobic conditions. Yeast may be used to ferment the glucose to alcohol under anaerobic conditions, but the xylose, a pentose, is not fermentable.

**Summary of Hydrolytic Behavior of Carbohydrates.** The hydrolytic behavior of carbohydrates is presented in a simplified graphic form in Fig. 5-1. All di- and polysaccharides yield glucose. Sucrose yields fructose, lactose yields galactose, and hemicellulose yields xylose in addition to glucose.

## 5-21. Fats, Oils, and Waxes

*Fats*, *oils*, and *waxes* are all esters. Fats and oils are esters of the trihydroxy alcohol, glycerol, while waxes are esters of long-chain mono-hydroxy alcohols. All serve as food for humans as well as bacteria, since they can be hydrolyzed to the corresponding fatty acids and alcohols.

**Fats and Oils.** Fats and oils are both glycerides of fatty acids. The fatty acids are generally of 16- or 18-carbon atoms, although butyric, caproic, and caprylic acids are present to a significant extent as components of the esters of butter fat. The acids may also be unsaturated. Oleic and linoleic are important acids in cottonseed oil. Linseed oil contains large amounts of linoleic and linolenic acids. The glycerides of fatty acids that are liquid at ordinary temperatures are called *oils* and those that are solids are called *fats*. Chemically they are quite similar. The oils have a predominance of short-chain fatty acids or fatty acids with a considerable degree of unsaturation, such as linoleic or linolenic.

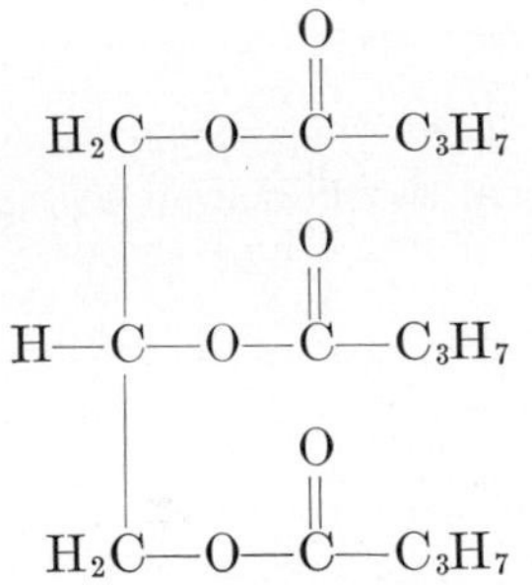

$$H_2C-O-\overset{\overset{\displaystyle O}{\|}}{C}-C_3H_7 \qquad H_2C-O-\overset{\overset{\displaystyle O}{\|}}{C}-C_{17}H_{35}$$

$$H-C-O-\overset{\overset{\displaystyle O}{\|}}{C}-C_3H_7 \qquad H-C-O-\overset{\overset{\displaystyle O}{\|}}{C}-C_{17}H_{35}$$

$$H_2C-O-\overset{\overset{\displaystyle O}{\|}}{C}-C_3H_7 \qquad H_2C-O-\overset{\overset{\displaystyle O}{\|}}{C}-C_{17}H_{35}$$

Glyceryl (or glycerol)      Glyceryl (or glycerol)
tributyrate, tributyrin      tristearate, tristearin

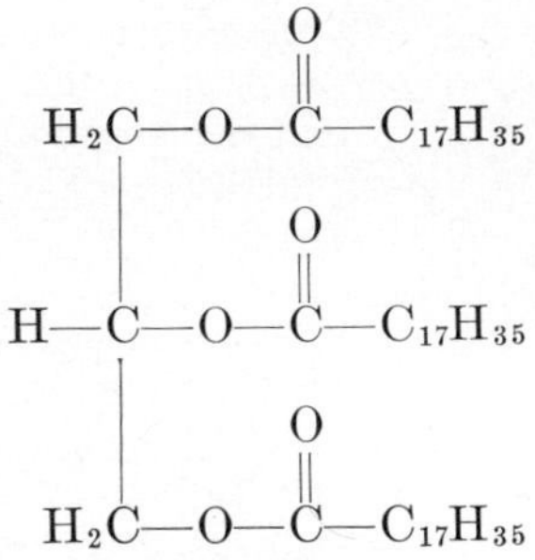

The fatty acids in a given molecule of a glyceride may all be the same, as shown above, or they may all be different.

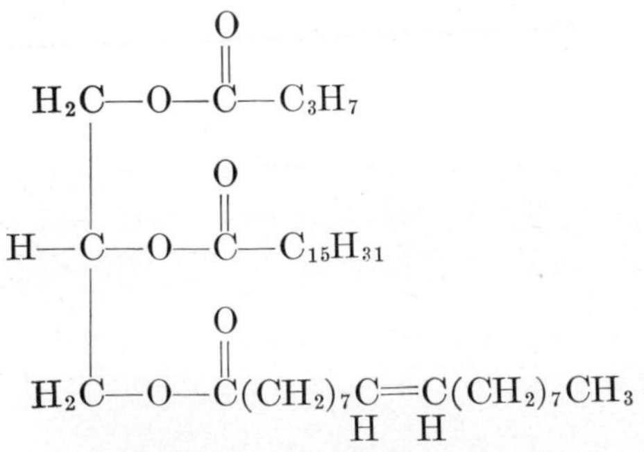

$$H_2C-O-\overset{\overset{\displaystyle O}{\|}}{C}-C_3H_7 \qquad \overset{\alpha}{H_2C}-O-\overset{\overset{\displaystyle O}{\|}}{C}-C_{17}H_{35}$$

$$H-C-O-\overset{\overset{\displaystyle O}{\|}}{C}-C_{15}H_{31} \qquad \beta H-C-O-\overset{\overset{\displaystyle O}{\|}}{C}-C_{15}H_{31}$$

$$H_2C-O-\overset{\overset{\displaystyle O}{\|}}{C}(CH_2)_7C\!\!=\!\!C(CH_2)_7CH_3 \qquad H_2C-O-\overset{\overset{\displaystyle O}{\|}}{C}-C_{17}H_{35}$$
$$\qquad\qquad\qquad H\ \ H$$

Glyceryl (or glycerol) oleo-
butyropalmitate (found in butter
fat)

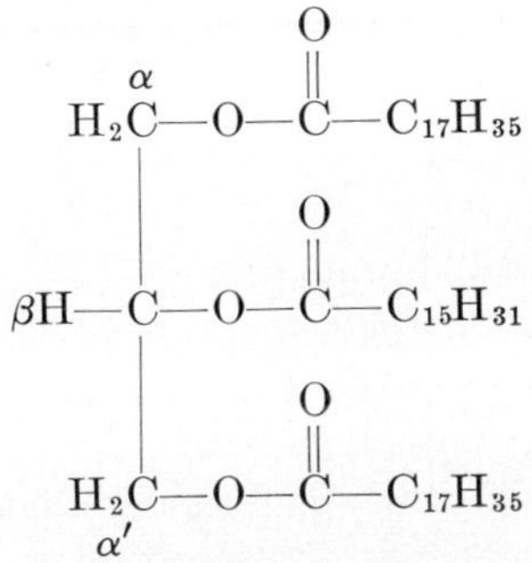

$\beta$-Palmito-$\alpha,\alpha'$-distearin

The principal acids composing the glycerides of fats and oils are shown in Table 5-12.

The relative amounts of the major fatty acids contained in various fats and oils are shown in Table 5-13.

Fats and oils undergo three types of chemical reactions that are of interest to sanitary engineers.

*Hydrolysis.* Since fats and oils are esters they undergo hydrolysis with more or less ease. The hydrolysis may be induced by chemical

TABLE 5-12. ACIDS OF FATS AND OILS*

| Name | Formula | Mp, °C | Source |
|------|---------|--------|--------|
| Butyric | $C_3H_7COOH$ | − 4.7 | Butter |
| Caproic | $C_5H_{11}COOH$ | − 2 | Butter, coconut oil |
| Caprylic | $C_7H_{15}COOH$ | 16 | Palm oil, butter |
| Capric | $C_9H_{19}COOH$ | 31.5 | Coconut oil |
| Lauric | $C_{11}H_{23}COOH$ | 44 | Coconut oil, spermaceti |
| Myristic | $C_{13}H_{27}COOH$ | 58 | Nutmeg, coconut oil |
| Palmitic | $C_{15}H_{31}COOH$ | 64 | Palm oil, animal fats |
| Stearic | $C_{17}H_{35}COOH$ | 69.4 | Animal and vegetable fats, oils |
| Arachidic | $C_{20}H_{40}O_2$ | 76.3 | Peanut oil |
| Behenic | $C_{22}H_{44}O_2$ | 84 | Ben oil |
| Oleic | $C_{18}H_{34}O_2$ | 14 | Animal and vegetable fats, oils |
| Erucic | $C_{22}H_{42}O_2$ | 33.5 | Rape oil, mustard oil |
| Linoleic | $C_{18}H_{32}O_2$ | −11 | Cottonseed oil |
| Linolenic | $C_{18}H_{30}O_2$ | | Linseed oil |
| Clupanodonic | $C_{22}H_{34}O_2$ | < −78 | Fish oils |

* From E. Wertheim and H. Jeskey, "Introductory Organic Chemistry," 3d ed., McGraw-Hill Book Company, Inc., New York, 1956. Table reproduced by permission of the authors.

means, usually by treatment with NaOH, or by bacterial enzymes that split the molecule into glycerol plus fatty acids. Hydrolysis with the aid of NaOH is called *saponification*. Hydrolysis by bacterial action produces *rancid* fats or oils and renders them unpalatable. Rancid butter and margarine are notorious.

*Addition.* The fats and oils containing unsaturated acids add chlorine at the double bonds, as other unsaturated compounds do. This reaction is often slow because of the relative insolubility of the compounds. It may represent a significant part of the chlorine demand of some sewages and industrial wastes.

Oils that contain significant amounts of oleic and linoleic acids may be converted to fats by the process of *hydrogenation*. In this process hydrogen is caused to add at the double bonds, and saturated acids result. Thus low-priced oils such as soybean and cottonseed can be converted into a product commonly called oleomargarine, which is acceptable as human food. Many cooking fats or shortenings such as Spry, Crisco, Fluffo, and other proprietary products are made in the same manner. The hydrogenation can be controlled to produce any degree of hardness desired in the product.

TABLE 5-13. ACID CONTENT OF FATS AND OILS[a]

| Name | Oleic | Linoleic | Linolenic | Stearic | Myristic | Palmitic | Arachidic |
|---|---|---|---|---|---|---|---|
| Butter[b] | 27.4 | | | 11.4 | 22.6 | 22.6 | |
| Mutton tallow | 36.0 | 4.3 | | 30.5 | 4.6 | 24.6 | |
| Castor oil[c] | 9 | 3 | | 3 | | | |
| Olive oil | 84.4 | 4.6 | | 2.3 | trace | 6.9 | 0.1 |
| Palm oil | 38.4 | 10.7 | | 4.2 | 1.1 | 41.1 | |
| Coconut oil[d] | 5.0 | 1.0 | | 3.0 | 18.5 | 7.5 | |
| Peanut oil[e] | 60.6 | 21.6 | | 4.9 | | 6.3 | 3.3 |
| Corn oil[f] | 43.4 | 39.1 | | 3.3 | | 7.3 | 0.4 |
| Cottonseed oil | 33.2 | 39.4 | | 1.9 | 0.3 | 19.1 | 0.6 |
| Linseed oil | 5 | 48.5 | 34.1 | | | | |
| Soybean oil[g] | 32.0 | 49.3 | 2.2 | 4.2 | | 6.5 | 0.7 |
| Tung oil[h] | 14.9 | | | 1.3 | | 4.1 | |

[a] From E. Wertheim and H. Jeskey, "Introductory Organic Chemistry," 3d ed., McGraw-Hill Book Company, Inc., New York, 1956. Table reproduced by permission of the authors.

[b] Contains caproic, 1.4 per cent; caprylic, 1.8 per cent; capric, 1.8 per cent; butyric, 3.2 per cent; lauric, 6.9 per cent.

[c] Contains about 85 per cent of ricinoleic acid, 12-hydroxy-9-octadecenoic acid (mp, 17°), $CH_3(CH_2)_5CHOHCH_2CH=CH(CH_2)_7COOH$.

[d] Contains caprylic, 9.5 per cent; capric, 4.5 per cent; lauric, 51 per cent.

[e] Contains 2.6 per cent lignoceric acid.

[f] Contains 0.2 per cent lignoceric acid.

[g] Contains 0.1 per cent lignoceric acid.

[h] Contains 79.7 per cent eleostearic acid.

*Oxidation.* The oils with appreciable amounts of linoleic and linolenic acids or other highly unsaturated acids, such as linseed and tung oil, are known as *drying oils.* In contact with the air, oxygen adds at the double bonds and forms a resin-like material. The drying oils are the major vehicle in all oil-base paints.

**Waxes.** Waxes, with the exception of paraffin wax, are esters of long-chain acids and alcohols of high molecular weight. *Beeswax* is an ester of palmitic acid and myricyl alcohol $(C_{15}H_{31}COOC_{31}H_{63})$. It also contains cerotic acid $(C_{25}H_{51}COOH)$. Spermaceti is obtained from the heads of sperm whales and is principally an ester of palmitic acid and cetyl alcohol $(C_{15}H_{31}COOC_{16}H_{33})$. Cetyl esters of lauric and myristic acids are also present to a limited extent.

## 5-22. Proteins and Amino Acids

*Proteins* are complex compounds of carbon, hydrogen, oxygen, and nitrogen. Phosphorus and sulfur are present in a few. They are among the most complex of the organic compounds produced in nature and are widely distributed in plants and animals. They form an essential part of all protoplasm and are a necessary part of the diet of all higher animals, in which they serve to build and repair muscle tissue. Like polysaccharides, which may be considered to be made up of glucose units, proteins are formed by the union of $\alpha$-amino acids. Since there are 27 known amino acids, the variety of proteins is considerable.

**Amino Acids.** *$\alpha$-Amino acids* are the building blocks from which proteins are constructed. Plants and bacteria have the ability to synthesize the amino acids from which they build proteins. Animals are unable to synthesize certain of the amino acids and must depend upon plants to supply them in the form of proteins. Such amino acids are considered to be indispensable.

The amino acids that occur in proteins all have an amino group attached to the alpha carbon atom and, therefore, are called $\alpha$-amino acids.

$$\begin{array}{c} NH_2 \\ | \\ R\text{---}C\text{---}COOH \\ | \\ H \end{array}$$

$\alpha$-Amino acid

*Chemistry of Amino Acids.* The free amino acids behave like acids and also like bases because of the amino group that they contain. Thus they are *amphoteric* in character and form salts with acids or bases.

Salt formation with an acid:

$$H_2NCH_2COOH + HCl \rightarrow Cl^{-+}H_3NCH_2COOH \qquad (5\text{-}48)$$

Salt formation with a base:

$$H_2NCH_2COOH + NaOH \rightarrow H_2O + H_2NCH_2COO^-Na^+ \qquad (5\text{-}49)$$

The amino acids having one amino and one carboxyl group are essentially neutral in aqueous solution. This is considered to be due to a case of self-neutralization in which the hydrogen ion of the carboxyl group migrates to the amino group and a positive-negative (dipolar) ion known as a *zwitterion* results.

$$\begin{array}{c} NH_2 \\ | \\ R\text{---}C\text{---}COOH \\ | \\ H \end{array} \rightleftharpoons \begin{array}{c} NH_3^+ \\ | \\ R\text{---}C\text{---}COO^- \\ | \\ H \end{array} \qquad (5\text{-}50)$$

Zwitterion

In Sec. 5-9, it was shown that organic acids can react with ammonia to form amides. The amino and carboxyl groups of separate amino acid molecules can react in the same manner.

$$R-\overset{\overset{H}{|}}{\underset{NH_2}{C}}-\overset{\overset{O}{||}}{C}-\boxed{OH \quad H}\,\overset{\overset{H}{}}{N}-\overset{\overset{R}{|}}{\underset{H}{C}}-COOH \longrightarrow R-\overset{\overset{H}{|}}{\underset{NH_2}{C}}-\overset{\overset{O}{||}}{C}-\overset{\overset{H}{}}{N}-\overset{\overset{R}{|}}{\underset{H}{C}}-COOH + H_2O \quad (5\text{-}51)$$

A dipeptide

It is this ability to form linkages between the amino and carboxyl groups that allows the large complex molecules of proteins to be formed. In the example given above, the resulting molecule contains one free amino and one free carboxyl group. Each can combine with another molecule of an amino acid. In turn, the resulting molecule will contain free amino and carboxyl groups and the process can be repeated, presumably, *ad infinitum*. Natural forces, however, direct the synthesis to produce the type and size of protein molecules desired.

The molecule formed by the union of two molecules of amino acids is known as a *dipeptide;* if there are three units the name is *tripeptide;* if more than three units the compound is called a *polypeptide.* The particular linkage formed when amino acids join is called the *peptide link* and is formed by loss of water between an amino and a carboxyl group.

$$-\overset{\overset{O}{||}}{C}-\underset{\text{-----}}{[OH \quad H]}-\overset{\overset{H}{}}{N}- \longrightarrow -\overset{\overset{O}{||}}{C}-\overset{\overset{H}{}}{N}- + H_2O \quad (5\text{-}52)$$

Peptide link

*Classes of Amino Acids.* Twenty-seven different α-amino acids have been isolated from proteins by hydrolysis of protein matter. The simplest have one amino group and one carboxyl group per molecule. Some have sulfur in the molecule. Some have two amino groups and one carboxyl group and, consequently, are basic in reaction. Some have one amino group and two carboxyl groups and are acid in reaction. Others have aromatic or heterocyclic groups.

All the amino acids, except glycine, are optically active. In the list below[1] the symbols $d$ and $l$ refer to the actual optical rotation of the acids. The dates in parentheses show when the amino acids were first isolated from proteins and when first synthesized, respectively. Those marked with an asterisk are considered indispensable in human nutrition.

[1] Data adopted from E. Wertheim and H. Jeskey, "Introductory Organic Chemistry," 3d ed., McGraw-Hill Book Company, Inc., New York, 1956, by permission of the authors.

*Monoamino monocarboxy acids:*

$$H_2NCH_2COOH$$

Glycine, glycocoll, $\alpha$-amino-acetic acid (1820, 1858)

$$CH_3CHNH_2COOH$$

$d$-Alanine, $\alpha$-aminopropionic acid (1888, 1850)

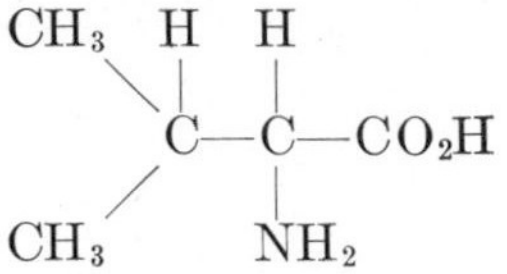

*$d$-Valine, $\alpha$-isopropyl-$\alpha$-amino-acetic acid (1901, 1880)

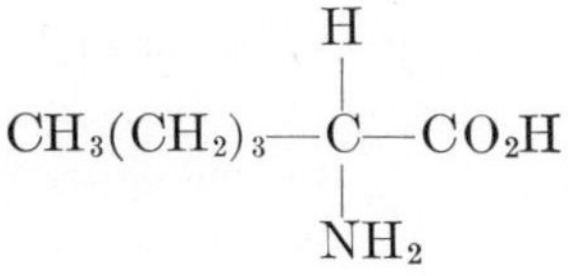

$d$-Norleucine, $\alpha$-amino-$n$-caproic acid (1901, 1870)

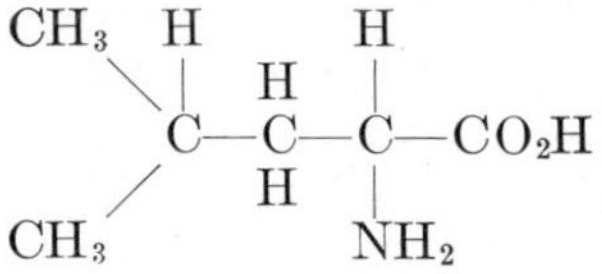

*$l$-Leucine, $\beta$-isopropyl-$\alpha$-amino-propionic acid (1820, 1855)

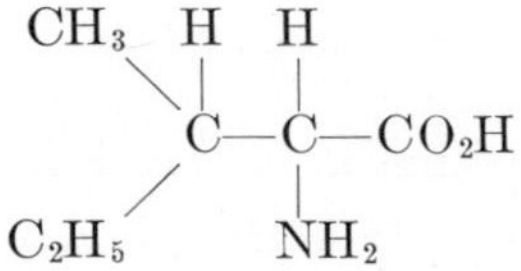

*$d$-Isoleucine, $\alpha$-amino-$\beta$-ethyl-$\beta$-methyl-propionic acid (1904, 1905)

*Monoamino monocarboxy monohydroxy acids:*

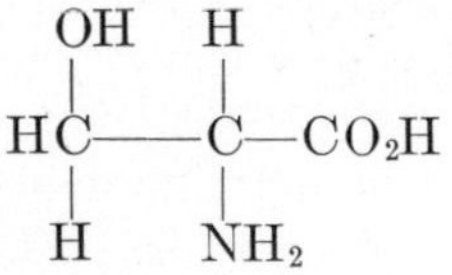

$l$-Serine, $\beta$-hydroxy-$\alpha$-aminopropionic acid (1865, 1902)

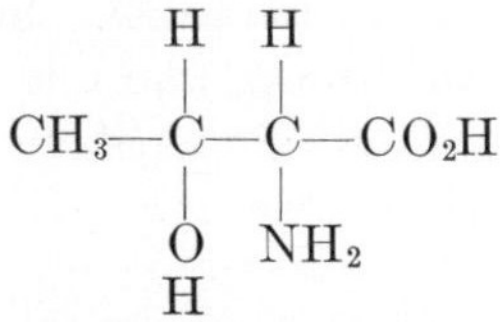

*$l$-Threonine, $\alpha$-amino-$\beta$-hydroxybutyric acid (1926, 1936)

*Sulfur-containing acids:*

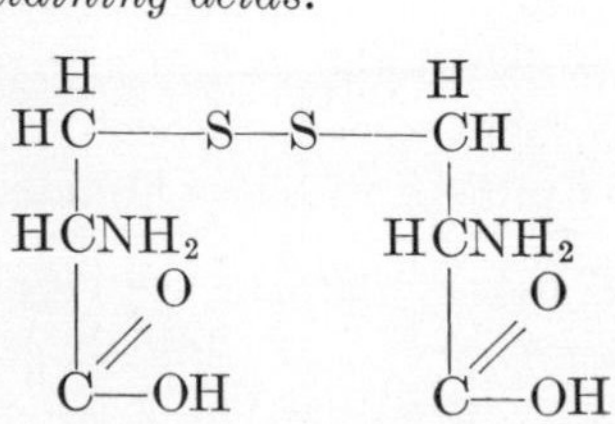

$l$-Cystine (1899, 1903)

$$\begin{matrix} H & & O \\ S & H & \diagup\!\!\diagup \\ HC\!-\!C\!-\!C\!-\!OH \\ H & NH_2 \end{matrix}$$

The reduced form of cystine is cysteine, $\beta$-thiol-$\alpha$-amino-propionic acid

$$\begin{matrix} H_2C\!-\!S\!-\!CH_2\!-\!S\!-\!CH_2 \\ H_2N\overset{}{C}H \qquad\qquad H\overset{}{C}NH_2 \\ \overset{}{C}O_2H \qquad\qquad \overset{}{C}O_2H \end{matrix}$$

Djenkolic acid, cysteine thioacetal of formaldehyde (1935, 1936)

$$CH_3\!-\!S\!-\!CH_2\!-\!CH_2\!-\!\overset{\displaystyle H}{\underset{\displaystyle NH_2}{C}}\!-\!CO_2H$$

*$l$-Methionine, $\gamma$-methylthiol-$\alpha$-aminobutyric acid (1922, 1928)

*Monocarboxy diamino acids:*

$$H_2N\!-\!\overset{\overset{\displaystyle H}{\underset{\displaystyle \|}{N}}}{C}\!-\!\overset{\displaystyle H}{N}\!-\!CH_2(CH_2)_2\!-\!\overset{\overset{\displaystyle H}{}}{\underset{\displaystyle NH_2}{C}}\!-\!\overset{\displaystyle O}{\overset{\diagup\!\!\diagup}{C}}\!-\!OH$$

$d$-Arginine, $\alpha$-amino-$\vartheta$-guanidinevaleric acid (1895, 1910)

$$H_2N\!-\!CH_2\!-\!CH_2\!-\!CH_2\!-\!\overset{\displaystyle H}{\underset{\displaystyle NH_2}{C}}\!-\!CO_2H$$

The hydrolysis of arginine yields $d$-ornithine, $\alpha,\vartheta$-di-aminovaleric acid

$$\overset{\displaystyle H}{\underset{\displaystyle H}{H_2N}}C(CH_2)_3\!-\!\overset{\overset{\displaystyle H}{}}{\underset{\displaystyle NH_2}{C}}\!-\!\overset{\displaystyle O}{\overset{\diagup\!\!\diagup}{C}}\!-\!OH$$

*$d$-Lysine, $\alpha,\epsilon$-diaminocaproic acid (1889, 1902)

$$H_2N\!-\!\overset{\overset{\displaystyle O}{\underset{\displaystyle \|}{}}}{C}\!-\!\overset{\displaystyle H}{N}\!-\!CH_2\!-\!CH_2\!-\!CH_2\!-\!\overset{\overset{\displaystyle H}{}}{\underset{\displaystyle NH_2}{C}}\!-\!CO_2H$$

Citrulline, $\vartheta$-car-bamido-$\alpha$-amino-valeric acid

*Aromatic homocyclic acids:*

$$\bigcirc\!\!-\!CH_2\!-\!\overset{\overset{\displaystyle H}{}}{\underset{\displaystyle NH_2}{C}}\!-\!\overset{\displaystyle O}{\overset{\diagup\!\!\diagup}{C}}\!-\!OH$$

*$l$-Phenylalanine, $\beta$-phenyl-$\alpha$-amino-propionic acid (1881, 1882)

$$HO\!-\!\bigcirc\!\!-\!CH_2\!-\!\overset{\overset{\displaystyle H}{}}{\underset{\displaystyle NH_2}{C}}\!-\!\overset{\displaystyle O}{\overset{\diagup\!\!\diagup}{C}}\!-\!OH$$

$l$-Tyrosine, $\beta$-[$p$-hydroxyphenyl]-$\alpha$-aminopropionic acid (1849, 1882)

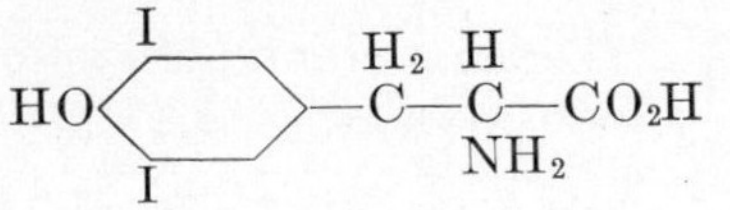

$$\text{HO} \diagdown \underset{\text{I}}{\overset{\text{I}}{\diagup}} \text{—} \overset{\text{H}_2}{\underset{}{\text{C}}} \text{—} \overset{\text{H}}{\underset{\text{NH}_2}{\text{C}}} \text{—CO}_2\text{H}$$

*d*-Iodogorgoic acid, 3,5-di-iodotyrosine (1896, 1905)

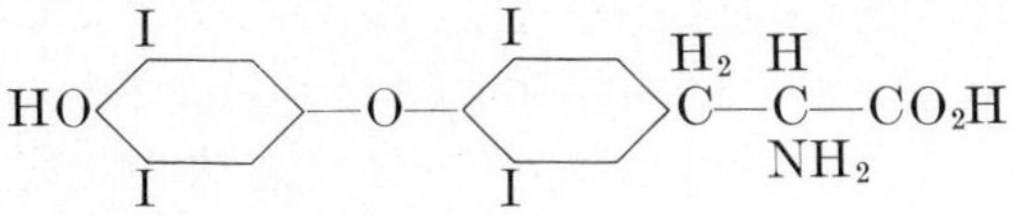

$$\text{HO} \diagdown \overset{\text{I}}{\diagup} \text{—O—} \diagdown \overset{\text{I}}{\diagup} \overset{\text{H}_2}{\underset{}{\text{C}}} \text{—} \overset{\text{H}}{\underset{\text{NH}_2}{\text{C}}} \text{—CO}_2\text{H}$$

*l*-Thyroxine (1915, 1927)

*Heterocyclic acids:*

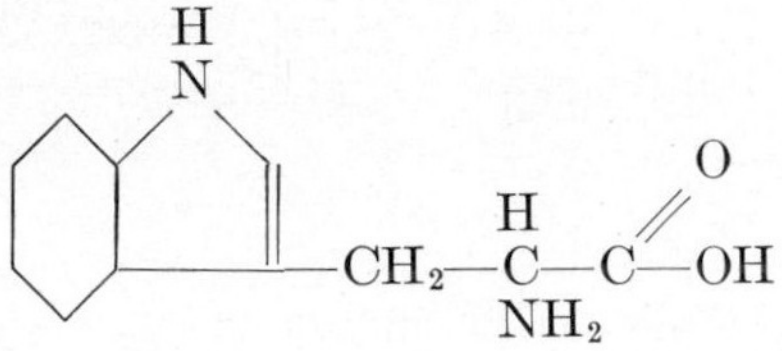

$$\text{—CH}_2\text{—}\overset{\text{H}}{\underset{\text{NH}_2}{\text{C}}}\text{—}\overset{\text{O}}{\text{C}}\text{—OH}$$

*l*-Tryptophan, α-amino-β-3-indolepropionic acid (1901, 1907)

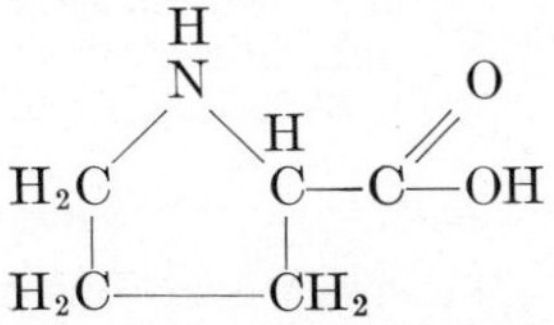

$$\text{H}_2\text{C} \quad \overset{\text{H}}{\text{C}}\text{—}\overset{\text{O}}{\text{C}}\text{—OH}$$
$$\text{H}_2\text{C}\text{——CH}_2$$

*l*-Proline, pyrrolidine-α-carboxylic acid (1901, 1900)

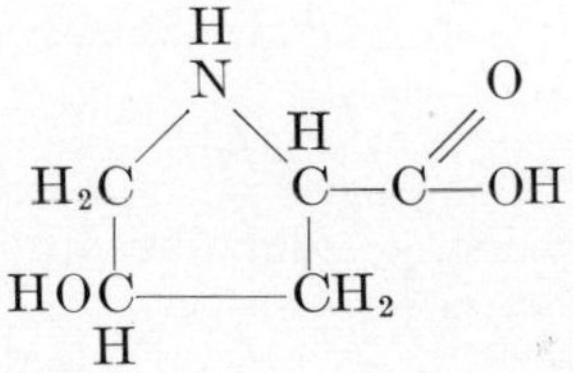

$$\text{H}_2\text{C} \quad \overset{\text{H}}{\text{C}}\text{—}\overset{\text{O}}{\text{C}}\text{—OH}$$
$$\text{HOC}\text{——CH}_2$$
$$\text{H}$$

*l*-Hydroxyproline (1902, 1905)

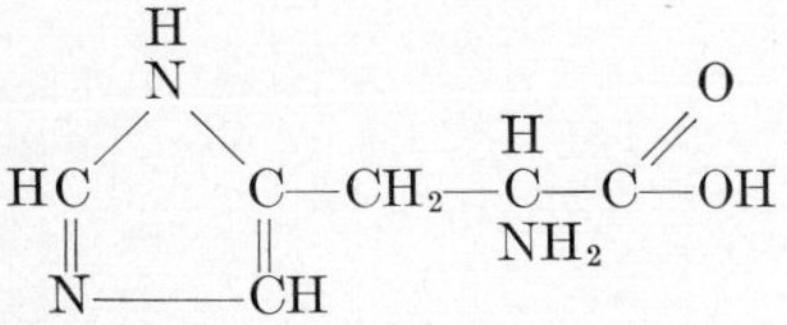

$$\text{HC} \quad \text{C—CH}_2\text{—}\overset{\text{H}}{\underset{\text{NH}_2}{\text{C}}}\text{—}\overset{\text{O}}{\text{C}}\text{—OH}$$
$$\text{N——CH}$$

*l*-Histidine, α-amino-β-imidazolepropionic acid (1896, 1911)

Proteins from different sources yield varying amounts of the different amino acids upon hydrolysis. The protein from a given source, however, normally yields the same amino acids and in the same ratio. All proteins yield more than one amino acid.

**Proteins.** Proteins constitute a very important part of the diet of humans, particularly in the form of meats, cheeses, eggs, and certain vegetables. The processing of these materials, except for eggs, results in the production of industrial wastes that are the concern of sanitary engineers.   Wastes produced in the meat-packing industry alone have a population equivalent in excess of 15 million.

*Properties of Proteins.*   Protein molecules are very large, and molecular weights are difficult to obtain.   Minimum values can be obtained by calculation from chemical analysis.   That for hemoglobin is calculated to be 16,669, based upon one atom of iron per molecule.   The ultracentrifuge also is used to obtain molecular weights.   By this method hemoglobin is estimated to have a molecular weight of 68,000; that for hemocyanin is estimated to be 6,740,000.

All proteins contain carbon, hydrogen, oxygen, and nitrogen.   Regardless of their source, be it animal or vegetable, the ultimate analysis of all proteins falls within a very narrow range, as shown below:

|            | Percentage |
|------------|------------|
| Carbon     | 51  –55    |
| Hydrogen   | 6.5– 7.3   |
| Oxygen     | 20  –24    |
| Nitrogen   | 15  –18    |
| Sulfur     | 0.0– 2.5   |
| Phosphorus | 0.0– 1.0   |

The nitrogen content varies from 15 to 18 per cent and averages about 16 per cent.   Since carbohydrates and fats do not contain nitrogen, advantage is taken of this fact in food analysis to calculate protein content.   The value for nitrogen as determined by the Kjeldahl digestion procedure (Sec. 25-3), when multiplied by the factor 100/16 or 6.25, gives the protein content.   Sanitary engineers often use this procedure to estimate the protein content of sewages, of industrial wastes, and of sludges from their organic nitrogen (Sec. 25-3) content.

*Biological Treatment of Protein Wastes.*   In general, satisfactory treatment of wastes containing significant amounts of proteins requires the use of biological processes.   In these processes the first step in degradation of the protein is considered to be hydrolysis, induced by hydrolytical enzymes.   The hydrolysis is considered to progress in steps in reverse manner to those in which proteins are synthesized.

*Hydrolysis products of proteins:*

$$\text{Protein} \rightarrow \text{proteoses} \rightarrow \text{peptones} \rightarrow \text{polypeptides}$$
$$\downarrow \qquad\qquad (5\text{-}53)$$
$$\alpha\text{-amino acids} \leftarrow \text{dipeptides}$$

The $\alpha$-amino acids are then deaminized by enzymic action, and free fatty and other acids result.   The free acids serve as food for the microorganisms, and they are converted to carbon dioxide and water.

DETERGENTS

## 5-23. Detergents

The term *detergent* is applied to a wide variety of organic surface-active materials used to remove soil from clothes, dishes, and a host of other things. All detergents have rather large polar molecules. One end of the molecule is particularly soluble in water and the other is readily soluble in oils. The solubility in water is due to carboxyl, sulfate, hydroxyl, or sulfonate groups. The detergents with carboxyl, sulfate, and sulfonate groups are all used as sodium salts.

$$
\begin{array}{cl}
\textit{Oil-soluble part} & \textit{Water-soluble part} \\[4pt]
\text{Organic group} \Big\} &
\begin{array}{l}
-\text{COO}^-\text{Na}^+ \\
-\text{SO}_4^-\text{Na}^+ \\
-\text{SO}_3^-\text{Na}^+ \\
-\text{OH}
\end{array}
\end{array}
$$

The nature of the organic part of the molecule varies greatly with the various detergent types.

## 5-24. Soaps

Ordinary *soaps* are derived from fats and oils by *saponification* with sodium hydroxide. Saponification is a special case of hydrolysis in which an alkaline agent is present to neutralize the fatty acids as they are formed. In this way the reaction is caused to go to completion.

$$
\begin{array}{l}
\text{H}_2\text{COOCC}_{17}\text{H}_{35} \\
\quad | \\
\text{H--COOCC}_{17}\text{H}_{35} + 3\text{NaOH} \rightarrow \\
\quad | \\
\text{H}_2\text{COOCC}_{17}\text{H}_{35}
\end{array}
\quad
\begin{array}{l}
\text{H}_2\text{COH} \\
\quad | \\
\text{H--COH} + 3\text{C}_{17}\text{H}_{35}\text{COONa} \quad (5\text{-}54) \\
\quad | \qquad\qquad \text{Sodium stearate,} \\
\text{H}_2\text{COH} \qquad\quad \text{a soap}
\end{array}
$$

Stearin                          Glycerol

The fats and oils are split into glycerol and sodium soaps. The nature of the soap depends upon the type of fat or oil used. Beef fat and cottonseed oil are used to produce low-grade heavy-duty soaps. Coconut and other oils are used in the production of toilet soaps.

All sodium and potassium soaps are soluble in water. If the water is hard, the calcium, magnesium, and any other ions causing hardness precipitate the soap in the form of metallic soaps.

$$
2\text{C}_{17}\text{H}_{35}\text{COONa} + \text{Ca}^{++} \rightarrow \underline{(\text{C}_{17}\text{H}_{35}\text{COO})_2\text{Ca}} \downarrow + 2\text{Na}^+ \quad (5\text{-}55)
$$

Soap must be added to precipitate all the ions causing hardness before it can act as a detergent, usually indicated by the onset of frothing upon agitation. This characteristic is the basis of a method of determining hardness in waters (Sec. 18-4).

## 5-25. Synthetic Detergents

Since 1945 a wide variety of *synthetic detergents*, commonly called *syndets*, have been accepted as substitutes for soap. Their major advantage is that they do not form insoluble precipitates with the ions causing hardness. As marketed, most of them contain from 20 to 30 per cent of surface-active agent and 70 to 80 per cent of *builders*. The builders are usually sodium sulfate, sodium tripolyphosphate, sodium silicate, and other materials that enhance the detergent properties of the active ingredient. The syndets are of three major types: *anionic, nonionic,* and *cationic.*

**Anionic Syndets.** The *anionic* syndets are all sodium salts and ionize to yield $Na^+$ plus a negatively charged, surface-active ion. The common ones are all sulfates and sulfonates.

*Sulfates.* Long-chain alcohols when treated with sulfuric acid produce sulfates (inorganic esters) with surface-active properties. Dodecyl or lauryl alcohol is commonly used.

$$C_{12}H_{25}OH + H_2SO_4 \rightarrow C_{12}H_{25}\!-\!O\!-\!SO_3H + H_2O \qquad (5\text{-}56)$$

Lauryl
alcohol

The sulfated alcohol is neutralized with sodium hydroxide to produce the syndet.

$$C_{12}H_{25}\!-\!O\!-\!SO_3H + NaOH \rightarrow C_{12}H_{25}\!-\!O\!-\!SO_3Na + H_2O \quad (5\text{-}57)$$

Sodium lauryl sulfate

The sulfated alcohols were the first syndets to be produced commercially. Dreft and Vel were formerly compounded entirely with this surface-active agent. The sulfated alcohols are used in combination with other syndets to produce blends with desirable properties.

*Sulfonates.* The principal sulfonates of importance are derived from esters, amides, and alkyl benzenes.

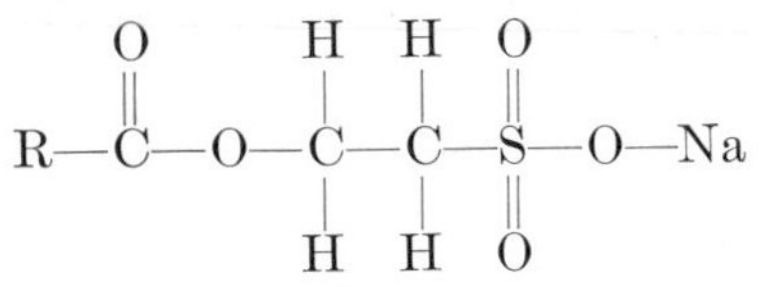

Ester

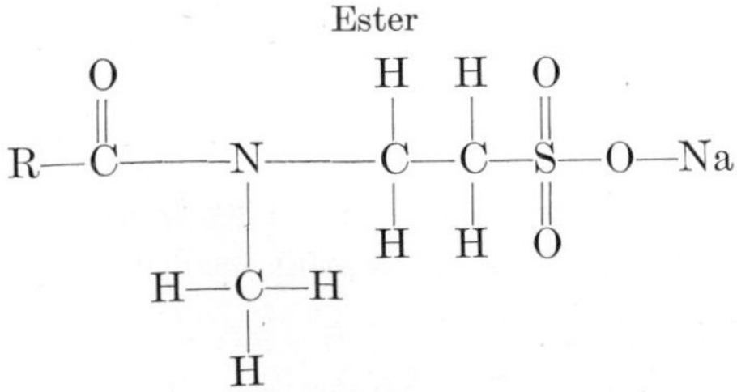

Amide

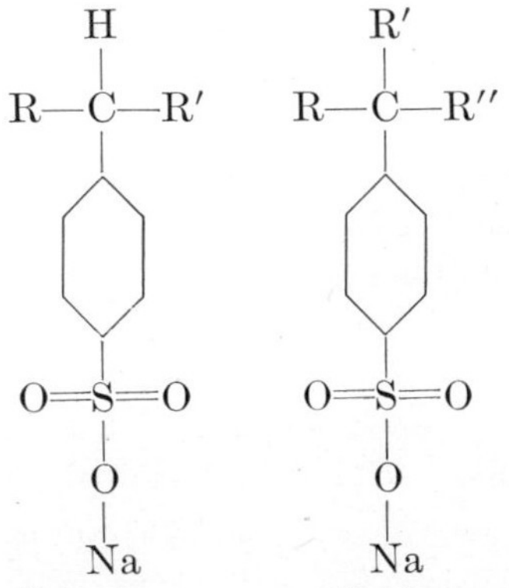

Secondary
Tertiary
Sulfonated alkyl benzenes

The esters and amides are of organic acids with 16- or 18-carbon atoms. The alkyl benzenes are derived largely from polymers of propylene and average 12-carbon atoms in the alkyl group.

**Nonionic Syndets.** The *nonionic* detergents do not ionize and have to depend upon groups in the molecule to render them soluble. All depend upon polymers of ethylene oxide to give them this property.

$$R—\overset{\overset{\textstyle O}{\|}}{C}—O—[C_2H_4O]_xH$$
Ester type

$$R—\overset{\overset{\textstyle O}{\|}}{C}—\underset{\underset{\textstyle R}{|}}{N}—[C_2H_4O]_xH$$
Amide type

Aryl type

$$HO[C_2H_4O]_xH$$
Ethylene oxide
polymer type

The nonionic type of syndet has been more expensive to produce than the anionic type. It is gaining in popularity, however.

**Cationic Syndets.** The *cationic* syndets are salts of quaternary ammonium hydroxide. In quaternary ammonium hydroxide, the hydrogens of the ammonium ion have all been replaced with alkyl groups. The surface-active properties are contained in the cation.

$$\left[ R—\overset{\overset{\textstyle R'}{|}}{\underset{\underset{\textstyle R''}{|}}{N}}—R'' \right]^+ Cl^-$$
A cationic syndet

The cationic syndets are noted for their disinfecting (bactericidal) properties. They are used as sanitizing agents for dishwashing where hot water is unavailable or undesirable. They are also useful in the washing of babies' diapers where sterility is important. If diapers are not sterilized by some means, bacterial infestations may occur which release enzymes that will hydrolyze urea to produce free ammonia [Eq. (5-43)]. The high pH resulting is harmful to the tender skin of babies, and the odor of free ammonia is unpleasant to all concerned.

**Biological Degradation of Detergents.** Detergents vary greatly in their biochemical behavior, depending upon their chemical structure.[1] Common soaps and the sulfated alcohols are readily used as bacterial food. The syndets with ester or amide linkages are readily hydrolyzed.

[1] C. N. Sawyer and D. W. Ryckman, Anionic Detergents and Water Supply Problems, *J. Am. Water Works Assoc.*, **49**, 480 (1957).

The fatty acids produced serve as sources of bacterial food.   The other hydrolysis product may or may not serve as bacterial food, depending upon its chemical structure.   The alkyl benzene sulfonates derived from propylene are resistant to biological attack because of branched-chain structure of alkyl groups and because the benzene rings are attached principally to tertiary carbon atoms of the branched-chain groups.   The syndets prepared from polymers of ethylene oxide are resistant to biological attack, presumably because of the ether (C—O—C) bonds that they contain.

## REFERENCES

Cason, J.: "Essential Principles of Organic Chemistry," Prentice-Hall, Inc., Englewood Cliffs, N.J., 1956.

Conant, J. B., and A. H. Blatt: "Fundamentals of Organic Chemistry," The Macmillan Company, New York, 1950.

Fuson, R. C., and H. R. Snyder: "Organic Chemistry," 2d ed., John Wiley & Sons, Inc., New York, 1954.

Wertheim, E., and H. Jeskey: "Introductory Organic Chemistry," 3d ed., McGraw-Hill Book Company, Inc., New York, 1956.

# 6. Basic Concepts from Physical Chemistry

## 6-1. Introduction

That portion of science dealing with laws or generalizations related to chemical phenomena is called *physical chemistry*. A sound knowledge of physics is fully as important in the study of physical chemistry as a good grounding in chemistry. Some physical chemistry has always been taught in general, qualitative, and quantitative chemistry without describing it as such. The trend has been to include more and more physical chemistry in such courses, and even in high school chemistry, as those in the teaching profession have realized the need and gained the stimulation of teaching "why" as well as "what" chemical reactions occur.

The subject of valency, oxidation-reduction reactions, the gas laws, Raoult's law, the law of mass action, the theory of ionization, the solubility-product principle, and other discussions pertaining to heterogeneous equilibrium are all examples of topics in physical chemistry which have been developed previously. Some of them require further amplification, and a great many additional concepts need to be developed.

## 6-2. Avogadro's Number

It has been demonstrated by several experimental methods that gram molecular volumes of all gases (22.4 liters under standard conditions) contain the same number of molecules, as illustrated in Fig. 6-1. Values for this number of molecules obtained by the various methods have differed somewhat, and a value of $6.06 \times 10^{23}$ was called *Avogadro's number* until recent years. By more refined methods, the value has been determined to be $6.02 \times 10^{23}$. The enormous size of this number is incomprehensible. Some concept of its magnitude may be gained from a consideration that the life span of the ordinary United States citizen is on the order of $2.2 \times 10^9$ sec and a person would have to live about $3 \times 10^{14}$ lives to count to Avogadro's number.

It is important to remember that the gram molecular volume and gram molecular weight of any given gas represent the same mass. From this relationship it becomes obvious that the gram molecular weight of any substance, be it solid or gaseous, contains Avogadro's number of molecules. This knowledge is fundamental to an understanding of many chemical and physical phenomena, such as Gay-Lussac's law of combining volumes (Sec. 2-8) and Raoult's law (Sec. 2-9).

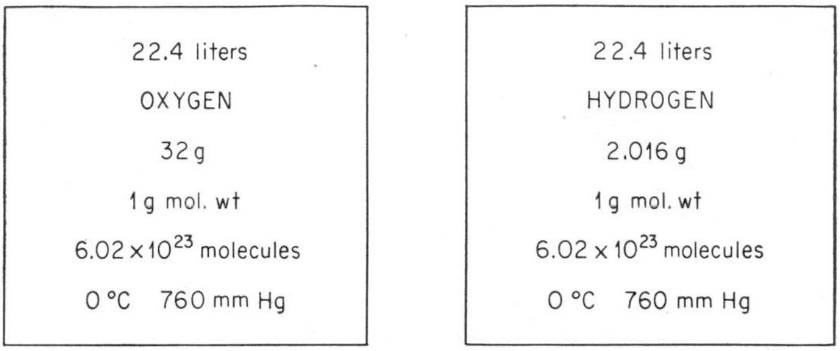

| 22.4 liters | 22.4 liters |
|---|---|
| OXYGEN | HYDROGEN |
| 32 g | 2.016 g |
| 1 g mol. wt | 1 g mol. wt |
| $6.02 \times 10^{23}$ molecules | $6.02 \times 10^{23}$ molecules |
| 0 °C   760 mm Hg | 0 °C   760 mm Hg |

FIG. 6-1. A comparison of oxygen and hydrogen in relation to Avogadro's number.

## 6-3. Vapor Pressure of Liquids

According to the kinetic theory, liquids, as well as gases, are in constant agitation and molecules are constantly flying from the surface of the liquid into the atmosphere above. In open systems most of these particles never return, and the liquid is said to be undergoing evaporation. In a closed system, however, particles return to the liquid phase in proportion to their concentration in the gaseous phase, and eventually the rate of return equals the rate of flight and a condition of equilibrium is established. The vapor is then said to be saturated. The pressure exerted by the vapor under these conditions is known as the *vapor pressure*. The vapor pressure of all liquids increases with temperature. The vapor-pressure values of water and a few organic liquids are given in Table 6-1. It will be noted that vapor pressures do not rise in a regular manner. For rough approximations, the vapor pressure may be considered to increase about 1.5 times for each 10°C rise in temperature.

The Rankine formula,

$$\log p = \frac{A}{T} + B \log T + C \tag{6-1}$$

or one of its modifications is commonly used to calculate vapor pressures. Sanitary engineers will find vapor-pressure data for many of the compounds with which they are concerned in the "International Critical Tables" or standard handbooks of chemistry. Appropriate formulas and constants are usually given to allow calculation of vapor-pressure values for any temperature.

When the vapor pressure of a liquid becomes equal to the pressure of the atmosphere above it, the liquid is said to have reached its *boiling point*. Violent agitation of the liquid occurs under these conditions as a result of the transformation of liquid to gas at the source of heat, migration of the bubbles of vapor through the liquid, and their escape from the liquid surface.

Liquids with appreciable vapor pressure may be caused to boil over a wide range of temperatures by decreasing or increasing the pressure.

TABLE 6-1. VAPOR PRESSURE OF LIQUIDS, MM HG

| Temp., °C | Water | Ethyl alcohol | n-Hexane | Benzene |
|---|---|---|---|---|
| 0 | 4.58 | 12.2 | 45.4 | 26.5 |
| 10 | 9.21 | 23.6 | 75.0 | 45.4 |
| 20 | 17.54 | 43.9 | 120.0 | 74.7 |
| 30 | 31.82 | 78.8 | 185.4 | 118.2 |
| 40 | 55.32 | 135.3 | 276.7 | 181.1 |
| 50 | 92.51 | 222.2 | 400.9 | 269.0 |
| 60 | 149.4 | 352.7 | 566.2 | 388.6 |
| 70 | 233.7 | 542.5 | 787.0 | 547.4 |
| 80 | 355.1 | 812 | 1,062 | 735.6 |
| 90 | 525.8 | 1,187 | 1,407 | 1,016 |
| 100 | 760.0 | 1,693 | 1,836 | 1,344 |

Water boils at room temperature if the pressure above it is reduced to about 17 mm Hg. On the other hand, the boiling point of water in a steam boiler operating at 200 lb pressure is 194.4°C. Chemical engineers make particular application of this principle in multiple-effect and thermal compression evaporators.

## 6-4. Heat of Vaporization

Heat is required to transform a liquid into a vapor. The amount needed to transform one gram of a liquid at its boiling point into vapor is known as the *heat of vaporization*, and values are commonly expressed in calories. Engineers in the United States, however, commonly use the British system in which the unit of weight is the pound, and heats of vaporization are expressed in British thermal units (Btu). Sanitary engineers encounter a wide variety of evaporation, drying, and incineration problems involving a knowledge of heats of vaporization. Many industrial processes involve evaporation or drying in which cooling water is needed. In essence, the heat of vaporization is transferred to the coolant during condensation, and the warmed water may become a thermal pollution problem in terms of the receiving body of water. This is a matter of growing concern as water use by industry and the public increases.

## 6-5. Surface Tension

According to the kinetic theory, molecules of a liquid attract each other. At the surface, the molecules are subjected to an unbalanced force since the molecules in the gaseous phase are so widely dispersed. As a result, the molecules at the *surface* are under *tension* and form a thin skinlike layer that adjusts itself to give a minimum surface area. This

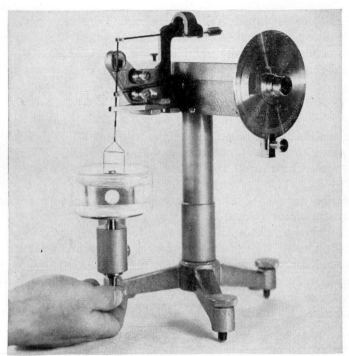

FIG. 6-2. The Du Nuoy tensiometer used for surface-tension measurements. (*Central Scientific Co.*)

property of surface tension causes liquid droplets to assume a spherical shape; water to rise in a capillary tube; and liquids, such as water, to move through porous materials that they are capable of wetting. The movement of water through soils is an excellent example.

Surface tension may be most accurately determined by measuring the height to which a liquid will rise in a capillary tube. Most liquids, like water, wet the walls of a glass tube and the liquid adhering to the walls pulls liquid up into the tube to decrease the total surface area in relation to its surface tension. This is the basis of capillary action so important in supplying water and nutrients to plant and animal tissues. Under static conditions, such as occur in a glass tube used to measure surface tension, the opposing forces are equal. The downward force may be expressed as $\pi r^2 h \rho g$, and the upward force as $2\pi r \gamma \cos \theta$.

$$\pi r^2 h \rho g = 2\pi r \gamma \cos \theta \tag{6-2}$$

or

$$\gamma = \frac{h \rho g r}{2 \cos \theta} \tag{6-3}$$

In Eqs. (6-2) and (6-3), $\gamma$ is the surface tension in dynes per centimeter when the height $h$ and the radius $r$ are expressed in centimeters. Rho ($\rho$) is the density of the liquid, $g$ is the acceleration due to gravity, and $\theta$ is the angle of contact the liquid makes with the wall of the capillary tube. For water and for many other liquids, $\theta$ is so small that $\cos \theta$ may be considered equal to 1. Then

$$\gamma = \frac{1}{2} h \rho g r \qquad \text{or} \qquad h = \frac{2\gamma}{\rho g} \frac{1}{r} \tag{6-4}$$

and the relationship between the height to which a liquid will rise in a capillary and its radius is readily apparent. The capillaries in the giant sequoia trees, which reach a height of nearly 300 ft, must be extremely small.

The surface tension of liquids is commonly measured by means of the *Du Nuoy tensiometer* (Fig. 6-2). This method employs a platinum ring, and the force required to pull the ring through the surface film is measured. The method is satisfactory for most measurements needed in sanitary engineering practice.

**Poiseuille's Law.** The behavior of liquids when flowing through capillary tubes in relation to their viscosity was studied by Poiseuille. He summarized his findings in the equation

$$\mu = \frac{\pi P r^4}{8 V l} t \tag{6-5}$$

where $V$ denotes the volume of liquid of viscosity $\mu$, flowing through a capillary tube of length $l$ and radius $r$, in time $t$, and under pressure $P$.

Sanitary engineers are often confronted with problems involving the flow of liquids through capillaries. A notable example is in the filtration of sewage sludge in which the void areas are considered as tortuous capillaries. Since water of a uniform viscosity is the liquid to be removed and the volume or rate of movement is of interest, *Poiseuille's equation* is of importance and is usually written

$$V = \frac{\pi P r^4}{8 \mu l} \tag{6-6}$$

where $P$ is pressure, $r$ is the radius of the capillaries, $\mu$ is the viscosity of the liquid, and $l$ is the length of the capillaries. The value of $t$ is usually dropped as unit time is understood. From this equation, the importance of the diameter of the capillaries is immediately apparent as being the principal factor in determining the pressure differential needed to maintain a constant liquid volume flow. A knowledge of Poiseuille's law is helpful in explaining how filter aids and chemical-conditioning agents such as lime are beneficial in filtration operations and as a basic concept for planning research on filtration or related problems.

### 6-6. Binary Mixtures

*Binary mixtures* of miscible liquids such as water and ethanol are of interest because of the differences in vapor pressure which they exhibit and the influence which vapor pressure has upon their separation by distillation. All mixtures fall into one of three classes, and their properties are considerably different.

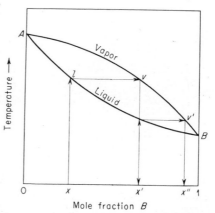

FIG. 6-3. Composition of liquid and vapor phases during distillation of Class I binary mixtures.

**Class I.** Class I includes all mixtures whose vapor pressure, regardless of the composition of the mixture, is always less than that of the most volatile component and always more than that of the least volatile component; consequently, the boiling point of Class I mixtures is always between that of the two components. The composition of the vapor is always richer in the more volatile component than the liquid from which it distills. Such mixtures are amenable to essentially complete separation by means of fractional distillation.

A diagram showing the composition of the liquid and vapor phases and how separation of the two components of Class I mixtures can be accomplished by fractional distillation is given in Fig. 6-3. If a mixture of A and B having the composition represented by $x$ is heated to its boiling point, the liquid will have a temperature corresponding to $l$, and the vapor produced will have a composition corresponding to $v$ on the vapor curve. If the vapor at $v$ is condensed, a liquid corresponding to $x'$, much richer in B, is obtained. Redistillation of the mixture $x'$ results in a vapor with a composition $x''$. Through successive condensations and evaporations, normally accomplished by a fractionating column, a distillate of essentially pure B can be obtained, and A will remain as a

relatively pure residue in the still.   A wide variety of compounds form
Class I binary mixtures.

**Class II.**   Class II binary mixtures include those that at certain mole
ratios have vapor pressures less than either of the components and, consequently, at these ratios have boiling points that are greater than that
of either of the components.   Upon distillation of such mixtures, one or
the other of the components may be fractionated into relatively pure form
until the liquid mixture reaches a composition of minimum vapor pressure or maximum boiling point.   From that point on, a constant boiling
mixture is obtained, the composition of the vapor and liquid is identical,
and further separation is impossible by this means.

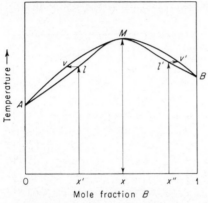

Fig. 6-4. Composition of liquid and vapor
phases during distillation of a Class II
binary mixture.

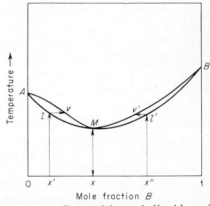

Fig. 6-5. Composition of liquid and
vapor phases during distillation of a
Class III binary mixture.

A diagram showing the composition of the liquid and vapor phases of
a Class II binary mixture is given in Fig. 6-4.   If a mixture corresponding to $x'$ is distilled, the vapor formed is rich in component A and may be
recovered in part in relatively pure form by fractionation.   However,
as A is removed from the liquid phase, the liquid phase grows richer in B
until it equals the composition shown by $x$.   At this point the composition of the vapor and liquid phases is identical, and a constant boiling
mixture that cannot be fractionated results.   Likewise, if a mixture with
a composition represented by $x''$ is distilled, a distillate of B can be
obtained, the liquid remaining will approach a composition equal to $x$,
and a constant boiling mixture will result.   Hydrochloric, hydrobromic,
hydroiodic, hydrofluoric, nitric, and formic acid in aqueous solution are
all binary mixtures of Class II.   The constant boiling mixture of hydrochloric acid at 760 mm pressure contains 20.2 per cent HCl and is often
used as a primary standard in quantitative analysis.

**Class III.**  Class III binary mixtures include those that at certain mole ratios have vapor pressures greater than that of either of the components, and, therefore, the boiling points at such mole ratios are lower than that of either component.  Upon distillation of Class III mixtures, the results are opposite to those obtained with Class II mixtures.  A distillate is obtained that contains both components in a constant ratio, and the residue remaining in the flask consists of one or the other component in pure form.

A diagram showing the composition of the liquid and vapor phases of a Class III binary mixture is given in Fig. 6-5.  A mixture corresponding to $x'$ will produce a vapor with composition $v$.  Fractionation of this vapor will produce a distillate with composition $x$, and the liquid phase will grow richer in component A.  Distillation of a mixture corresponding to $x''$ will produce a vapor with a composition $v'$.  Fractionation will yield a distillate with composition $x$, and the liquid will become richer in component B.  Eventually either pure A or pure B will remain in the liquid phase.  Ethyl alcohol and water form a binary mixture of this class.  The distillate, regardless of the composition of the original mixture, will always contain 95.6 per cent of alcohol at 760 mm pressure as long as both components are present in the liquid phase.

## 6-7. Solutions of Solids in Liquids

The amount of a solid that will dissolve in a liquid is a function of the temperature, the nature of the solvent, and the nature of the solute. The broad concepts of unsaturated, saturated, and supersaturated solutions are generally treated quite adequately in courses in general science and chemistry.  However, the significance of crystal or particle size and the influence of temperature on solubility are not always adequately discussed.

**Significance of Particle Size.**  The solubility of solids has been shown to increase as particle size diminishes.  For example, coarse granular $CaSO_4$ dissolves to the extent of 2.08 g/l at 25°C whereas finely divided $CaSO_4$ dissolves to the extent of 2.54 g/l.  This phenomenon is considered to be due to the increased ratio of surface area to mass and an increase in vapor pressure of the solid as particle size decreases.  Particles of colloidal size are considered to have the greatest solubility because of their submicroscopic size.

In quantitative analysis, advantage is often taken of the fact that solubility varies with particle size.  In gravimetric analysis, such as in the determination of sulfate by precipitation as $BaSO_4$, the precipitate first formed is highly colloidal in nature.  However, if some care is used in the precipitation procedure, a few crystals of larger size will be formed. By allowing the precipitated material to stand for a period of time before filtration, the colloidal-size particles will pass into solution and precipitate out on the larger crystals present. The rate of transfer is a function of the number of crystals present, the differential in solubilities, and the temperature. The difference in solubility is known to increase with temperature, as well as the rate of exchange; consequently, "digestion" of precipitates is normally done at temperatures near the boiling point of the solvent.

**Temperature Relationships.** In general, the solubility of solids in liquids increases as the temperature increases. There are a number of exceptions, however. The influence of temperature on solubility depends mainly upon the total heat effects of the solution. If the heat of solution is endothermic, the solubility increases with an increase in temperature; if the heat of solution is exothermic, the solubility decreases with

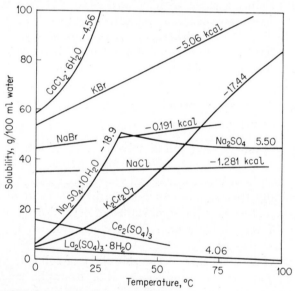

Fig. 6-6. Relationship between solubility in water and heats of solution.

an increase in temperature; and if there is little thermal change, the solubility is influenced very little by change of temperature. These considerations are all in accord with Le Chatelier's principle and the second law of thermodynamics.[1]

Figure 6-6 shows solubility curves for a number of solids in water and illustrates the relationship to heat of solution. The solubility curves for some solids, such as sodium sulfate, show abrupt changes because of a change in molecular composition and heat of solution.

[1] Thermodynamics is not discussed in this chapter as engineers are expected to have adequate training in this field.

## 6-8. Osmosis

*Osmosis* is defined as the passage of a solvent through a membrane from a dilute solution into a more concentrated one. For example, if a salt solution is separated from water by means of a semipermeable membrane, as shown in Fig. 6-7, water will pass through the membrane in both directions, but it will pass more rapidly in the direction of the salt solution. As a result, a difference in hydrostatic pressure develops that at equilibrium is termed the *osmotic pressure*.

Many theories have been advanced to explain the process of osmosis. Two are widely accepted. One applies to membranes not wetted by the solvent and holds that the transfer of solvent through the semipermeable membrane occurs in the vapor state. According to this concept, the controlling factor is the difference in the vapor pressures of the solutions on either side of the membrane. Because of this difference, the vapor within the membrane condenses more rapidly on the side containing the greater amount of solute, and evaporation is more rapid from the side with less solute. As a result, there is a net transfer of solvent across the membrane from the less concentrated solution to the more concentrated solution. The transfer will continue until the effects of hydrostatic pressure over-

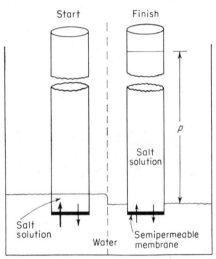

FIG. 6-7. The process of osmosis and the development of osmotic pressure.

come the driving force of the vapor-pressure differential. That the effects of hydrostatic pressure do not cancel in an arithmetical manner can be deduced from the fact that a 0.1 molal solution (approximately 33 g/l) of sucrose in water, having a vapor pressure 1.4 mm Hg less than water, exerts an osmotic pressure of about 2.6 atmospheres (atm) at 20°C.

The second important theory of osmosis relates to membranes that are wetted by the solvent. Animal membranes in aqueous solutions represent such systems. The transfer of solvent is in favor of the solution containing the greater amount of solute and is considered to be due to a greater physical hindrance to the movement of solvent molecules in the solution of greater concentration. As a result, there is a net transfer of solvent into the more concentrated solution, and this will continue until offset by adequate hydrostatic pressures.

## 6-9. Dialysis

The sanitary engineer does not have much opportunity to apply the principle of osmosis in its strictest sense. However, he does make use of a related phenomenon referred to as *dialysis*. By choice of a membrane, of a particular permeability, which is wetted by the solvent, it is possible for ions to pass through the membrane while large molecules of organic substances or colloidal particles are unable to pass. Thus, a separation of solutes can be accomplished, and the term dialysis is justified.

Dialysis is used extensively to remove electrolytes from colloidal suspensions to render the latter more stable. Chemical and sanitary engineers use dialysis to recover sodium hydroxide from certain industrial

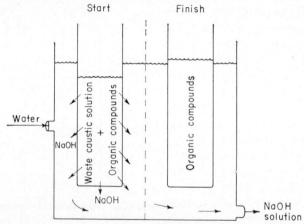

Fig. 6-8. A simple dialysis cell for recovery of sodium hydroxide from an industrial waste.

wastes that have become contaminated with organic substances, as shown in Fig. 6-8. In the process, the waste material is placed in cells with permeable membranes and the cells are surrounded with water. The sodium and hydroxide ions pass through the cell wall into the surrounding water. The water is evaporated to recover the sodium hydroxide, and the organic waste remaining in the cells is disposed of separately. Waste caustic solutions must be quite concentrated before recovery by dialysis can be justified economically. Mercerizing wastes of the cotton textile industry are an example.

## 6-10. Electrolytic Dissociation

The fundamental aspects of *electrolytic dissociation*, or ionization, were discussed in Sec. 2-11. The early concepts of Arrhenius have been modified somewhat in view of modern knowledge concerning the structure of inorganic crystalline materials. Such crystals have been shown by X-ray analysis to be made up of a latticework of ions arranged in very regular patterns, and any given ion in a crystal is not bound to any particular ion of opposite charge. From this viewpoint, the concept of molecules is no longer applicable to this type of compound, and, when solution of a crystal occurs in a solvent, the ions leave their sites at the surface of the crystal and pass into the solvent individually. Thus, solutions of most salts and other electrolytes are thought to exist in a completely dissociated form. From this point of view, the degree of dissociation $\alpha$, as calculated from the Arrhenius concept, appears to lose its significance.

Experimental evidence has shown that solutions of electrolytes do not exhibit freezing-point values which correspond to those that would be predicted from Raoult's law, assuming complete ionization of the electrolyte. Rather, the results are less and the divergence from the theoretical becomes greater as concentration of the solute increases. If this effect cannot be explained by the formation of un-ionized molecules, some other explanation is required. The *Debye-Hückel* or *interionic-attraction theory* is most often used to explain this anomalous situation. According to it, oppositely charged ions attract each other and cause deviations from those that would be produced by an equal number of uncharged particles. In order to correct for this deviation, the concept of *activity coefficient, f,* was developed. Physical chemists have found this concept to be of great value.

From the viewpoint of the sanitary engineer, it makes little difference whether he thinks in terms of molecules and incomplete dissociation or whether he thinks in terms of complete dissociation and activity coefficients. In the realm of weak electrolytes, such as bicarbonate buffered systems and other systems frequently encountered in sanitary engineering, the former has many advantages. It may be expected that ionization constants based upon the original concepts of Arrhenius will be used a long time in the future.

## 6-11. Principles of Solvent Extraction

Industrial wastes often contain valuable constituents which can be recovered most effectively and economically by means of extraction with an immiscible solvent, such as petroleum ether, diethyl ether, benzene, chloroform, or some other organic solvent. Because of the importance of this operation in sanitary engineering practice, a discussion of the principles involved is merited.

When an aqueous solution is intimately mixed with an immiscible solvent, the solutes contained in the water distribute themselves in relation to their solubilities in the two solvents. For low to moderate concentrations of solute, the ratio of distribution is always the same:

$$\frac{C_{\text{solvent}}}{C_{\text{water}}} = \frac{C_s}{C_w} = K \tag{6-7}$$

The value of $K$, or the ratio of distribution, is known as the *distribution coefficient*. In actual practice the immiscible solvent is selected for its ability to dissolve the desired material, and values for $K$ are normally greater than 1.

If the volume of solvent used is equal to the volume of the sample being extracted, the mathematics involved is rather simple. For a system with a distribution coefficient of 9, 90 per cent of the material would be extracted in the first step, and 90 per cent of the material remaining in each successive step. After three extractions with fresh solvent, 99.9 per cent of the material would be removed.

In actual practice it is seldom feasible to use a volume of solvent equal to the waste volume, and calculations become somewhat involved. The question in industrial waste treatment which usually requires answering is: How much remains in the aqueous phase after $n$ extractions? The expression defining the distribution coefficient may be written in terms of the amounts of the substance extracted and the volumes of the liquids involved,

$$K = \frac{C_s}{C_w} = \frac{(W_0 - W_1)/V_s}{W_1/V_w} \tag{6-8}$$

where $W_0$ is the weight of the substance originally present in the aqueous phase, $W_1$ is the weight remaining in the water after one extraction, and $V_s$ and $V_w$ are the volumes of solvent and water, respectively. Simplifying, we obtain

$$W_1 = W_0 \frac{V_w}{KV_s + V_w} \tag{6-9}$$

In the second step of the extraction,

$$W_2 = W_1 \frac{V_w}{KV_s + V_w} \tag{6-10}$$

or, in terms of the original sample,

$$\begin{aligned} W_2 &= W_0 \frac{V_w}{KV_s + V_w} \frac{V_w}{KV_s + V_w} \\ &= W_0 \left(\frac{V_w}{KV_s + V_w}\right)^2 \end{aligned} \tag{6-11}$$

and after $n$ extractions the weight of substance remaining in the water is

$$W_n = W_0 \left(\frac{V_w}{KV_s + V_w}\right)^n \tag{6-12}$$

Equation (6-12) has general application and may be used to calculate the volume of a solvent needed to reduce the concentration of a material in the aqueous phase to definite levels with a fixed number of extractions or the number of extractions needed with a fixed volume of a solvent, provided that the distribution coefficient is known.

## 6-12. Chemical Kinetics

Chemical kinetics is concerned with the speed or velocity of reactions. Reactions in which molecules do not react with each other but act individually are called *unimolecular reactions*. These are all decomposition reactions such as that of hydrogen peroxide, of nitrogen pentoxide, and of radioactive elements. Many other reactions appear to be unimolecular in nature from a mathematical viewpoint but in reality are not. Such reactions are known as *first-order reactions*. Reactions that occur because of collisions between two molecules, of either the same or different species, are termed *bimolecular reactions*. A few reactions are known that involve collision of three molecules. They are known as *termolecular reactions*.

The sanitary engineer is concerned with unimolecular- and binary-type reactions. In general, the binary-type reactions are so rapid that they cause him little difficulty. Examples are oxidation of cyanides [Eq. (3-8)] and of ferrous ion [Eq. (2-5)] by chlorine. Reactions of the unimolecular type, however, vary greatly in their speed, and it is this type which is of great concern to sanitary engineers.

**Unimolecular Reactions.** The decomposition of a radioactive element is the simplest example of a true unimolecular reaction. In such a reaction the rate of decomposition is directly proportional to the amount of undecayed material and may be expressed mathematically as

$$- \frac{dC}{dt} = kC \tag{6-13}$$

where the minus sign indicates a loss of material, $C$ is its concentration, and $k$ is a proportionality constant.

Upon integration of Eq. (6-13), we obtain

$$\log C = - \frac{k}{2.303} t - \text{const} \tag{6-14}$$

and, from this equation, it becomes evident that, if a plot is made of the logarithm of concentration versus time, a straight line results. In sanitary engineering practice, this is a common way of proving whether or not a reaction is unimolecular in nature. The velocity constant $k$ can be evaluated by multiplying the negative slope of the plotted line by 2.303.

If Eq. (6-14) is integrated between limits, we obtain

$$k = \frac{2.303}{t_2 - t_1} \log \frac{C_1}{C_2} = \frac{2.303}{t} \log \frac{C_0}{C} \tag{6-15}$$

where $C_0$ is the concentration at zero time and $C$ is the concentration after time $t$ has elapsed. The value of $k$ has real significance only when $t$ is defined; this may be in terms of seconds, minutes, hours, days, or even years.

Reaction rates are usually expressed in terms of numerical values for $k$. For radioactive substances it is customary to express decomposition rates in terms of half-life. There is a growing tendency to use this mode of expression for a variety of phenomena in sanitary engineering practice. The period of half-life is

$$t_{\frac{1}{2}} = \frac{0.693}{k} \tag{6-16}$$

Sanitary engineers find application for the concepts involved in unimolecular reactions in areas that do not involve decomposition reactions. For example, the solution of oxygen in water, under a given set of conditions, is a unimolecular reaction.

**First-order Reactions.** It was stated above that a number of chemical reactions appear to behave mathematically like unimolecular reactions, but in reality they are not. Most of these are bimolecular in nature, but, because of the preponderance of one reactant whose concentration does not change materially, the reactions progress as though only one substance was undergoing change. Two examples will be discussed to illustrate the case.

In Sec. 5-20 it was shown that di- and polysaccharides react with water to form simple sugars. For example,

$$\underset{\text{Sucrose}}{C_{12}H_{22}O_{11}} + H_2O \xrightarrow[\text{HCl}]{\text{cat.}} \underset{\text{Glucose}}{C_6H_{12}O_6} + \underset{\text{Fructose}}{C_6H_{12}O_6} \tag{6-17}$$

This is a binary reaction since it involves collisions between two molecules. However, under the conditions used for hydrolysis of sucrose, water is in such abundance that its concentration is not appreciably diminished as the reaction proceeds. As a result, the nature of the reaction is the same as though sucrose decomposed by itself, and the kinetics of the reaction is essentially the same as that of a unimolecular reaction.

The decomposition of organic matter by bacteria is another reaction which may be considered to be bimolecular in nature since decomposition depends upon oxidation of organic matter brought about by bacteria.

$$\text{Organic matter} + \text{bacteria} \xrightarrow{O_2} CO_2 + H_2O \tag{6-18}$$

In this reaction the population of bacteria does not diminish as the reaction progresses, but, instead, the population usually increases considerably; thus, from the viewpoint of the organic matter, its destruction will proceed more or less in a unimolecular manner. However, from the viewpoint of the bacterial population, the reaction rate should increase as long as bacterial numbers are on the increase; thus, the BOD reaction, as it is commonly called in sanitary engineering practice, has the elements of a first-order reaction, but it may not necessarily express itself in the form of a unimolecular reaction. If the initial population of bacteria is low, values for $k$ will be very low but will increase rapidly with bacterial reproduction or during the log-growth phase. When the population of bacteria becomes static, the reaction may become truly unimolecular from a mathematical viewpoint. If the initial population of bacteria is great and subsequent reproduction does not alter numbers materially, the reaction will approach a true unimolecular reaction, mathematically. The latter is the case in domestic sewage that is a few hours old. Industrial wastes, in general, correspond to the former case.

From a theoretical viewpoint, it would be impossible for the biological degradation of anything but substrates of pure organic compounds to approach a true unimolecular reaction. Domestic sewage and many industrial wastes consist of a mixture of many organic compounds. The rate of biological degradation of the several compounds may differ considerably. As a result, the gross rate of decomposition during the initial hours is influenced greatly by the materials with short half-lives, and the materials of longer half-lives determine the $k$ value during the later stages. This phenomenon of decreasing $k$ value with time has been observed by several investigators and has a sound theoretical basis.

## 6-13. Catalysis

*Catalysts* have the power to change the rate of a chemical reaction. They may be positive or negative in effect. Regardless of their actual role in the reaction, they are recoverable in their original form at the end of the reaction. It is important to remember that catalysts have no influence on the final equilibrium of a reaction. They simply alter the speed with which the equilibrium is attained by changing the energy of activation. Positive catalysts have one other property of interest to sanitary engineers. They can initiate and maintain reactions at concentration levels below those at which ordinary reactions would occur.

Applications of catalysis in the field of sanitary engineering are largely concerned with control of air pollution. Hydrogen sulfide is catalytically oxidized to sulfur dioxide at concentrations normally incapable of supporting combustion. Catalytic devices are being sought to oxidize olefinic compounds in the exhaust gases of trucks and buses as one means of controlling the "smog" problem at Los Angeles. Such devices as are available at the present time cannot be used on motor vehicles using "leaded" fuels because of "poisoning" of the catalyst.

## 6-14. Electromotive Force

Any extended discussion of electromotive force involves concepts from thermodynamics, physics, and electrochemistry that are beyond the scope of this book. Reference should be made to standard texts on physical or theoretical chemistry for such information. However, there are several fundamental considerations which may be approached from a qualitative viewpoint that should be helpful to sanitary engineers in understanding corrosion and other phenomena.

**Single Electrode Potentials.** According to modern concepts, a metallic electrode when placed in water tends to dissolve to a limited extent. In this reaction, metallic ions are considered to pass into solution, and the electrode becomes negatively charged, as shown in Fig. 6-9. Of course, metallic ions are attracted to the negatively charged electrode and an equilibrium condition results. The extent of the negative charge that accumulates on a metallic electrode is a function of the solution pressure of the metal. This corresponds to the well-known electromotive-force series of the metals. When the potentials are measured in terms of a reference electrode (such as the normal hydrogen electrode) and in a solution containing 1 g ionic weight of the metallic ion per 1,000 g of water instead of in pure water, *single electrode potentials* are obtained which are called *normal electrode potentials*. It is impractical to attempt measurement of single electrode potentials in pure water because of secondary reactions which often occur that destroy the reversibility of the reaction. Table 6-2 shows the normal electrode potentials for a number of the common metals.

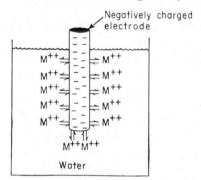

FIG. 6-9. Development of single electrode potential on a metal electrode immersed in water.

Considering the single electrode potentials for Zn, Fe, and Sn, the conditions at equilibrium may be represented in a qualitative manner, as shown in Fig. 6-10. The potential on each electrode in terms of electrons is a function of the number of metallic ions that have passed into solution and exist in equilibrium with the electrode. If the Zn cell is connected to the Fe cell by a conducting salt bridge and a connection is made between the zinc and iron electrodes, a *galvanic cell* results, and electrons flow from the electrode of high potential (Zn) to the electrode of low potential (Fe). As a result, the potential of the zinc electrode falls, and more zinc ionizes and passes into solution in an attempt to maintain a state of equilibrium. As electrons flow from the zinc elec-

TABLE 6-2. NORMAL ELECTRODE POTENTIALS* FOR A NUMBER OF
COMMON METALS

| Electrode | $E_0$, volts† | Electrode reaction |
|-----------|---------------|--------------------|
| K | −2.92 | $K° \rightarrow K^+ + e$ |
| Ca | −2.87 | $Ca° \rightarrow Ca^{++} + 2e$ |
| Zn | −0.76 | $Zn° \rightarrow Zn^{++} + 2e$ |
| Fe | −0.44 | $Fe° \rightarrow Fe^{++} + 2e$ |
| Cd | −0.40 | $Cd° \rightarrow Cd^{++} + 2e$ |
| Sn | −0.13 | $Sn° \rightarrow Sn^{++} + 2e$ |
| Pb | −0.12 | $Pb° \rightarrow Pb^{++} + 2e$ |
| H | 0.00 | $\frac{1}{2}H_2° \rightarrow H^+ + e$ |
| Cu | 0.34 | $Cu° \rightarrow Cu^{++} + 2e$ |
| Ag | 0.79 | $Ag° \rightarrow Ag^+ + e$ |

\* Actually, single electrode potentials measured under special conditions.
† Relative to normal hydrogen electrode, $Pt(\frac{1}{2}H_2° \rightarrow H^+)$.

trode to the iron electrode, an excess of electrons accumulate on the iron electrode, and ferrous ions are recalled from solution to plate out on the electrode; thus, the iron is kept from passing into solution while the zinc acts in a *sacrificial* manner. This is an example of *galvanic protection* and is the basic principle involved in the protection of iron by galvanizing with zinc.

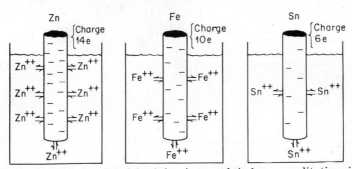

FIG. 6-10. Single electrode potentials of zinc, iron, and tin from a qualitative viewpoint.

If the Fe cell is connected with the Sn cell of Fig. 6-10 by a conducting salt bridge and a connection is made between the iron and tin electrodes, a galvanic cell results and electrons flow from the iron to the tin electrode. The iron electrode will dissolve in an attempt to maintain equilibrium conditions, and the tin electrode will be protected because of the excess electrons flowing from the iron electrode.

From the above considerations, it becomes obvious that when two metals are in electrical contact, the metal with the greater single electrode potential or higher in the electromotive-force series will sacrifice itself to protect the other. The sacrificial electrode is known as the *anode*, and the protected electrode is the *cathode*. From these considerations, the engineer can explain why discontinuous zinc coatings protect iron from corroding whereas discontinuous coatings of tin aggravate the rusting of iron. The principles developed above are also the basis of regulations prohibiting the joining of copper and iron pipe without the use of insulating connectors. The same principles are involved in cathodic protection of steel pipelines, tanks, and structures by means of sacrificial anodes or artificially impressed negative potentials.

**Concentration Cells.** *Concentration cells* are of two types: those with electrodes of different concentrations and those with solutions of different concentrations. The former are of little concern to sanitary engineers. The latter, however, are of considerable importance as a factor

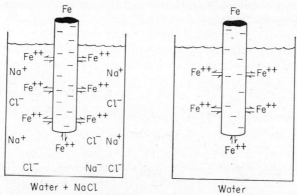

Fɪɢ. 6-11. Concentration cells, showing the effect of water quality on single electrode potentials.

that often aggravates corrosion of steel pipelines passing through soils of varying character or soils containing zones of brackish and fresh waters.

If electrodes of the same metal, such as iron, are placed in aqueous solutions containing different salt concentrations, the extent to which the iron passes into solution will differ, and, as a result, the potential developed on the electrodes will be different, as shown in Fig. 6-11. In general, the electrode in the salt solution will have the higher potential and, therefore, becomes sacrificial. As a result, that part of the metal immersed in brackish water or passing through soils of high soluble salt content tends to corrode very rapidly. Water lines laid under such adverse conditions on Treasure Island in San Francisco Bay in preparation for the 1938 Golden Gate International Exposition failed because of corrosion before the fair was started.[1] Some of the pipe passed through "land-fill" areas

[1] C. E. Lee, *J. Am. Water Works Assoc.*, **32**, 305 (1940).

where the soil character varied radically. Ground water varied considerably in salt concentration.

**Reference Electrodes.** Since the absolute potentials of single electrodes are unknown, it is necessary to accept one as standard and relate the others to it. The *hydrogen electrode* is often used as the standard. It consists of a strip of sheet platinum coated with platinum black, immersed in a solution that is 1.0 $N$ with respect to hydrogen ions and bathed with a stream of hydrogen gas under 1 atm of pressure. Hydrogen gas is adsorbed on the platinum black, and the electrode is considered to be $Pt(H_2^\circ \rightleftharpoons 2H^+)$ whose characteristics are dominated by the hydrogen. The hydrogen electrode is assigned a value of zero, and potentials related to it are designated by the prefix $E_0$ or $E_H$.

The hydrogen electrode is cumbersome to use, and a variety of other electrodes have been suggested as substitutes. Of these, the calomel electrode has found greatest favor. The elements of a calomel reference electrode, as used on electrometric pH meters and other devices, are shown in Fig. 6-12.

Calomel electrodes are of three types: normal, tenth normal, and saturated, depending upon the concentration of KCl solution used in preparing them. The potential that each develops is a function of the concentration of the potassium chloride solution used. The potential of each with respect to the hydrogen electrode is as shown in Table 6-3.

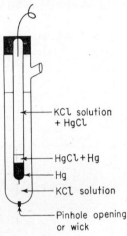

Fig. 6-12. Calomel reference electrode.

(labels: KCl solution + HgCl; HgCl+Hg; Hg; KCl solution; Pinhole opening or wick)

TABLE 6-3. POTENTIAL OF CALOMEL REFERENCE ELECTRODES

| Concentration of KCl | $E_0$ or $E_H$ at 25°C, volts |
|---|---|
| 0.1 $N$ | 0.336 |
| 1.0 $N$ | 0.281 |
| Saturated | 0.246 |

From the data given in Table 6-3, it becomes apparent that knowledge of the concentration of KCl used in preparing a calomel reference electrode is necessary for proper interpretation of information gathered with its aid. In general, the saturated type of calomel electrode is used, and its use is so common that results are often reported in terms of $E_{cal}$ rather than $E_0$.

**The Glass Electrode.** The *glass electrode* is used almost universally for measurement of pH. It functions in highly colored solutions where colorimetric methods are useless and in oxidizing media, reducing media, and colloidal systems where other electrodes have failed almost completely.

The action of the glass electrode is not completely understood. The glass used in the sensitive part of the electrode must have special characteristics with respect to thickness. Construction of the electrode is essentially the same as that of the calomel reference electrode except that the cell does not have an opening or wick to make direct electrical connection with the surrounding fluid. Also, the electrolyte within the glass electrode is an acid solution of definite strength rather than a KCl solution. The glass electrode is used in conjunction with a standard calomel reference cell, and the system may be described as shown in Fig. 6-13.

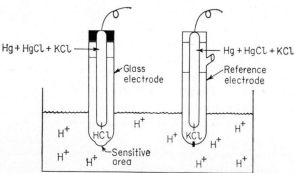

FIG. 6-13. Electrode system employing the glass electrode for measurement of pH.

The single electrode potential established on the glass electrode is determined by the concentration of hydrogen ions in the solution in relation to the concentration in the electrolyte within the electrode. It is generally considered that the potential is actually determined by the relative concentrations of adsorbed $H^+$ on the two sides of the glass membrane.

Since the glass electrode is, in essence, a calomel electrode, its inherent electromotive force cancels that of a calomel reference electrode, and the potential established on a glass electrode in relation to a calomel electrode may be expressed as

$$E = \frac{RT}{F} \ln \frac{[H_1^+]a}{[H_2^+]a} \tag{6-19}$$

where $[H_1^+]a$ and $[H_2^+]a$ are actual molar concentrations of $H^+$ corrected for activity.

The potential developed by a glass electrode is so small that measurements cannot be made by ordinary galvanometers. As a result, a vacuum-tube voltmeter (pH meter) is commonly employed and calibrated to read pH directly.

**Oxidation-Reduction Potentials.**   *Oxidation-reduction potentials* are of interest to sanitary engineers for at least two reasons.   They are of importance in the selection of internal indicators to show the stoichiometric end point during oxidation-reduction type of titration, as discussed in Sec. 4-4.   They are of even greater interest as a means of showing the conditions which exist in biological systems.   This is of particular value at sewage or industrial waste treatment plants designed to operate as aerobic processes.   The potentials are measured by means of a noble-metal electrode, such as gold or platinum, in conjunction with a reference electrode, as shown in Fig. 6-14.

In any system undergoing biological oxidation, there is a continual change in the ratio between the materials in the reduced form (reductants) and the materials in the oxidized forms (oxidants).   At the start of the treatment process, the concentration of reductants (organic waste materials) is high and the amount of oxidized material including dissolved oxygen is usually very low.   Such a system has a low $E_{cal}$ or $E_H$ value. As biological oxidation progresses,

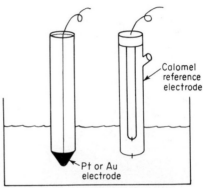

Fig. 6-14. Electrode assembly for measurement of oxidation-reduction potentials (ORP).

the concentration of reductants decreases and the concentration of oxidized materials including dissolved oxygen increases.   As a result, the $E_{cal}$ or $E_H$ of the system increases.   This is in accordance with the general equation

$$E = E_0 - \frac{RF}{nf} \ln \frac{[\text{reductants}]}{[\text{oxidants}]} \tag{6-20}$$

where $E$ denotes the potential required to transfer electrons from the oxidant to the reductant.   It is not possible to apply Eq. (6-20) in a quantitative manner to biological systems because of the variety of reductants and oxidants present.   The concept expressed is of great value, and experience in actual operations will soon establish critical values that are extremely helpful in the operation of aerobic treatment facilities.

## 6-15. Adsorption

*Adsorption* may be defined as the tendency exhibited by all solids to condense upon their surfaces a layer of any gas or liquid with which they are in contact.   Charcoal is used extensively for adsorptive purposes because of its tremendous surface area in relation to mass. At a given temperature and pressure a sample of charcoal will adsorb a definite quantity of a gas. If the pressure is increased, it will adsorb more; if the pressure is decreased, it will adsorb less. If the quantities of adsorbed gas are plotted against pressure, curves of the nature shown in Fig. 6-15 are obtained.

Adsorption by charcoal of solutes from solution follows the same law as gases. This is illustrated in Fig. 6-16 which shows data for the adsorption of acetic and benzoic acids. The curves are of the same nature as those shown in Fig. 6-15. From these data; it may be con-

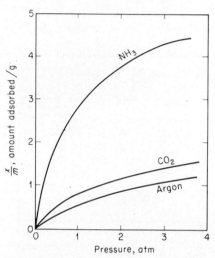

FIG. 6-15. Adsorption of gases on charcoal in relation to pressure at constant temperature.

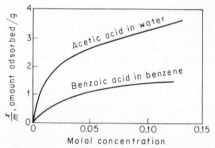

FIG. 6-16. Adsorption of solutes on charcoal. Temperature and pressure constant.

cluded that the quantity of substance adsorbed by a given sample of adsorbent depends upon the nature of the material and its concentration. Temperature is also a factor which is not demonstrated by the data presented.

Freundlich studied the adsorption phenomenon extensively and showed that adsorption from solutions by charcoal could be expressed by the equation

$$\frac{x}{m} = kC^{1/n} \quad \text{or} \quad \left(\frac{x}{m}\right)^n = k_1 C \tag{6-21}$$

where $C$ is the concentration of solute, $x/m$ is the amount of material adsorbed per unit weight of the adsorbent, and $k$, $k_1$, and $n$ are constants which must be evaluated for each solute and temperature.

The Freundlich isotherm is often expressed in its logarithmic form

$$\log \frac{x}{m} = \log k + \frac{1}{n} \log C \tag{6-22}$$

Adsorption data, when plotted according to Eq. (6-22), yield straight lines, as shown in Fig. 6-17.    Experimental data are often plotted in this manner as a convenient way of determining whether removal of materials

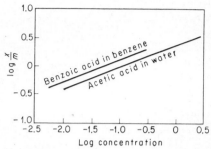

FIG. 6-17. Logarithmic plot of adsorption data.

from solution is accomplished by adsorption and as a means of evaluating the constants $k$ and $n$.

## REFERENCES

Daniels, F., and R. A. Alberty: "Physical Chemistry," John Wiley & Sons, Inc., New York, 1955.

Millard, E. B.: "Physical Chemistry for Colleges," 7th ed., McGraw-Hill Book Company, Inc., New York, 1953.

Moore, W. J.: "Physical Chemistry," 2d ed., Prentice-Hall, Inc., Englewood Cliffs, N.J., 1955.

# 7. Basic Concepts from Colloid Chemistry

## 7-1. Introduction

*Colloid chemistry* is concerned with dispersions.  These may exist in solids, liquids, or gases.  Dispersions in solids are of little consequence to sanitary engineers; consequently, discussion will be directed toward those that occur in liquids or in gases.  Eight classes of colloidal dispersions are known, as shown in Table 7-1.  Classes 4 through 8 of

TABLE 7-1. CLASSES OF COLLOIDAL DISPERSIONS

| Class | Dispersed phase | Dispersion medium | Common name |
|-------|-----------------|-------------------|-------------|
| 1 | Solid | Solid | |
| 2 | Liquid | Solid | |
| 3 | Gas | Solid | |
| 4 | Solid | Liquid | |
| 5 | Liquid | Liquid | Emulsions |
| 6 | Gas | Liquid | Foams |
| 7 | Solid | Gas | Smokes |
| 8 | Liquid | Gas | Fogs |

this table are commonly encountered in sanitary engineering practice, and classes 5 through 8 are readily recognized by laymen by their common names.

**Size.**  Colloidal dispersions consist of discrete particles that are separated by the dispersion medium.  The particles may be aggregates of atoms, molecules, or mixed materials that are considered larger than individual atoms or molecules but are small enough to possess properties greatly different from coarse dispersions.  Colloidal particles normally range in size from about 1 to 100 millimicrons ($m\mu$) and are not visible even with the aid of the ordinary high-powered microscope.  Their relation to other dispersions is as follows:

140

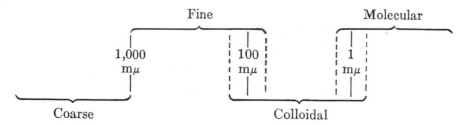

Colloidal dispersions may be considered as ultrafine dispersions and occupy a size range between fine and molecular.    The boundaries between fine, colloidal, and molecular dispersions are by no means hard-and-fast values.

**Methods of Formation.**    Any material that is reasonably insoluble in the dispersion medium can be caused to form a colloidal dispersion. Colloidal-sized particles can be produced by grinding coarse materials. Devices designed for such purposes are called *colloid mills.*    Colloidal particles are formed in considerable amounts in hard-rock drilling and blasting operations.    Colloidal-sized particles may be formed from ions that react to form insoluble compounds.    Under the proper conditions, aggregates of molecules result that do not grow into crystals of a size large enough to settle or be filtered out.    This often happens in gravimetric analysis, as discussed under crystal growth in Sec. 6-7.

Certain organic substances and compounds that are considered to be soluble in water do not form true solutions; instead, they form colloidal dispersions.    Soap, starch, gelatin, agar-agar, gum arabic, and albumin are examples.    Bentonite, a volcanic clay, is an example of an inorganic material that acts likewise.    In these cases, the dispersion medium, water, has the ability to disintegrate the material sufficiently to carry it into colloidal suspension, but it does not necessarily have the ability to complete the dispersion into molecular particles.    In certain cases, such as with gelatin, gum arabic, and albumin, the individual molecules may be so large as to fall into the colloidal range, even though dispersion might be complete.

**General Properties.**    Because colloidal particles are so small, their surface area in relation to mass is very great.    Some concept of this relation can be obtained by consideration of how the surface area of a cube 1 cm side length increases when it is reduced to colloidal-sized cubes.    If colloidal-sized cubes of 10 m$\mu$ are formed, the surface area is increased from 6 sq cm to 600 sq m, or about $\frac{1}{7}$ acre.    It is difficult to conceive of such a small mass of material having such a tremendous surface area. As a result of this large area, surface phenomena predominate and control the behavior of colloidal suspensions.    This is so much so that colloidal chemistry is often considered synonymous with surface chemistry.

The mass of colloidal particles is so small that gravitational effects are unimportant.

*Electrical Properties.* All colloidal particles are electrically charged. The charge varies considerably in its magnitude with the nature of the colloidal material and may be positive or negative, as shown in Fig. 7-1. Many colloidal dispersions are dependent upon the electrical charge for their stability. Like charges repel, and, as a result, similarly charged colloidal particles cannot come close enough together to agglomerate into larger particles.

The *electrokinetic* properties of colloids are of great importance to sanitary engineers, as destruction of many forms depends upon a knowledge of them. More detailed discussion is given in Sec. 7-2.

When colloidal particles are placed in an electrical field, the particles migrate toward the pole of opposite charge. This phenomenon is known

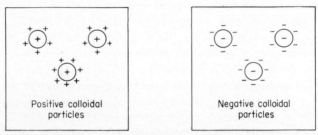

Positive colloidal particles

Negative colloidal particles

Fig. 7-1. Positive and negative colloidal particles.

as *electrophoresis* and is used extensively to determine the nature of the charge on the colloidal particle and other properties.

*Brownian Movement.* Colloidal particles are bombarded by molecules of the dispersion medium, and, because of their small mass, the colloids move about under the impetus of the bombardment in a helter-skelter manner. This movement may be observed in some colloidal suspensions with the aid of a high-powered microscope but is seen best with the aid of the ultramicroscope. It was originally thought to be a characteristic of living matter, but a botanist, Robert Brown, in 1827, showed that non-living material exhibited this same phenomenon. The term *Brownian movement* has been used to describe this action, whether the particles are living or inanimate.

*Tyndall Effect.* Because colloidal particles have dimensions greater than the average wavelength of white light, they interfere with the passage of light. Light which strikes them may be reflected. As a result, a beam of light passing through a colloidal suspension is visible to an observer who is at or near right angles to the beam of light. This phenomenon is called the *Tyndall effect* in honor of the English physicist who studied it extensively. This test is often used to prove the presence of a colloid, as true solutions and coarse suspensions do not produce the phenomenon.   Oftentimes, rays of sunlight piercing between clouds are seen when the atmosphere is charged with colloidal dust particles.   Students often see the Tyndall effect illustrated in classrooms when chalk or other dust is present in colloidal form in the air.   The Tyndall effect is used as a basis of determining turbidity when the Baylis or St. Louis type of turbidimeter is used.

*Adsorption.*   Colloids have tremendous surface area and, of course, great adsorptive powers.   Adsorption is normally preferential in nature, with some ions being chosen and others excluded.   This selective action yields charged particles and is the fundamental basis of the stability of many colloidal dispersions.

*Effect on Freezing and Boiling Point.*   Colloidal dispersions affect the freezing and boiling points of liquids the same as dispersions of other particles; see Raoult's law (Sec. 2-9).   Their effect, however, is not measurable with ordinary instruments because the actual number of particles is so very few as compared with Avogadro's number.   This is because colloidal suspensions normally fall into the realm of very dilute solutions, and, in addition, each particle is made up of, perhaps, hundreds or even thousands of molecules.

*Dialysis.*   Colloids, because of their large particle size, do not pass through ordinary semipermeable membranes.   Thus a separation of crystalloids and colloids can be accomplished by dialysis, as discussed in Sec. 6-9.

**Nomenclature.**   The nomenclature applied to colloidal systems varies considerably with the type; consequently, there are few terms generally applicable.

## 7-2. Colloidal Dispersions in Liquids

Colloidal dispersions of solids, liquids, and gases in liquids are commonly encountered in sanitary engineering practice.   The nomenclature and behavior of each type differ somewhat; consequently, discussions of each will be given.

**Solids in Liquids.**   Colloidal dispersions of solids in liquids are of two types, solvent-hating and solvent-loving.   In terms of water, the solvent-hating are called *hydrophobic* and the solvent-loving are called *hydrophilic*.   Colloidal dispersions of solids in liquids are often referred to as *sols* or *suspensoids.*

*Hydrophobic Colloids.*   Hydrophobic colloids are all electrically charged.   The charge on all particles in a given dispersion is the same. It may be positive or negative, depending upon the nature of the sol. Most metallic oxide sols become positively charged, and nonmetallic oxide, as well as metallic sulfide, sols are usually negatively charged.

The nature of the charge, however, may be the opposite when formation of the sol occurs under a different set of conditions.

In the realm of liquids, the sanitary engineer is concerned with the removal of colloidal solids from water, sewage, and industrial wastes. These colloids are not always well-defined hydrophobic sols; but they do lend themselves to separation when treatment designed to remove hydrophobic sols is used. The natural coloring matter of surface waters and the colloidally suspended matter of sewage are examples of quasi hydrophobic-hydrophilic, negatively charged colloids encountered in sanitary engineering practice.

ELECTROKINETIC PROPERTIES. The stability of hydrophobic colloids depends upon the electrical charge that they possess. This charge is gained by adsorption of ions from the surrounding medium, as illustrated in Fig. 7-2. Ions of opposite charge then arrange themselves in a diffuse second layer about the first layer. As a result, the colloidal particle assumes a distinct charge that is determined by the layer nearest it. The stability of the colloid is generally a function of the magnitude of the charge, commonly referred to as the *zeta potential*, $\zeta$. The zeta potential is defined by the equation

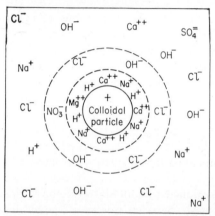

FIG. 7-2. A positively charged colloidal particle with adsorbed cations and diffuse layer of ions of opposite charge.

$$\zeta = \frac{4\pi\delta q}{D} \qquad (7\text{-}1)$$

where $q$ is the charge on the particle, $\delta$ is the thickness of the zone of influence of the charge on the particle, and $D$ is the dielectric constant of the liquid.

All hydrophobic colloidal particles are subject to two opposing forces: The $\zeta$ potential, which is a repelling force, and an intermolecular or interparticle attractive force commonly called the *Van der Waals force*. As long as the $\zeta$ potential is great enough to produce repulsive forces in excess of the Van der Waals force, the particles cannot coalesce. The objective of chemical coagulation is to reduce the magnitude of the $\zeta$ potential so that repulsive forces between particles are less than the Van der Waals attractive force. Then coalescence of colloidal particles will occur and coagulation can be accomplished.

DESTRUCTION. The destruction of hydrophobic colloids may be accomplished in four major ways. Only two are applied to a significant extent in sanitary engineering practice. The four methods are (1) boiling, (2) freezing, (3) addition of electrolytes, and (4) mutual precipitation by addition of a colloid of opposite charge.

Boiling of a hydrophobic colloidal suspension often results in coagulation of the colloidal particles. This action is not usually attributed to a reduction in the $\zeta$ potential but rather to modification in the degree of hydration of the particles, or sometimes to increased kinetic velocities which increase $\zeta$-potential requirements to maintain stability. Chemists often boil materials to accomplish coagulation of colloids, but boiling is too expensive for general application in sanitary engineering practice.

Freezing is another method by which colloids may be coagulated. During the freezing process, crystals of relatively pure water form. Thus the colloidal and crystalloidal materials are forced into a more and more concentrated condition. Two additive effects cause coagulation to occur. As the colloidal suspension becomes more concentrated, the $\zeta$ potential required to maintain stability increases. At the same time, the concentration of electrolytes increases and this tends to decrease the $\zeta$ potential. The net result is coagulation of the colloid.

Freezing has been proposed as a practical means of destroying the colloidal character of sludges in preparation for vacuum filtration. However, it is usually less costly to condition sludges for filtration by the use of chemicals.

The common method of destroying hydrophobic colloids is by the addition of electrolytes. Electrolytes act in two ways to cause coagulation. Salts of monovalent ions, such as NaCl, act largely to reduce the zone of influence, $\delta$, of the charged particles. However, it has been noted that salts having divalent ions of charge opposite to that of the colloidal particle exert coagulation powers far beyond expectation. Salts having trivalent ions of opposite charge are even more effective. The significance of the relation between ionic charge and precipitating power was first pointed out by Schulze and verified by Hardy. Their findings are usually called the *Schulze-Hardy rule*, which states: *The precipitation of a colloid is effected by that ion of an added electrolyte which has a charge opposite in sign to that of the colloidal particles, and the effect of such ion increases markedly with the number of charges it carries.*

Table 7-2 lists a number of electrolytes and gives their relative coagulating powers for positive and negative colloids. From the data given in Table 7-2 it becomes obvious why aluminum and iron salts are so widely used as coagulants in sanitary engineering practice. The greater value of the sulfates as compared with the chlorides is not readily apparent but will be discussed shortly. Multivalent ions of opposite charge are considered to be able to force their way into the zone of influence of colloidal particles and in this way neutralize, in part, the charge on the colloid.   This results in lowering the $\zeta$ potential and, if enough of the ion of opposite charge is added, in coagulation of the colloid.

Mutual precipitation occurs when colloids of opposite charge are mixed. If they are added in essentially equivalent amounts, in terms of electrostatic charge, coagulation occurs and is quite complete.   This method is not used per se in sanitary engineering practice because of the large volumes of water that would be needed to carry the second colloid and because of the relatively long time required for flocculation of the colloidal dispersions.

TABLE 7-2. RELATIVE COAGULATING POWER OF SEVERAL ELECTROLYTES

| Electrolyte | Relative power* of coagulation | |
| --- | --- | --- |
| | Positive colloids | Negative colloids |
| NaCl | 1 | 1 |
| $Na_2SO_4$ | 30 | 1 |
| $Na_3PO_4$ | 1,000 | 1 |
| $BaCl_2$ | 1 | 30 |
| $MgSO_4$ | 30 | 30 |
| $AlCl_3$ | 1 | 1,000 |
| $Al_2(SO_4)_3$ | 30 | >1,000 |
| $FeCl_3$ | 1 | 1,000 |
| $Fe_2(SO_4)_3$ | 30 | >1,000 |

* Values given are approximate and are for solutions of equivalent ionic strength.

The trivalent salts of iron and aluminum used in coagulation of water to remove colloidal color and turbidity are considered to act in three capacities, all of which have significance from the viewpoint of colloidal chemistry.   These salts, when added to water, do ionize to yield trivalent metallic ions, the amount and life of which are a function of the pH of the water.   Some of the trivalent ions, undoubtedly, reach the target and neutralize the charge on some of the colloidal particles.   The majority of the trivalent ions, however, unite with the available hydroxyl ions to give colloidal metallic hydroxides which carry a positive charge. The amount of positively charged metallic hydroxide is normally much in excess of the amount needed to react with any negatively charged color or turbidity particles that may have escaped neutralization by trivalent metallic ions.   The excess colloidal metallic hydroxides must be coagulated in some manner.   This is where the negative ion of the metallic salt used is of importance.   If sulfates are used instead of chlorides, the divalent sulfate ions act to neutralize the charge on the excess colloidal metallic hydroxide and thereby complete the coagulation of the colloidal system.

*Hydrophilic Colloids.* A wide variety of hydrophilic colloidal materials are known. Most of them are products of plant or animal life and, therefore, of considerable concern to sanitary engineers. Soap, soluble starch, soluble proteins, protein degradation products, blood serum, agar-agar, gum arabic, pectins, and synthetic detergents are examples. These materials occur in domestic sewage and in many industrial wastes. Soap, however, is usually precipitated by calcium and magnesium ions and does not often occur as a colloidal suspension except in laundry wastes.

The hydrophilic colloids are readily dispersed in water, and their stability depends upon their love for the solvent rather than upon the slight charge (usually negative) that they possess. This property makes it difficult to remove them from aqueous suspension. Certain of them, such as the proteins and protein degradation products, form heavy metal salts that are insoluble; thus their removal is effected by aluminum and ferric salts. Proteins, proteoses, peptones, polypeptides, and amino acids have a minimum solubility at their isoelectric point. The isoelectric point varies from about pH 4.0 to 6.5 for the majority; consequently, it is usually uneconomical to attempt their removal by pH adjustment in wastes that are well buffered with bicarbonates.

Most hydrophilic colloids serve in a protective capacity for hydrophobic colloids. When acting in this capacity they are called *protective colloids*. It is believed that they envelope the hydrophobic colloid in a manner to shield it from the action of electrolytes. Coagulation of such systems requires rather drastic treatment with massive doses of coagulant salts, often ten to twenty times the amount used in conventional water treatment. Information concerning the action of coagulants on many hydrophilic colloids is lacking. Further research is needed.

**Liquid-in-liquid Systems.** Colloidal systems involving the dispersion of one liquid in another are known as *emulsions*. Obviously, the two liquids must be immiscible in each other. The emulsions of interest to sanitary engineers usually are composed of oil and water. The oil may be dispersed in the water (the usual case) or water may be dispersed in oil. Most emulsions depend upon a third component, an *emulsifying agent*, for their stability.

Soap and synthetic detergents are excellent emulsifying agents, as would be suspected from their common use for laundering, dishwashing, and other cleaning purposes. Many natural materials such as proteins, protein degradation products, egg yolk, lanolin, saponin, and gum arabic act as emulsifying agents. Egg yolk serves as the emulsifying agent in salad dressings, as in mayonnaise, for example. Kaolin, fuller's earth, colloidal clay, and lampblack have been found to act as good emulsifiers of mineral oil in water.

*Water-in-oil Emulsions.*    Water-in-oil emulsions are quite common in the petroleum industry.    They can be readily broken by heating, and such treatment is practical because of the value of the oil that can be recovered.

*Oil-in-water Emulsions.*    Oil-in-water emulsions are usually milky white in appearance, and their destruction depends upon treatment to inactivate the emulsifying agent.    This inactivation may be accomplished in a variety of ways, but economics usually dictates the use of chemical coagulating agents such as aluminum or ferric salts.

**Gas-in-liquid Systems.**    Dispersions of gas bubbles in liquids are considered to be colloidal in character regardless of the bubble size; therefore foams fall in this category.    Foams have become of considerable importance to sanitary engineers, particularly those concerned with the treatment of domestic sewage, since the advent of synthetic detergents that are resistant to biological degradation.    They are of concern, also, in the treatment of certain industrial wastes such as those from the wood-pulping and the meat-packing industries.

Foams are normally stabilized by hydrophilic colloidal materials that are highly surface-active and tend to concentrate at air-water interfaces. Foams have been aptly described as a collection of interfaces separated by air bubbles.    Destruction is usually accomplished in either of two ways.    Water sprays are used to break the foam by dilution and mechanical action, or antifoaming materials may be added.    The antifoaming material, to be effective, must lower the surface tension more than the hydrophilic colloid.    It will then displace the colloid and cause the foam to collapse.

### 7-3. Colloidal Dispersions in Air

The sanitary engineer is becoming more and more involved in air pollution problems.    The control of "smog" and of smoke are two important phases of air pollution that have colloidal aspects.

**Fog and "Smog."**    *Fog* consists of a colloidal dispersion of a liquid in air.    The sanitary engineer has no special interest in ordinary fog.    However, in areas where atmospheric inversions are common, such as at Los Angeles, photochemical reactions may occur in the polluted atmosphere near the ground to produce an artificial fog.    These fogs are commonly referred to as "*smog.*"    At the present time, "smog" is believed to be formed by the reaction between olefinic hydrocarbons and nitrogen dioxide in the presence of sunlight.    Ozone is formed in the reaction and a nitro derivative of the olefin is believed to be formed.    The latter is suspected of condensing water from the atmosphere to produce the colloidal dispersion called "smog." Like fog, the amounts involved are so tremendous that destruction is out of the question. Control appears to rest on limitation of the olefin-type compounds allowed to reach the atmosphere. Automobile exhaust gases are considered to be the major source.

**Smoke.** Dispersions of solid matter in air are called *smokes*. They may originate from a wide variety of industrial processing, the principal one being the power industry. The colloidal particles in smoke are charged, and their removal can be accomplished by passage through electrostatic precipitators, such as the Cottrell precipitator.

## REFERENCES

Fischer, E. K.: "Colloidal Dispersions," John Wiley & Sons, Inc., New York, 1950.
Hauser, E. A.: "Colloidal Phenomena," McGraw-Hill Book Company, Inc., New York, 1939.
Weiser, H. B.: "Colloid Chemistry," John Wiley & Sons, Inc., New York, 1949.

# 8. Basic Concepts from Biochemistry

## 8-1. Introduction

Biological engineering has been defined as the science of controlling the actions of living organisms to produce desired end products. Most sanitary engineers can be classed as biological engineers because they spend considerable time and effort in designing and operating treatment facilities that utilize living organisms to bring about the destruction of waste organic materials. Therefore, an important facet of their training is concerned with biochemistry.

*Biochemistry* deals with chemical changes that are brought about by living organisms. The reactions may be *extracellular* or *intracellular*. Hydrolytic reactions (splitting by water) are extracellular in character and necessarily so, because such reactions are often required to reduce the complexity of organic compounds to a point where they can dialyze through the cell wall. The energy requirement for hydrolytic reactions is considered to be nil. Oxidative reactions occur intracellularly and produce energy in accordance with the free energy of the particular reaction involved.

Biochemical reactions occur at temperatures with a normal range from about 0 to 60°C. Organisms that thrive at 0 to 10, 10 to 40, and 40° upward are classed as *psychrophilic*, *mesophilic*, and *thermophilic*, respectively. The majority of the chemical reactions that these organisms bring about occur at far lower temperatures than would be needed in their absence. For this reason, catalysts that lower markedly the activation energy of the reactions are required. The catalysts are supplied by the living organisms as part of their life processes and are known as *enzymes*. They serve to initiate the reactions and also to control their speed in a manner that serves the best interests of the particular organism. This mechanism sometimes leads to an interference between groups of organisms when operating in mixed culture.

150

## 8-2. Enzymes

Enzymes have been defined as temperature-sensitive catalysts of organic nature, elaborated by living cells and capable of action outside or inside the cell. Certain of the enzymes are secreted by the cell and are known as *extracellular* enzymes. Others are associated with the protoplasm of the cell and perform their function within the cell, and so they are called *intracellular* enzymes.

Enzymes are proteinaceous in character. Some are simple proteins

TABLE 8-1. CLASSIFICATION OF ENZYMES

| Enzyme | Substrate | Products |
|---|---|---|
| Hydrolytic: | | |
| 1. Carbohydrases: | | |
|   *a.* Glycosidases (sugar splitters): | | |
|     Sucrase | Sucrose | Glucose + fructose |
|     Maltase | Maltose | Glucose |
|     Lactase | Lactose | Glucose + galactose |
|   *b.* Amylases (starch splitters): | | |
|     Diastase &#125; Ptyalin | Starch | Maltose |
|   *c.* Cellulase | Cellulose | Cellobiose |
| 2. Esterases: | | |
|   *a.* Lipases: | | |
|     Lipase | Glycerides | Glycerol + fatty acids |
|   *b.* Phosphatases | Phosphoric esters | $H_3PO_4$ + alcohols |
| 3. Proteases: | | |
|   *a.* Proteinases: | | |
|     Pepsin &#125; Trypsin | Proteins | Polypeptides |
|   *b.* Peptidases | Polypeptides | Amino acids |
| 4. Amidases: | | |
|   *a.* Urease | Urea | $NH_3 + CO_2$ |
| 5. Deaminases | Amino acids | $NH_3$ + organic acids |
| | | |
| Desmolytic or respiratory: | | |
| 1. Dehydrogenases* | | |
| 2. Oxidases* | | |
| 3. Activators of $H_2O_2$: | | |
|   *a.* Peroxidase | $H_2O_2$ + organic compound | $H_2O$ + oxidized compound |
|   *b.* Catalase | $H_2O_2$ | $H_2O + O_2$ |
| 4. Decarboxylases* | | |
| 5. Transaminases* | | |
| 6. Phosphorylases* | | |

\* Action of desmolytic enzymes is beyond the scope of this book. Consult any standard text on biochemistry.

whereas others are of a complex conjugated type. They are highly specific for the reactions that they catalyze. Enzymes are grouped into two major classes, depending on the nature of the reaction that they control. Those that catalyze hydrolytic reactions are known as *hydrolases* and those that catalyze the rupture of linkages that are not hydrolyzable are known as *desmolases* or *respiratory enzymes*. The enzymes involved in oxidation-reduction reactions are of the latter type. In general, hydrolases are extracellular and desmolases are intracellular. The *-ase* ending is used to designate enzymes. A classification of enzymes according to their function is given in Table 8-1.

A great number of enzyme and bacterial preparations with a wide variety of trade names (Sea Chem, Bionetic, Enzymatic, Septic Aid, etc.) have been marketed as agents capable of solving problems related to the operation of septic tanks, sludge digestion units, and other treatment facilities. Research has indicated that domestic sewage and sewage sludges contain bacteria capable of producing the necessary enzyme systems in adequate amounts and that no beneficial effects can be demonstrated by the addition of enzymes from outside sources. In the case of malfunctioning units, reports from field studies (usually conducted without controls) have often been favorable. Laboratory studies, however, have failed to show any beneficial effects when the materials were used in amounts recommended in practice.[1]

### 8-3. Coenzymes

*Coenzymes* are complex heat-stable compounds that must be present for certain enzymes to act. The best known are associated with the action of dehydrogenases in which they serve as "carriers" of hydrogen. Coenzymes are able to perform this function because they can be alternately reduced and oxidized by taking on or giving up electrons; thus they serve as hydrogen acceptors or as hydrogen donors. Approximately 10 coenzymes are known. Some of the more important are as follows:

**Coenzyme I.** A dinucleotide, usually designated as diphosphopyridine nucleotide (DPN), it serves as a hydrogen carrier in a number of reactions catalyzed by dehydrogenases.

**Coenzyme II.** Related to DPN, it has three phosphoric acid radicals in the molecule. It is triphosphopyridine nucleotide (TPN). Its best-known function is in the oxidation of glucose.

**Cocarboxylase or Coenzyme A.** A derivative of pantothenic acid, it functions in fatty-acid metabolism (β oxidation) and synthesis.

**Flavoproteins.** A mononucleotide, riboflavin phosphate, and a dinucleotide, adenine-riboflavin phosphate, are known collectively as flavo-

[1] E. A. Pearson, et al., Biocatalytic Additives in Sludge Digestion, *Sewage and Ind. Wastes*, **29**, 1066 (1957).

proteins.    They are important in the transport of hydrogen from metabolites to oxygen.

## 8-4. Temperature Relationships

Biochemical reactions, in general, follow the van't Hoff rule of a doubling of reaction rate for a 10°C increase in temperature, over a restricted temperature range.    Studies with activated sludge have shown the reaction rate to be more than doubled for a 10°C rise in temperature, as shown in Fig. 8-1.[1]

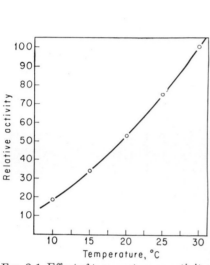

FIG. 8-1. Effect of temperature on activity of activated sludge as measured by oxygen requirements per unit time.

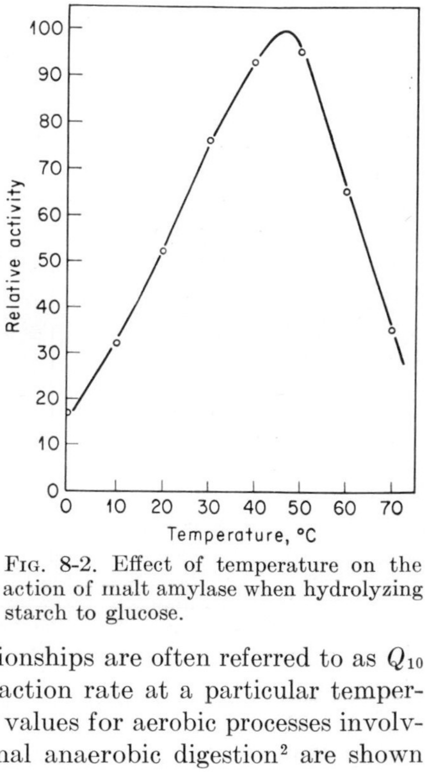

FIG. 8-2. Effect of temperature on the action of malt amylase when hydrolyzing starch to glucose.

In biochemistry, temperature relationships are often referred to as $Q_{10}$ values, which are the ratio of the reaction rate at a particular temperature to the rate at 10°C lower.    $Q_{10}$ values for aerobic processes involving activated sludge[1] and conventional anaerobic digestion[2] are shown in Table 8-2.

The data in Table 8-2 illustrate that the influence of temperature varies considerably, depending upon the range of temperature and also the nature of the reaction involved.    A great deal of study has been given to the effect of temperature on the rate of enzyme-induced reactions.    Since all biological reactions are dependent upon enzymes, the data are of considerable interest to sanitary engineers.    Table 8-3 shows the effect of temperature on a number of enzymes, and Fig. 8-2 shows

[1] C. N. Sawyer and G. A. Rohlich, *Sewage Works J.*, **11,** 946 (1939).

[2] G. M. Fair and E. W. Moore, *Sewage Works J.*, **6,** 3 (1934).

TABLE 8-2. EFFECT OF TEMPERATURE ON AEROBIC AND
ANAEROBIC BIOCHEMICAL PROCESSES

| Biological system | Temperature, °C | $Q_{10}$ |
|---|---|---|
| Activated sludge | 10–20 | 2.85 |
| | 15–25 | 2.22 |
| | 20–30 | 1.89 |
| Anaerobic sludge | 10–20 | 1.67 |
| | 15–25 | 1.73 |
| | 20–30 | 1.67 |
| | 25–35 | 1.48 |
| | 30–40 | 1.0 |

TABLE 8-3. THE EFFECT OF TEMPERATURE ON THE ACTIVITY OF
CERTAIN ENZYMES

| Enzyme | Temperature, °C | $Q_{10}$ |
|---|---|---|
| Amylase | 10–20 | 1.34 |
| | 15–25 | 1.59 |
| | 20–30 | 1.44 |
| | 25–35 | 1.27 |
| | 30–40 | 1.17 |
| Pepsin | 0–10 | 2.60 |
| | 10–20 | 2.00 |
| | 20–30 | 1.80 |
| | 30–40 | 1.60 |
| Steapsin | 0–10 | 1.50 |
| | 10–20 | 1.34 |
| | 20–30 | 1.26 |

the activity of amylase at several temperatures when hydrolyzing starch.

The data in Fig. 8-2 illustrate the point that increasing temperature has a favorable effect upon biochemical reactions, within limits. As the temperature is increased, eventually a point is reached where the enzyme becomes less active. This change is considered to be due to *denaturation* of the enzyme. In systems containing living organisms, the adverse effects of high temperature may be explained by considering that the enzymes are denaturized or that the ability of the organisms to produce enzymes has been destroyed. The net effect is the same in either case.

The importance of temperature as a factor in determining the rate of biological reactions has been recognized by sanitary engineers for some time in connection with anaerobic sludge digestion. Its significance in relation to aerobic processes was largely ignored until recently. At the present time, design standards for trickling filters recognize temperature as a factor, since accepted design loadings in the United States vary with the latitude. The significance of temperature in activated sludge treatment has not been given direct recognition. This effect is a complicated matter that does not lend itself to simple mathematical treatment. It involves three major factors all of which are temperature-dependent: (1) required detention time, (2) oxygen requirements per unit volume per unit time, and (3) variation in solubility of oxygen with temperature.

## 8-5. pH

Hydrogen-ion concentration is one of the most important factors that influence the speed of biochemical reactions, and, since such reactions

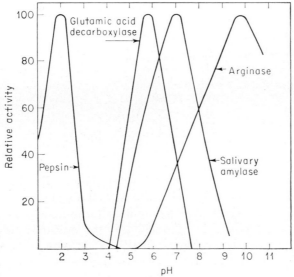

FIG. 8-3. Effect of pH on enzyme activity, illustrating the rather narrow range of optimum action.

are induced and controlled by enzymes, it is necessary to have a knowledge of how pH affects enzyme activity. The range of pH through which a particular enzyme can act effectively is usually quite narrow. Some enzymes act best at low pH levels; others require high pH; but the majority are most effective in neutral solutions. The optimum pH and the effective range of pH for a few enzymes are given in Fig. 8-3.

Most biological processes employed in sanitary engineering practice involve the use of soil organisms operating in mixed culture. The enzyme systems of these organisms are adapted to operating in essentially neutral solutions; therefore it is important that pH be controlled over a

rather narrow range of about 6 to 9.    Control of pH is best accomplished
by means of buffer systems.

## 8-6. Buffers

*Buffers* may be defined as substances in solution that offer resistance
to changes of pH as acids or alkalies are added to or formed within the
mixture.    Natural buffering materials are usually salts of weak acids,
such as bicarbonates.    Any salt of a weak acid or of a weak base will
serve as an excellent buffer over a particular pH range.    The fundamental basis for an understanding of buffer action was developed in
the discussion on acidimetry and alkalimetry as presented in Sec. 4-4.
Inspection of Figs. 4-3 and 4-5 will illustrate the point that only the
weak acids and weak bases offer marked resistance to pH change in the
range of pH 6 to 9.    This is the range in which biological reactions occur
with maximum facility and is of greatest interest to sanitary engineers.

Weak acids and bases have very small ionization constants.    Accordingly, the number of undissociated molecules is large with respect to the
number of ions present.    In the case of acetic acid, the condition might
be depicted graphically and mathematically as follows:

$$HAc \rightleftharpoons H^+ + Ac^-$$

and
$$\frac{[H^+][Ac^-]}{\left[ HAc \right]} = K = 10^{-5} \tag{8-1}$$

Acetic acid is a very good buffer toward alkalies, for the reason that,
as hydroxyl ions are added, they unite with the hydrogen ions available
to form water.    This disturbs the equilibrium represented in Eq. (8-1),
and more acetic acid dissociates to maintain the ionization constant equal
to $10^{-5}$; thus it would seem that the pH would remain essentially constant.    Inspection of the titration curves mentioned above shows that
this is not exactly true, the reason being as follows: Although hydrogen
ions are removed from solution, the acetate ions are not, and, as more
and more acetic acid dissociates to maintain a $K$ value of $10^{-5}$, the concentration of acetate ions increases.    This establishes a new set of conditions as follows:

$$\frac{[H^+] \left[ Ac^- \right]}{\left[ HAc \right]} = 10^{-5} \tag{8-2}$$

Under the new set of conditions, less acetic acid will have to ionize to
keep $K$ equal to $10^{-5}$ because of the increased concentration of acetate
ions.    As a result, the pH gradually increases as the titration progresses,
but it does not rise rapidly until all the un-ionized acetic acid is consumed.

All weak acids act in this manner. A similar discussion can be developed to illustrate the buffering character of weak bases.

In a solution of acetic acid that has been neutralized with sodium hydroxide to a pH of about 8, sodium, acetate, and hydrogen ions are present. The equilibrium can be expressed as follows:

$$\frac{[H^+]\left[Ac^-\right]}{[HAc]} = 10^{-5} \tag{8-3}$$

If a strong acid is added to the solution, the added hydrogen ions combine with acetate ions to form undissociated acetic acid, and the new equilibrium is essentially as shown in Eq. (8-2); thus the process of neutralization is reversed, and the pH falls in accordance with the hydrogen-ion concentration that can exist in equilibrium with the remaining acetate ions.

From the above discussion, it should be obvious that solutions can be buffered in the range of about 4 to 8 by use of proper mixtures of acetic acid and sodium acetate. The degree of buffering, usually called *buffering capacity*, is related to the amounts used.

Bicarbonates serve as the buffer in natural waters and many industrial wastes; therefore they are of great interest to sanitary engineers. The equilibrium of importance in biological systems is primarily that which exists between carbon dioxide and bicarbonate ion.

$$CO_2 + H_2O \rightleftharpoons H_2CO_3 \rightleftharpoons H^+ + HCO_3^- \tag{8-4}$$

In a system containing appreciable amounts of bicarbonate, the equilibrium conditions may be represented as follows:

$$\frac{[H^+]\left[HCO_3^-\right]}{CO_2 + H_2O \rightleftharpoons [H_2CO_3]} = 10^{-7} \tag{8-5}$$

Addition of a base, such as sodium hydroxide, results in a momentary reduction in the concentration of $H^+$. However, the carbonic acid ionizes to maintain $K = 10^{-7}$, and part of the carbonic acid is replaced by a union of $CO_2$ and $H_2O$. The net result is an increase in $[HCO_3^-]$ and a slight decrease in $[H^+]$. The pH increases slightly. Addition of hydroxide may be continued without rapid increases in pH until all the free carbon dioxide has been converted to bicarbonate at pH 8.3.

Addition of an acid to a bicarbonate system such as that illustrated in Eq. (8-5) results in a momentary increase in $[H^+]$. In order for $K$ to remain equal to $10^{-7}$, hydrogen and bicarbonate ions must combine to form un-ionized carbonic acid. This disturbs the equilibrium between

$CO_2$ and carbonic acid, and more free carbon dioxide is formed. When the new equilibrium has been established, the $[H^+]$ is only slightly greater than it was at the start, and the pH has been depressed very little. Thus, significant amounts of strong acid may be added with little change in pH. Inspection of Fig. 4-4 will show bicarbonate systems to have extremely good buffering capacity at pH values in the range of 5.5 to 7.5.

In sanitary analysis, buffering capacity is normally measured by alkalinity determinations. Although the buffering capacity of natural waters is largely due to bicarbonate, the sanitary engineer should remember that alkalinity determinations measure the buffering capacity of all salts of weak acids. This is particularly pertinent in the analysis of industrial wastes. The best way of evaluating the buffer capacity of an industrial waste is to perform an electrometric titration, using a standard acid. If observations of pH versus titrant additions are made, curves can be plotted that show its capacity and the pH range over which the buffer is especially effective.

Buffer capacity is an important characteristic of wastes that are submitted to biological treatment. The oxidation of neutral compounds, sugar for example, results in the production of organic acids as intermediates. If the buffering capacity is not sufficient, the pH may fall to levels that inhibit the action of the bacteria. In an instance where formaldehyde was involved, the pH was reduced to 4.5 within a matter of minutes, and the process was considered a failure until adequate buffer was supplied. The initiation of anaerobic digestion to produce methane from sewage sludge is hampered by limitations of buffer capacity. Liming of digesters is often practiced to maintain favorable pH conditions. In effect, the lime combines with the organic acids to form water and salts of weak acids. Although the calcium salts of the organic acids that result would have a buffering capacity toward mineral acids, they have little or no buffering action toward additional organic acids that may be released in the system. However, in a system containing calcium salts of fatty acids, the following equilibrium may be considered to exist:

$$M^{++}* + 2Ac^- + H_2O \rightleftharpoons M^{++} + 2OH^- + 2HAc \qquad (8\text{-}6)$$

As the organic acids are destroyed (represented by HAc in the above equation) by methane bacteria to form carbon dioxide and methane, the carbon dioxide combines with the hydroxyl ions to form bicarbonate.

$$M^{++}* + 2OH^- + 2CO_2 \rightarrow M^{++} + 2HCO_3^- \qquad (8\text{-}7)$$

Equations (8-6) and (8-7) are fundamental reactions for buffer formation. The metallic ion is usually $Ca^{++}$, $Mg^{++}$, $Na^+$, $K^+$, or $NH_4^+$.

* $M^{++}$ represents metallic ions normally present in biological systems.

## 8-7. Major and Trace Elements

Bacteria are among the simplest forms of living matter, and like all living matter, in order to survive, they must reproduce. Many bacteria can thrive upon very simple substrates, such as sugar, provided that certain essential elements are present in the form of ions or inorganic salts. Bacterial cell tissue has an empirical formula which approximates $C_5H_7NO_2$, corresponding to about 12 per cent nitrogen.

It is known that bacteria are capable of synthesizing protein from a wide variety of carbonaceous materials. If the species is to be preserved, sufficient nitrogen must be present to produce daughter cells exactly like the parent cells. This growth would require, on an average, enough nitrogen to produce cells with about 12 per cent nitrogen; therefore nitrogen is considered a major nutrient element in bacterial nutrition. Phosphorus and sulfur are other elements essential to the formation of some conjugated proteins and are considered major nutrient elements.

Certain other elements are needed in trace amounts for cell metabolism. Many are known to be important in enzyme function or in other physiological capacity. Calcium, cobalt, copper, iron, magnesium, manganese, potassium, selenium, and zinc are probably essential for most bacteria. Other elements are necessary for certain bacteria. Molybdenum, for example, is required by nitrogen-fixing bacteria.

Sanitary engineers may safely assume that domestic sewage will provide all the major and trace elements needed in its stabilization by bacteria. This may or may not be the case with industrial wastes. Many industrial wastes are deficient in the major nutrient elements nitrogen and phosphorus. Some may be deficient in sulfur and in trace elements, depending upon the nature of the carriage water.

## 8-8. Biochemistry of Carbohydrates

The primary function of carbohydrate matter in higher animals is to serve as a source of energy. With microscopic organisms, however, the differentiation of foods for particular purposes is not a rigid matter. Bacteria, for example, utilize carbohydrate matter for the synthesis of fats and proteins as well as for energy. In addition, of course, carbohydrate is also used in building cell tissue and may be stored as polysaccharide inside or outside the cell wall.

The mechanisms by which bacteria and other microorganisms transform carbohydrates are believed to be essentially the same as those occurring in plants and animals. The first stage in carbohydrate metabolism involves hydrolysis (see Fig. 5-1). This degradation must progress to at least the disaccharide stage before transfer through the cell wall can occur. Once within the cell wall, the simple sugars are used for energy or synthesis.    The mechanisms involved are beyond the scope of this book.

## 8-9. Biochemistry of Proteins

Proteins are essential in the diets of higher animals and are used to build and repair muscle tissue.    Amounts in excess of these requirements may be consumed for energy or converted to carbohydrates and fats. Saprophytic[1] bacteria are much less demanding in their protein requirements.    Most of them are capable of synthesizing protein from inorganic nitrogen and carbohydrates.    This ability is most fortunate, for many industrial wastes from the food industry have very low protein content. It would add greatly to the cost of biological treatment if proteinaceous matter had to be added.

The first step in biological utilization of proteins involves their hydrolysis, which progresses in steps as shown in Sec. 5-22.    It is fairly well established that hydrolysis must yield $\alpha$-amino acids before passage through the cell wall is possible.    Within the cell, *deamination* of the amino acids occurs.    The nature of the deamination reactions vary under aerobic and anaerobic conditions.

**Deamination under Aerobic Conditions.**    Bacteria deaminize amino acids under aerobic conditions to produce saturated acids with one less carbon atom,

$$R-\underset{\underset{H}{|}}{\overset{\overset{NH_2}{|}}{C}}-COOH + O_2 \xrightarrow[\text{enzymes}]{\text{bact.}} R-COOH + CO_2 + NH_3 \quad (8\text{-}8)$$

or hydroxy acids with the same number of carbon atoms,

$$R-\underset{\underset{H}{|}}{\overset{\overset{NH_2}{|}}{C}}-COOH + H_2O \xrightarrow[\text{enzymes}]{\text{bact.}} R-\underset{\underset{H}{|}}{\overset{\overset{OH}{|}}{C}}-COOH + NH_3 \quad (8\text{-}9)$$

**Deamination under Anaerobic Conditions.**    Bacterial deamination under anaerobic conditions may proceed with or without reduction to form the corresponding saturated or unsaturated acids.

$$R-\underset{\underset{H}{|}}{\overset{\overset{NH_2}{|}}{C}}-COOH + H_2 \xrightarrow[\text{enzymes}]{\text{bact.}} R-CH_2COOH + NH_3 \quad (8\text{-}10)$$

$$R-CH_2-\underset{\underset{H}{|}}{\overset{\overset{NH_2}{|}}{C}}-COOH \xrightarrow[\text{enzymes}]{\text{bact.}} R-CH{=}CH-COOH + NH_3 \quad (8\text{-}11)$$

[1] From the Greek words *sapros* meaning death or decay and *phytos* (plant).

The acids formed under aerobic or anaerobic conditions submit to further oxidation, as discussed in Sec. 8-10.

## 8-10. Biochemistry of Fats and Oils

The degradation or assimilation of fatty materials is often restricted because of their relative insolubility. This difficulty is overcome in animals by emulsifying agents (bile salts) that are contained in bile secreted by the liver. It is highly improbable that bacteria are capable of secreting similar emulsifying agents. In any event, it is known that segregation of fatty materials is a serious problem in anaerobic sludge digestion units. Because of their low specific gravity, the fatty materials tend to float and complicate scum conditions. In the scum layer, these fatty materials may be rather remote from the bacteria that are capable of utilizing them.

The biological degradation of fatty materials in its initial phases is known to progress along similar lines under aerobic and anaerobic conditions. The first step is hydrolysis, with the production of glycerol and fatty acids, as discussed in Sec. 5-21. The free fatty acids derived from the hydrolysis of fatty materials and those produced in the deaminization of amino acids undergo further breakdown by oxidation. Oxidation is believed to occur at the beta carbon atom in accordance with *Knoop's theory*, sometimes called the *beta-oxidation theory*. According to this theory, oxidation proceeds in four steps. Coenzyme A is known to be active in these transformations.

$$
\underset{\substack{| \quad | \\ H \quad H}}{R\!-\!\overset{\substack{H \quad H \\ | \quad |}}{C}\!-\!C\!-\!COOH} + O \xrightarrow[\text{enzyme}]{\text{bact.}} \underset{\substack{| \quad | \\ H \quad H}}{R\!-\!\overset{\substack{H \\ | \\ O \quad H \\ | \quad |}}{C}\!-\!C\!-\!COOH} \qquad (8\text{-}12)
$$

$$
R\!-\!C\!-\!C\!-\!COOH + O \xrightarrow[\text{enzymes}]{\text{bact.}} R\!-\!C\!-\!C\!-\!COOH \qquad (8\text{-}13)
$$

$$
R\!-\!C\!-\!C\!-\!COOH \xrightarrow[\text{enzymes}]{t.} R\!-\!C\!-\!C\!-\!COOH + H_2O \qquad (8\text{-}14)
$$

$$
R\!-\!C\!-\!C\!-\!COOH + H_2O \xrightarrow[\text{enzymes}]{\text{bact.}} R\!-\!COOH + CH_3COOH \qquad (8\text{-}15)
$$

In the final step, rupture of the molecule occurs, with formation of one molecule of acetic acid, and the original molecule of acid appears as a new acid with two less carbon atoms. Thus, by successive oxidations at the beta carbon atom, long-chain fatty acids are "whittled" into fragments consisting of acetic acid. It is the accumulation of acetic acid and fragments of the original molecules that causes radical decreases in the pH of mixtures undergoing anaerobic digestion, unless adequate buffers are present. In anaerobic sludge digesters, the accumulation of acetic and other low-molecular-weight acids is measured by the volatile-acids determination.

The fatty acids of low molecular weight are capable of passing through the cell wall. There they are used for energy or synthetic purposes. The mechanisms involved, like those for carbohydrates, are beyond the scope of this book.

### 8-11. Biochemistry of Man

Since sanitary engineers are concerned with the disposal of human wastes, it is important that they be familiar with the major changes that organic matter, taken as food, undergoes in its passage through the body.

**Carbohydrates.** Much of the carbohydrate consumed by man is utilized by the body. The remainder, consisting of undigestible matter, is eliminated in the feces. Most of the rejected carbohydrate matter is cellulose and other higher polysaccharides for which the human body does not provide enzymes to accomplish its hydrolysis, or the detention time in the intestine is too short to complete hydrolysis. The short detention time is aggravated by improper chewing of food and by diarrhetic conditions.

The carbohydrate matter that is assimilated into the blood stream is used for energy, stored as glycogen (animal starch) in the liver, or converted to fat and stored as fatty tissue. The carbohydrates that are oxidized to produce energy are converted to carbon dioxide and water. The carbon dioxide is carried away, by the blood, from the cells where it is formed. The blood is buffered to such an extent that it can carry considerable amounts of $CO_2$ and release it to the air in the lungs in accordance with the principles of Henry's law.

The human body contains a remarkable mechanism for controlling the amount of sugar (glucose) in the blood stream. If excessive amounts accumulate, the excess is released into the urine. This is a part of the kidney function. Persons with diabetes suffer from improper metabolism of sugar. As a result, blood sugar exceeds the amount acceptable to the kidney (renal threshold), and the excess is separated in the kidneys and escapes in the urine. The urine of diabetics shows the presence of glucose consistently. If the carbohydrate intake of a diabetic exceeds the capacity of his kidneys to excrete sugar, blood-sugar levels build up to a point where he may pass into a coma.

**Fats.** Crude fatty materials contain certain substances that are not hydrolyzed in the human alimentary system. These materials and some of the undigested fats are passed in the feces. Fats are hydrolyzed to a considerable extent by lipase in the stomach. Further hydrolysis occurs in the intestine where the reaction is facilitated through the emulsifying properties of the bile salts. The fatty acids that enter the blood stream are oxidized to produce energy or stored in fatty tissue for future use. The end products of oxidation are principally carbon dioxide and water, but some ketones, principally acetone, are formed. The carbon dioxide is expelled by the lungs. The ketones are excreted in the urine. Ketones are found in unusual amounts in the urine of diabetics and people suffering from faulty fat metabolism.

**Proteins.** Hydrolysis of proteins is started in the stomach and continues in the intestine. Amino acids, when released by hydrolysis, are absorbed into the blood stream. Fractions that are not completely hydrolyzed are excreted in the feces. The amino acids are used mainly for the building and repair of muscle tissue, and in these capacities they become fixed in body tissues.

The end products of protein metabolism that require excretion as waste products result principally from two processes: the "wearing" of muscle tissue and oxidation of amino acids to obtain energy. Deamination of amino acids precedes their use as energy sources. The ammonia is released principally as urea but small amounts of $NH_4^+$ are normally present. Excretion is by way of the urine. The major function of the kidneys is to separate waste nitrogen compounds from the blood. That protein metabolism involves a variety of complicated processes may be deduced from the considerable number of nitrogenous compounds present in urine. Creatine, creatinine, uric acid, hippuric acid, and traces of purine bases are normally present in addition to urea and ammonium ion.

**Vitamins.** *Vitamins* are very potent organic substances that occur in minute quantities in natural foodstuffs. They must be supplied in the diet of animals if they are not synthesized naturally within the animal from essential dietary or metabolic precursors. They exert a hormone-like or enzymic action in the control of specific chemical reactions in the animal body, and the absence or lack of a sufficient supply of certain ones leads to the development of vitamin-deficiency diseases, e.g., beriberi, rickets, pellagra, scurvy, etc.

A wide variety of vitamins are known. They are generally classified into two groups, the *fat-soluble* and the *water-soluble*, as shown in Table 8-4.

The role of vitamins in biological processes employed by sanitary engineers has not been explored. Several of the vitamins are recovered from industrial wastes, particularly those from the fermentation industry, and their economic value has been an important factor in helping to solve the waste-disposal problem in the distilling industry. Recently, activated sludge has been found to be a rich source of vitamin $B_{12}$. A plant for extracting the vitamin has been constructed at Milwaukee, Wisconsin. In view of these developments, the sanitary engineer should be informed on the subject of vitamins and their economic importance.

TABLE 8-4. CLASSIFICATION AND FUNCTION OF VITAMINS

| Vitamin | Good sources | Function |
|---|---|---|
| Fat-soluble: | | |
| A | Butter, liver oils | Eye health |
| D | Liver oils, egg | Ca metabolism, i.e., antirachitic |
| E | Cottonseed oil, cereals | Prevents sterility |
| K | Green plants, egg yolk | Clotting of blood |
| Water-soluble: | | |
| $B_1$ Thiamine | Pork, whole wheat, peanuts | Antiberiberi |
| $B_2$ Riboflavin | Eggs, liver, cereals, milk | General health |
| Nicotinic acid | Meat, whole wheat, yeast | Antipellagra |
| $B_6$ Pyridoxine | Egg yolk, liver, yeast | Skin tone |
| Biotin | Egg yolk, liver, yeast | Skin tone |
| Pantothenic acid | Egg yolk, liver, milk | Skin tone, growth |
| Choline | Egg yolk | Fat function |
| Folic acid group | Green leafy vegetables | Antianemia |
| Inositol | Fruits, vegetables | Hair, growth |
| $B_{12}$ group | Liver, activated sludge | Antianemia |
| C Ascorbic acid | Citrus fruits, apples | Antiscurvy |

## REFERENCES

Fruton, J. H., and S. Simmonds: "General Biochemistry," John Wiley & Sons, Inc., New York, 1953.

Gortner, R. A., and W. A. Gortner: "Outlines of Biochemistry," 3d ed., John Wiley & Sons, Inc., New York, 1949.

Mitchell, P. H.: "Textbook of Biochemistry," 2d ed., McGraw-Hill Book Company, Inc., New York, 1950.

# 9. Basic Concepts from Radiochemistry

## 9-1. Introduction

The science of *radiochemistry* deals with atomic transformations and may be considered to date from 1895 when Roentgen discovered a new form of radiation from cathode-ray tubes. The rays caused certain salts to become luminescent and also affected photographic plates. They are called *roentgen rays* or *X rays*. With a few modifications, the cathode-ray tube became the modern roentgen or X-ray tube which is used so extensively in medical and industrial applications. Gamma rays released by radioactive materials and X rays are both electromagnetic waves, the gamma rays usually having somewhat shorter wavelengths.

Roentgen's discovery of a new ray that affected photographic plates stimulated a great deal of testing of materials for similar characteristics. Becquerel and his father had been interested in phosphorescence for some time prior to 1891. They had noted that potassium uranyl sulfate [$K_2UO_2(SO_4)_2 \cdot 2H_2O$] exhibited pronounced phosphorescence when excited by ultraviolet light. It was natural that Becquerel would want to test his uranyl salts for emanation of X rays. He found them to do so, and subsequent observations on a wide variety of salts and materials containing uranium showed them to produce X rays in proportion to their content of uranium.

In 1898, Pierre and Marie Curie concluded that the X rays from uranium were an atomic phenomenon characteristic of the element, and they introduced the name *radioactivity*. The Curies pursued their studies of radioactive materials with much vigor. They found that compounds of thorium emitted rays similar to those of uranium. They also noted that certain ores of uranium were more radioactive than uranium itself. This led to a search for other materials in the residues remaining after uranium extraction. Two new radioactive elements were isolated, polonium and radium. Radium is several thousand times more radioactive than uranium.

## 9-2. Atomic Structure

Modern concepts of atomic structure are largely the result of knowledge gained from the behavior of radioactive materials. It is difficult, therefore, to discuss one without considering the other. Prior to the discovery of radioactivity, atoms were considered to be indivisible. With the discovery that radioactive elements emitted positively and negatively charged particles, the foundation was laid for new concepts.

**Nuclear Theory.**  By 1900 it was realized that atoms are not indivisible. However, it was not until 1911 that Rutherford proposed the nuclear concept of the atom. This theory held that atoms were composed of a small positively charged nucleus, containing most of the mass of the atom, with a cloud of negatively charged electrons surrounding it.

**Electron Orbits.**  Bohr was the first to propose that the electrons about the nucleus of an atom are arranged in a methodical manner and revolve in orbits about the nucleus. Although his theory, issued in 1913, has undergone some refinements, it remains the basis of our modern-day knowledge. The present tendency is to think of the electrons as being arranged in shells about the nucleus. A major contribution was made to the Bohr theory by Sommerfeld who has shown that the electrons within a given shell occur in several energy levels. Other contributions, particularly with respect to chemical properties, were made by Langmuir (octet theory), Mosely, G. N. Lewis, and W. Kossel.

The simplest atoms, hydrogen and helium, have one shell of electrons, and the most complex have seven. The shells or rings are designated as K, L, M, N, O, P, and Q in the order of their increasing remoteness from the nucleus. The arrangement of electrons for a number of elements is given in Table 9-1. Over the course of ensuing years, the positively charged nucleus was considered to consist of protons and electrons, except in the case of the hydrogen atom ($_1H^1$). The protons were always in excess of the electrons in the nucleus, and this excess was equal to the planetary electrons; thus the net charge on the atom was zero.

**Neutron-Proton Concept of Nuclear Structure.**  In 1930, Bothe and Becker discovered a very penetrating secondary radiation when light elements, such as beryllium and lithium, were subjected to bombardment by alpha particles from polonium. The new rays were first thought to be X rays of very short wavelength. In 1932, Chadwick showed this secondary radiation to be made up of neutral particles having a mass comparable to that of the proton. The new particles were given the name *neutrons*, and, since their source was obviously the nucleus of the bombarded atoms, a new concept of nuclear structure evolved.

According to present-day knowledge, the nucleus of all atoms, except the simple hydrogen atom ($_1H^1$), consists of neutrons plus protons. The

TABLE 9-1. ARRANGEMENT OF ELECTRONS FOR SOME COMMON ELEMENTS

| Symbol | Atomic number | Number of electrons in shells | | | | | | |
|--------|---------------|---|---|---|---|---|---|---|
| | | K | L | M | N | O | P | Q |
| H | 1 | 1 | | | | | | |
| He* | 2 | 2 | | | | | | |
| N | 7 | 2 | 5 | | | | | |
| Ne* | 10 | 2 | 8 | | | | | |
| Na | 11 | 2 | 8 | 1 | | | | |
| Cl | 17 | 2 | 8 | 7 | | | | |
| A* | 18 | 2 | 8 | 8 | | | | |
| Ca | 20 | 2 | 8 | 8 | 2 | | | |
| Zn | 30 | 2 | 8 | 18 | 2 | | | |
| Br | 35 | 2 | 8 | 18 | 7 | | | |
| Kr* | 36 | 2 | 8 | 18 | 8 | | | |
| Ag | 47 | 2 | 8 | 18 | 18 | 1 | | |
| Xe* | 54 | 2 | 8 | 18 | 18 | 8 | | |
| Ba | 56 | 2 | 8 | 18 | 18 | 8 | 2 | |
| Hg | 80 | 2 | 8 | 18 | 32 | 18 | 2 | |
| Pb | 82 | 2 | 8 | 18 | 32 | 18 | 4 | |
| Rn* | 86 | 2 | 8 | 18 | 32 | 18 | 8 | |
| Ra | 88 | 2 | 8 | 18 | 32 | 18 | 8 | 2 |

* Inert gases.

number of protons corresponds to the atomic number and is equal to the number of electrons about the nucleus. The number of neutrons is equal to the atomic weight expressed as the nearest whole number less the number of protons. The structure of the atom may be represented as shown in Fig. 9-1. The nucleus has a diameter on the order of $10^{-12}$ to $10^{-13}$ cm and the atom a diameter of about $10^{-8}$ cm. The density of nuclear matter is tremendous. It is estimated that 1 cu cm would weigh $10^8$ tons.

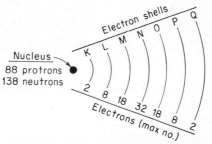

FIG. 9-1. Structure of radium atom ($_{88}Ra^{226}$).

**Nomenclature of Isotopes.** All isotopes of the same element have the same number of electrons and, of course, the same number of protons. Since the masses of the isotopes vary, the number of neutrons must vary. In order to differentiate between isotopes, a new system of symbol writing had to be developed. The system in vogue in the United States includes the atomic number as a subscript just before the symbol and the atomic weight, or mass number, as a superscript after the symbol. For example, $_{82}Pb^{204}$, $_{82}Pb^{206}$, $_{82}Pb^{207}$, and $_{82}Pb^{208}$ represent four isotopic

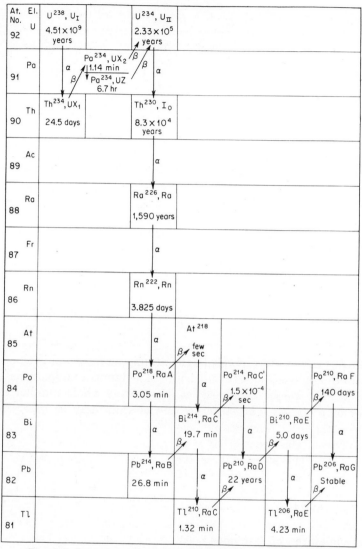

FIG. 9-2. Steps in radioactive decay of $U^{238}$ to stable $Pb^{206}$.

forms of lead all of which have 82 protons and 82 electrons. Since the atomic number of a given element is always the same, it is frequently eliminated when discussing isotopes. However, in radioactive changes involving transmutation of one element into another, such as in the conversion of $U^{238}$ to $Pb^{206}$, the change is best shown by $_{92}U^{238} \rightarrow {}_{82}Pb^{206}$. Anyone familiar with radiochemistry knows that such a change cannot occur in one step and that several intermediate steps are involved (see Fig. 9-2).

## 9-3. Natural Radioactivity

Over 40 kinds of atoms are known that display the property of natural radio-activity, and most have atomic weights greater than 200. The heavy-metal radioactive elements fall into three series: uranium, thorium, and actinium. The uranium series has $U^{238}$ as its parent substance and, after 14 successive transformations have occurred, the end product is $Pb^{206}$. Thorium ($Th^{232}$) is the parent substance of the thorium series. After 10 transformations, it remains as $Pb^{208}$. The parent element of the actinium series is $U^{235}$ and, after 11 transformations, it remains as $Pb^{207}$. This series takes its name from the fact that $Pa^{231}$ (preactinium) and $Ac^{227}$ (actinium) are long-lived elements formed as steps in the transformation. The uranium series is sometimes called the

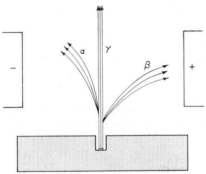

Fig. 9-3. Effect of a magnetic field upon alpha, beta, and gamma rays.

radium series for the same reason. The steps in the radioactive decay of $U^{238}$ are shown in Fig. 9-2. $Th^{232}$ and $U^{235}$ decompose through similar steps.

**Nature of Radiations.** Early workers with radioactive materials were cognizant of the presence of only one form of radiation, and its properties were similar to those of X rays. Later investigations established the presence of three kinds of rays designated as alpha, beta, and gamma rays. Separation and identification were accomplished by directing the rays through a magnetic field, as shown in Fig. 9-3. Certain of the rays were bent slightly toward the negative pole. This phenomenon indicated that they had a positive charge and, probably, were of considerable mass. They are called *alpha* rays. Other rays were bent radically toward the positive pole, showing them to be negatively charged and, probably, of small mass. They are called *beta* rays. A third group of rays were unaffected by the magnetic field. They do not have a charge and are called *gamma* rays.

*Alpha Rays.* Alpha rays are not true rays as are light and X rays. They consist of particles of matter and, therefore, should be referred to as *alpha particles*. Alpha particles are actually doubly charged ions of helium with a mass of 4. Although they are propelled from the nucleus of atoms at velocities ranging from 1.4 to $2 \times 10^9$ cm/sec (about 10 per cent of the speed of light), they do not travel much more than 10 cm in air at room temperature. They are stopped by an ordinary sheet of paper. The alpha particles emitted by a particular element are all released at the same velocity. The velocity varies, however, from element to element. The alpha particles have extremely high ionizing action within their range.

*Beta Rays.* Beta rays, like alpha rays, are not true rays since they consist of negatively charged particles moving at speeds ranging from 30 to 99 per cent of the speed of light. *Beta particles* are actually electrons, and the velocity of flight of individual electrons varies considerably for a given element as well as for different elements. The penetrating power of beta particles varies with their speed. They normally travel several hundred feet in air. Shielding with aluminum sheeting a few millimeters thick will stop the particles. The ionizing power of beta rays is much weaker than that of the alpha rays.

*Gamma Rays.* Gamma rays are true electromagnetic radiations which travel with the speed of light. They are similar to X rays but have shorter wavelengths and, therefore, greater penetrating power which increases as the wavelength decreases. Proper shielding from gamma rays requires several centimeters of lead or several feet of concrete. The unit of gamma radiation is the *photon*.

**Energies of Radiations.** It is important to know the energy of the various radiations produced by radioactive materials. Since alpha and beta particles have mass and gamma radiations do not, it would seem difficult to establish a single system of expressing energies. However, through Einstein's energy-mass equivalence formula

$$E = mc^2 \tag{9-1}$$

it is possible to evaluate all of them in the same terms. The term commonly used is the *electron volt* (ev) which is the energy necessary to raise one electron through a potential difference of one volt. The energies of alpha and beta particles and of gamma photons range from several thousands up to several millions of electron volts. For this reason, energies are usually expressed as million electron volts (Mev).

**Atomic Changes Resulting from Release of Radiations.** The change that atoms undergo when releasing alpha particles is considerably different from the change when beta particles are released. These changes are illustrated in Fig. 9-2 and were formulated into so-called *displacement laws* by Fajans, Rutherford, and Soddy as follows:

*Alpha-particle Release.*  *When an element emits an alpha particle, the product has the properties of an element two places to the left of the parent in the periodic table.*  In other words, emission of an alpha particle decreases the mass number by four units and the nuclear charge, or atomic number, by two units.

*Beta-particle Release.*  *When an element emits a beta particle, the product has the properties of an element one place to the right of the parent in the periodic table.*  In this change the mass remains the same and the atomic number increases one unit.

*Gamma Radiations.*  Gamma radiation may accompany the release of alpha or beta particles and is a result of energy released by nuclear transformations or shifts of orbital electrons.

**Units of Radioactivity.**  The unit of radioactivity is the *curie.*  Formerly, it was considered to be the number of disintegrations occurring per second in one gram of pure radium.  Since the constants for radium are subject to revision from time to time, the International Radium Standard Commission has recommended the use of a fixed value, $3.7 \times 10^{10}$ disintegrations per second, as the *standard curie* (c).

The curie is used mainly to define quantities of radioactive materials. A curie of an alpha emitter is that quantity which releases $3.7 \times 10^{10}$ alpha particles per second.  A curie of a beta emitter is that quantity of material which releases $3.7 \times 10^{10}$ beta particles per second, and a curie of a gamma emitter is that quantity of material which releases $3.7 \times 10^{10}$ photons per second.  The curie represents such a large number of disintegrations per second that the millicurie (mc) and microcurie ($\mu c$), corresponding to $10^{-3}$ curie and $10^{-6}$ curie, respectively, are more commonly used.

The *roentgen* (r) is a unit of gamma or X-ray radiation intensity.  It is of value in the study of the biological effects of radiation that result from ionization induced within cells by the radiations.  The roentgen is defined as the amount of gamma or X radiation that will produce in one cubic centimeter of dry air, at 0°C and 760 mm pressure, one electrostatic unit (esu) of electricity.  This is equivalent to $1.61 \times 10^{12}$ ion pairs per gram of air and corresponds to the absorption of 83.8 ergs of energy.

The roentgen is a unit of the total quantity of ionization produced by gamma or X rays, and dosage rates for these radiations are expressed in terms of roentgens per unit time.  In the United States, the maximum allowable continuous daily dose for humans is considered to be 0.06 r.

With the advent of atomic energy involving exposure to neutrons, protons, and alpha and beta particles which also have effects on living tissue, it has become necessary to have other means of expressing ionization produced in cells.  Three methods of expression have been used.

The *roentgen-equivalent-physical* (*rep*) is defined as that quantity of radiation (other than X rays or $\gamma$ radiation) which produces in one gram of human tissue ionization equivalent to the quantity produced in air by one roentgen of $\gamma$ radiation or X rays (equivalent to 83.8 ergs of energy). The rep has been replaced largely by the term *rad* which has wider application.

The *roentgen-absorption-dose* (*rad*) is a unit of radiation corresponding to an energy absorption of 100 ergs per gram of any medium. It can be applied to any type and energy of radiation that leads to the production of ionization. Studies on the radiation of biological materials have shown that the roentgen is approximately equivalent to 100 ergs/g of tissue and can be equivalent to 90 to 150 ergs/g of tissue, depending on the energy of the X and $\gamma$ radiation and type of tissue. The rad, therefore, is more closely related to the roentgen than is the rep, in terms of radiation effects on living tissues, and is the term preferred by biologists.

TABLE 9-2. HALF-LIVES OF COMMON RADIOACTIVE ELEMENTS

| Atomic number | Element | Half-life | Nature of radiation |
|:---:|:---:|:---:|:---:|
| 1 | $H^3$ | 12 yr | $\beta$ |
| 6 | $C^{14}$ | 6,400 yr | $\beta$ |
| 11 | $Na^{24}$ | 14.8 hr | $\beta, \gamma$ |
| 15 | $P^{32}$ | 14.3 days | $\beta$ |
| 16 | $S^{35}$ | 87.1 days | $\beta$ |
| 27 | $Co^{60}$ | 5.3 yr | $\beta, \gamma$ |
| 35 | $Br^{78}$ | 6.4 min | $\beta, \gamma$ |
| 38 | $Sr^{90}$ | 25 yr | $\beta$ |
| 88 | $Ra^{226}$ | 1,590 yr | $\alpha, \gamma$ |
| 92 | $U^{238}$ | $4.51 \times 10^9$ yr | $\alpha$ |

The rad represents such a tremendous radiation dosage, in terms of permissible amounts for human beings, that another unit has been developed specifically for man. The term *roentgen-equivalent-man* (*rem*) is used. It corresponds to the amount of radiation that will produce an energy dissipation in the human body that is biologically equivalent to one roentgen of $\gamma$ radiation or X rays, or approximately 100 ergs.

**Half-lives.** Radioactive decomposition is a true unimolecular reaction. The rate is constant over a wide variety of environmental conditions. Half-lives of the radioactive elements vary from fractions of a second to about $10^{12}$ yr. The half-lives of a number of elements are given in Table 9-2. The kinetics of unimolecular reactions are discussed in Sec. 6-12.

## 9-4. Atomic Transmutations and Artificial Radioactivity

The experimental conversion of one element into another was accomplished by Rutherford in 1919. When alpha particles derived from radium C were passed through nitrogen gas, protons were detected. The collisions between alpha particles and nitrogen nuclei resulted in the formation of an isotope of oxygen and a proton as follows:

$$_7N^{14} + {_2}He^4 \rightarrow {_8}O^{17} + {_1}H^1 \tag{9-2}$$

By 1922, Rutherford and Chadwick had shown that all elements in the periodic table between boron and potassium, except carbon and oxygen, underwent similar transmutations when submitted to bombardment by alpha particles.

It was not until 1930 that radiation other than protons was detected when elements were subjected to alpha-particle bombardment. In that year, Bothe and Becker discovered a very penetrating, neutral, secondary radiation when beryllium or lithium was subjected to alpha particles from polonium. In 1932, Chadwick showed the particles to be neutrons, and the changes were described as follows:

$$_3Li^7 + {_2}He^4 \rightarrow {_5}B^{10} + {_0}n^1 \tag{9-3}$$
$$_4Be^9 + {_2}He^4 \rightarrow {_6}C^{12} + {_0}n^1 \tag{9-4}$$

where the neutron is represented by $_0n^1$.

The third important step in transmutation of elements involved the discovery that a third particle was found in certain instances. In 1934, I. Curie and Joliot noted that, when either boron, magnesium, or aluminum was bombarded with alpha particles, the expected transmutation with neutron release occurred and that positrons[1] (positive electrons) were also produced. In addition, they found that positron emission continued after alpha bombardment was discontinued. The emission of positrons was shown to decrease in accordance with the decay law for radioactive materials. Through careful analysis of the materials produced, they were able to show that alpha bombardment of these elements had produced an atom with an unstable nucleus that underwent radioactive positron decay; thus the production of artificial radioactive materials by alpha bombardment was established.

$$_5B^{10} + {_2}He^4 \rightarrow {_7}N^{13} + {_0}n^1 \tag{9-5}$$
$$\quad\quad\quad\quad\quad\quad \hookrightarrow {_6}C^{13} + \beta^+ \quad\quad t_{\frac{1}{2}} = 9.9 \text{ min}$$

$$_{13}Al^{27} + {_2}He^4 \rightarrow {_{15}}P^{30} + {_0}n^1 \tag{9-6}$$
$$\quad\quad\quad\quad\quad\quad \hookrightarrow {_{14}}Si^{30} + \beta^+ \quad\quad t_{\frac{1}{2}} = 2.55 \text{ min}$$

[1] The existence of positrons had been predicted and confirmed previously in cosmic-ray studies.

It soon became apparent that there is no real distinction between a nuclear reaction leading to stable products and one leading to unstable products. According to the Bohr concept, all bombardments result in an absorption of the bombarding particle by the nucleus to produce an unstable compound nucleus. The life of the compound nucleus is extremely short ($10^{-12}$ to $10^{-14}$ sec), and decomposition occurs to a set of products. The products may be stable or they may be unstable.

The discovery of the neutron and the fact that radioactive elements could be produced artificially set the stage for the tremendous developments in the area of nuclear energy that have occurred in the past few years.

### 9-5. Nuclear Reactions

Nuclear reactions may be induced by bombardment with a wide variety of particles.

**Alpha-induced Reactions.** Because of the positive charge on the alpha particle, it has to overcome the repulsive forces of the positively charged nucleus of an atom before it can add to it. As the atomic number of elements increases, the repulsive force toward alpha particles increases. For this reason, alpha particles are unable to cause nuclear changes in elements of high atomic weight, and their use is restricted to action on the elements with light nuclei.

Alpha-induced reactions serve as the basis for the production of neutrons and, therefore, are extremely important.

**Proton-induced Reactions.** Protons suffer from the same limitations as do alpha particles, even more so, because the ratio of mass to charge is only one-half that of the alpha particle. Therefore they are repelled more easily by the positively charged nuclei.

**Deuteron-induced Reactions.** Deuterons $[(_1H^2)^+]$ are probably the most effective of the positively charged particles since they have only one charge and the ratio of mass to charge is the same as for the alpha particle. Certain deuteron-induced reactions are excellent sources of neutrons.

**Gamma-induced Reactions.** Gamma and X rays are extremely inefficient in producing nuclear reactions.

**Neutron-induced Reactions.** Neutrons, being neutral, are extremely efficient particles for bombarding the nuclei of all elements. By their use, all elements, with the exception of helium, have been transmuted into other elements. Bombardment of some high-mass elements results in nuclear fission, a special form of transmutation.

### 9-6. Nuclear Fission

Shortly after the discovery of the neutron, Fermi found neutron bombardment of some heavy metals to be followed by beta activity.

Bombardment of uranium produced beta particles of four distinct activities. The activities could not be correlated with those of any of the elements with a mass in the range of uranium. The answer was found by Hahn and Strassmann who conducted chemical analyses of the products. They found isotopes of barium, lanthanum, strontium, and yttrium as well as an inert gas (Xe or Kr) and an alkali metal (Cs or Rb) present. From this information it was concluded that neutron capture by the uranium atom was followed by a rupture of the nucleus to form several elements of lower atomic weight. This is termed *nuclear fission*.

Nuclear fission has been of great interest because of the tremendous amounts of energy released as a result of the fission process. This release results from a conversion of some of the mass to energy. The energy released during the fission of one gram atom of $U^{233}$, $U^{235}$, or $Pu^{239}$ corresponds to $5.3 \times 10^6$ kwhr. Since the gram atomic weights of these elements vary so little, the energy per pound of fissionable material is essentially as shown in Table 9-3.

TABLE 9-3. ENERGY LIBERATED PER POUND OF FISSIONABLE MATERIAL

$0.9 \times 10^{13}$ cal
$1.0 \times 10^7$ kwhr
$2.8 \times 10^{13}$ ft-lb
$3.6 \times 10^{10}$ Btu

*Nuclear Explosions.* Nuclear fission is initiated by neutron bombardment. During the fission of $U^{235}$, an average of 2.5 neutrons are released for each atom undergoing fission; thus the reaction can become self-perpetuating once fission is initiated. Fortunately, this had not been the case in early laboratory studies. Probability considerations, however, indicated that, if the mass of fissionable material was large enough, a self-sustaining chain reaction would occur. The *critical mass* of fissionable materials still remains a closely guarded secret. The fact that there is some such value, and that chain reactions do occur, has been proven many times, beginning with the first atomic bomb test at Alamagordo, New Mexico, in 1945.

Nuclear explosions are accompanied by release of tremendous amounts of radioactivity. The effect on the surrounding ground area depends upon the distance from the ground at which the explosion occurs. In any event, a great deal of the radioactive matter is projected into the upper atmosphere where it is carried around the world. It is constantly returning to the earth, particularly at times of rain and snowfall, as *fall-out*.

*Nuclear Power.* Control of fission reactions so that the great amount of energy released can be utilized for beneficial purposes has been the objective of a great deal of research, and power plants developing so-called "atomic power" are now in operation at several places in the United States.   The reactors, or "furnaces," in which the fission occurs of course must contain the fissionable matter in excess of the "critical mass."   To avoid an explosion, neutrons released in the fission process must be controlled in number to keep the chain reaction going at the desired speed. This is accomplished by means of neutron absorbers or moderators. Cadmium, graphite, and deuterium oxide are excellent neutron absorbers.

*Atomic Pile.*   The atomic pile operates on the same principle as the atomic power plant.   It uses $U^{233}$, $U^{235}$, or $Pu^{239}$ as fuel to maintain a controlled chain reaction.   Its function is to produce neutrons that can be used to transmute nonradioactive elements into fissionable or radioactive forms.   The atomic pile at Hanford, Washington, was used to convert $U^{238}$ to $Pu^{239}$, a fissionable element.   The one at Oak Ridge, Tennessee, has been used largely to produce a wide variety of radioactive isotopes for use in medical, biological, and industrial research.

Water-cooled atomic piles require large quantities of water to dissipate the heat released by the nuclear fission that produces neutrons.   Discharge of such cooling water to rivers has been of concern to sanitary engineers and biologists because of the induced radioactivity and possibly some fission products that it may contain.

### 9-7. Nuclear Fusion

The fusion of two or more light atomic nuclei to form the nucleus of a heavier element is generally more productive of energy than the fission of heavy elements.   The production of one atom of helium from the fusion of four atoms of hydrogen produces seven times as much energy per unit weight of material as the fission of $U^{235}$ or $Pu^{239}$.

The hydrogen bomb depends upon *nuclear fusion* for its tremendous explosive power, resulting from the nuclear fusion of heavy hydrogen isotopes.   Temperatures of over 50,000,000°C are needed to initiate the fusion process, and because of this the fusion process is known as a *thermonuclear reaction.*   The high temperatures required can be obtained only by incorporating an atomic bomb as the igniting device.   Thus development of the atomic bomb made the hydrogen bomb a possibility.

The usual fuel for the hydrogen bomb is deuterium ($_1H^2$) and tritium ($_2H^3$) which unite to produce $_2He^4$ with the release of a neutron.

$$_1H^2 + {}_2H^3 \xrightarrow{\Delta\Delta\Delta} {}_2He^4 + {}_0n^1 \qquad (9\text{-}7)$$
$$\llcorner\!\!\rightarrow \text{Energy}$$

Under the conditions, the neutron is converted to energy.   In this reaction about 20 per cent of the original mass of the hydrogen is converted to energy, and this accounts for the tremendous amount of heat and destructive power released. Hydrogen bombs are rated in terms of millions of tons of TNT, while atomic bombs are rated in tens of thousands of tons.

Nuclear fusion in itself does not release radioactive materials, and because of this a great deal of research is being conducted to produce a so-called "clean" bomb. Since the hydrogen bomb requires an atomic bomb as a triggering device, it produces intense radioactivity. Predictions are that a "clean" bomb can be made. If so, it will depend upon other ways of producing the high ignition temperatures required or the use of elements other than hydrogen so that an atomic bomb will not be needed to initiate the explosion.

At the International Conference on the Peaceful Uses of Atomic Energy, held in Geneva, Switzerland, in 1955, it was predicted that the fusion process would be harnessed to provide power for industrial uses within 20 yr.

## 9-8. Use of Radioactive Materials as Tracers

Compounds containing radioactive elements, particularly $C^{14}$ and $I^{125}$, have been used extensively by researchers in the fields of biology, chemistry, and medicine to determine the course of chemical and biochemical reactions. Tracers are being used in many industries to study various phenomena. Petroleum technologists have used tracers extensively to improve methods of processing crude oil and to evaluate the lubricating properties of oils and greases.

The sanitary engineering profession has been somewhat slow to adopt the use of radioactive tracers. Compounds containing $C^{14}$ were used to determine the mechanisms of methane formation. Recently, considerable attention has been given to their use for determining the "flow-through time" of sedimentation tanks and of "reaches" or "stretches" in rivers. They are being used to some extent to determine direction and rate of flow of ground water.

The major factor restricting application of radioactive tracers in the field of sanitary engineering has been the lack of devices for quantitative measurement of radioactivity. As more laboratories become equipped with such facilities, it may be expected that radioactive tracers will be used to a much greater extent. However, the large amounts of materials needed and the inherent hazards involved will remain a serious deterrent to their use in other than laboratory-scale studies.

The use of radioisotopes in chemical and biological research and in medical treatment creates a problem for sanitary engineers, since some of the materials contained in waste waters reach sewers and rivers. In sewers and sewage treatment plants, certain of the isotopes, such as radioiodine and radiophosphorus, accumulate in biological slimes and sludges. In rivers, radioactive material may be concentrated by microscopic forms that serve as food for fish and other forms of life consumed by man. Many water supplies are derived from rivers; hence the disposal of radioactive wastes to rivers becomes a matter of concern to all the consumers. A few large cities have initiated programs for monitoring their water supplies and sewage as a protection to the public. It is to be expected that this practice will grow as the use of radioisotopes increases.

**REFERENCES**

Friedlander, G., and J. W. Kennedy: "Nuclear and Radiochemistry," John Wiley & Sons, Inc., New York, 1955.
Etherington, Harold (ed.): "Nuclear Engineering Handbook," McGraw-Hill Book Company, Inc., New York, 1958.

# PART II

# Water, Sewage, and Industrial Waste Analysis

# 10. Introduction

## 10-1. Importance of Quantitative Measurements in Sanitary Engineering Practice

Quantitative measurements of one sort or another serve as the keystone of engineering practice. Sanitary engineering is perhaps most demanding in this respect, for it requires the use of not only the conventional measuring devices employed by engineers but, in addition, many of the techniques and methods of measurement used by chemists and some of those used by biologists.

Every problem in sanitary engineering must be approached initially in a manner that will define the problem. This approach necessitates the use of analytical methods and procedures, in the field and laboratory, that have been proven to yield reliable results in the hands of many people and on a wide variety of materials. Once the problem has been defined quantitatively, the engineer is usually in a position to design facilities that will provide a satisfactory solution.

After construction of the facilities has been completed and they have been placed in operation, usually constant supervision employing quantitative procedures is required to maintain economical and satisfactory performance. Records of performance are frequently needed for reports that have to be made to supervisory personnel and regulatory agencies.

The increase in population density and new developments in industrial technology are constantly intensifying old problems and creating new ones. In addition, engineers are forever seeking more economical methods of solving old problems. Research is continuously under way to find answers to the new problems and better answers to old ones. Quantitative analysis will continue to serve as the basis for such studies.

## 10-2. Character of Sanitary Engineering Problems

Most problems in sanitary engineering practice involve relationships between living organisms and their environment. Because of this, the analytical procedures needed to obtain quantitative information are often a strange mixture of chemical and biochemical methods, and interpretation of the data is usually related to the effect on microorganisms or human beings. Also, many of the determinations used fall into the realm of microanalysis on account of the small amounts of contaminants present in the samples. For these reasons, the usual course in quantitative analysis offered by most schools of chemistry is of limited value to sanitary engineers, other than to teach basic techniques. Specialized courses in sanitary analytical chemistry have been developed to meet this particular need at nearly all schools that train sanitary engineers.

## 10-3. Standard Methods of Analysis

Concurrent with the evolution of sanitary engineering practice, analytical methods have been developed to obtain the factual information required for the resolution and solution of problems. In many cases different methods were proposed for the same determination, and many of them were modified in some manner. As a result, analytical data obtained by analysts were often in disagreement. In cases involving litigation, judges often found it difficult to evaluate evidence based upon analytical methods. In an attempt to bring order out of chaos, the American Public Health Association appointed a committee to study the various analytical methods available and published the recommendations of the committee as "Standard Methods of Water Analysis" in 1905. Since that time, the scope of "Standard Methods" has been enlarged to include sewage and industrial wastes, and the American Water Works Association and the Federation of Sewage and Industrial Wastes Associations have become collaborators in its preparation. The tenth edition appeared in 1955[1] and the eleventh edition is expected in 1960.

"Standard Methods" as published today is the product of the untiring effort of hundreds of men who serve on committees and subcommittees, testing and improving analytical procedures for the purpose of selecting those best suited for inclusion in "Standard Methods." Evidence that is obtained by qualified analysts based upon methods recommended in "Standard Methods" is normally accepted in the courts of the United States without qualification.

## 10-4. Scope of a Course in Water, Sewage, and Industrial Waste Analysis

It would be impossible and unwise to attempt to teach a course in sanitary analysis dealing with all the determinations described in "Standard Methods." In the first place, space does not permit such treatment,

[1] "Standard Methods for the Examination of Water, Sewage and Industrial Wastes," American Public Health Association, Inc., New York.

and, in the second place, many of the determinations are highly specific for certain industrial wastes. On the other hand, it is important that a good foundation in analytical procedures be established so that any contingencies that may arise during one's career can be met and handled with a reasonable degree of confidence.

The choice of determinations and the order in which they are included in a particular course depend greatly upon the interests of the instructor. The selection of topics for discussion in the following chapters covers items that the author has found essential for the basic training of sanitary engineers. The order of presentation is a matter of personal opinion but is based upon a natural sequence of dependence and increasing complexity. The procedures for chemical coagulation and water softening are included to give experience in the application of certain determinations and to aid the student in other courses involving these processes.

A major objective of a course in the analysis of water, sewage, and industrial wastes should be to prepare the student for research, rather than as a technician. To this end, it is important that the student appreciate the nature and source of the materials under analysis, the limitations of the analytical methods, how to interpret his data, and how the information may be applied in sanitary engineering practice.

## 10-5. Expression of Results

Most materials subjected to sanitary analysis in the fields of water, sewage, and industrial wastes fall into the realm of dilute solutions, and it is impractical to express results in terms of per cent, as is the usual practice in analytical chemistry. Ordinarily, the amounts determined are a few milligrams per liter and oftentimes fractions of a milligram. Samples are usually measured by volume, using a volumetric pipet; therefore it is convenient to express results in terms of milligrams per liter (mg/l). Formerly, the term *parts per million* (ppm) was widely used but frequently led to misinterpretation.

**Parts per Million.** The term *parts per million* is a weight-to-weight ratio. Its use was more or less universal and unquestioned during the time that sanitary analysis was principally concerned with water, because a liter of water weighs approximately 1,000 g or 1,000,000 mg and hence 1 mg/l was considered to be equal to 1 ppm. With the development and inclusion of methods for the analysis of polluted waters, such as domestic sewage, the concept of the relation between parts per million and milligrams per liter did not change, because the specific gravity of domestic sewage is essentially the same as that of water. As industrial wastes were included in the materials subjected to sanitary analysis, many of them were found to have specific gravities considerably different from that of water and the close relationship between parts per million and milligrams per liter no longer applied. This discrepancy has led to abandonment of the term parts per million in water, sewage, and industrial waste analysis in favor of the use of milligrams per liter.

**Milligrams per Liter.** Milligrams per liter is a weight-volume relationship and, because sanitary engineers deal largely with liquids, it offers a convenient basis for calculation. The expression

$$\text{mg/l} \times 8.34 = \text{lb/million gal}$$

is widely used and has general application. It replaces the original expression

$$\text{ppm} \times 8.34 = \text{lb/million gal}$$

which may be safely applied to problems involving water and sewage and other liquids whose specific gravity is essentially 1.00 but may lead to serious errors with other liquids unless correction for specific gravity is applied.

The use of milligrams per liter eliminates any opportunity for misunderstanding and confusion. In the past many results have been reported in terms of parts per million with no reference to specific gravity. Obviously, the results should have been reported as milligrams per liter.

**Other Methods of Expression.** In certain determinations, such as color and turbidity, reference is made to arbitrary standards. In these cases results are expressed in units without designation, 0, 1, 5, etc.

Sludges and some industrial wastes contain sufficient suspended or dissolved solids so that results can be best expressed in terms of per cent. A rule of thumb often applied is as follows: When concentrations exceed 10,000 mg/l,[1] results are expressed as per cent. Wherever practice has established a precedent in opposition to the rule, the rule is ignored.

Water chemists often prefer to express results in terms of milliequivalents (me) per liter. This allows them to translate results directly in terms of other chemicals. Milliequivalents per liter are obtained by dividing milligrams per liter of the element or ion by its equivalent weight in grams.

## 10-6. Other Items

It is expected that the sanitary engineering student will become familiar with all the material in the Introduction to "Standard Methods." Particular attention should be directed to the sections on collection of samples; laboratory apparatus, reagents, and techniques; statistics for the analyst; and significant figures.

---

[1] 10,000 mg/l is equivalent to 1 per cent when the specific gravity is equal to 1.0.

# 11. Turbidity

## 11-1. General Considerations

The term *turbid* is applied to waters containing suspended matter that interferes with the passage of light through the water or in which visual depth is restricted. The *turbidity* may be caused by a wide variety of suspended materials which range in size from colloidal to coarse dispersions, depending upon the degree of turbulence. In lake or other waters existing under relatively quiescent conditions, most of the turbidity will be due to colloidal and extremely fine dispersions. In rivers under flood conditions, most of the turbidity will be due to relatively coarse dispersions.

Turbidity may be caused by a wide variety of materials. In glacier-fed rivers and lakes most of the turbidity is due to colloidal rock particles produced by the grinding action of the glacier. The beautiful blues and greens of the lakes and rivers in Glacier National Park are typical examples. As rivers descend from mountain areas onto the plains, they receive contributions of turbidity from farming and other operations that disturb the soil. Under flood conditions, great amounts of topsoil are washed to receiving streams. Much of this material is inorganic in nature but considerable amounts of organic matter are included. As the rivers progress toward the ocean, they pass through urban areas where domestic sewage and industrial wastes, treated or untreated, may be added. The domestic sewage may add great quantities of organic and some inorganic materials that contribute turbidity. Certain industrial wastes may add large amounts of organic substances and others inorganic substances that produce turbidity. Street washings contribute much inorganic and some organic turbidity. Organic materials reaching rivers serve as food for bacteria, and the resulting bacterial growth and other microorganisms that feed upon the bacteria produce additional turbidity.

From the above considerations, it is safe to say that the materials causing turbidity may range from nearly pure inorganic substances to those that are largely organic in nature.    This disparity in the nature of the materials causing turbidity makes it impossible to establish hard and fast rules for its removal.

## 11-2. Sanitary Significance

Turbidity is an important consideration in public water supplies for three major reasons.

**Aesthetic.**    Consumers of public water supplies expect and have a right to demand turbidity-free water.    Laymen are aware that domestic sewage is highly turbid.    Any turbidity in the drinking water is automatically associated with possible sewage pollution and the health hazards occasioned by it.    This fear has a sound basis historically, as anyone knows who is familiar with the water-borne epidemics that formerly plagued the water works industry.

**Filterability.**    Filtration of water is rendered more difficult and costly when turbidity increases.    The use of slow sand filters has become impractical in most areas because high turbidity shortens filter runs and increases cleaning costs.    Satisfactory operation of rapid sand filters depends upon effective removal of turbidity by chemical coagulation before the water is admitted to the filters.    Failure to do so results in short filter runs and production of an inferior-quality water.

**Disinfection.**    Disinfection of public water supplies is usually accomplished by means of chlorine or ozone.    To be effective, there must be contact between the agent and the organisms that the disinfectant is to kill.

In turbid waters, most of the harmful organisms are exposed to the action of the disinfectant.    However, in cases where turbidity is caused by sewage solids, many of the pathogenic organisms may be encased in the particles and protected from the disinfectant.    For this and aesthetic reasons the U.S. Public Health Service has placed a limit of 10 units of turbidity as the maximum amount allowable in public water supplies.

## 11-3. Standard Unit of Turbidity

Because of the wide variety of materials that cause turbidity in natural waters, it has been necessary to use an arbitrary standard.    The standard chosen was

$$1 \text{ mg } SiO_2/l = 1 \text{ unit of turbidity}$$

and the silica used must meet certain specifications as to particle size.

Standard suspensions of pure silica are not used in ordinary practice for measuring turbidity.    They were used originally to calibrate the Jackson candle turbidimeter which was chosen as the standard instrument for turbidity measurement. Today all instruments are copies of the original, and the glass tubes employed are calibrated in conformity with the original data obtained (see "Standard Methods," 10th ed., Table 15).

For routine work employing the Jackson turbidimeter no standards are required. Where other methods are employed, standard suspensions must be prepared for reference. The usual procedure is to use natural materials, where available, or fuller's earth (diatomaceous earth) suspensions. The suspensions are standardized by means of the Jackson turbidimeter.

## 11-4. Methods of Determination

Turbidity values may range from essentially zero in pure water to several thousand in highly turbid rivers; consequently no one method of measurement is applicable to all samples. Three methods are commonly employed, and the ranges of turbidity that they will measure with reasonable accuracy are as follows:

| Method | Range |
|---|---|
| Jackson candle turbidimeter | 100–1,000 (short tube) |
| Jackson candle turbidimeter | 25–1,000 (long tube) |
| Jackson candle turbidimeter | 1,000 upward (by dilution) |
| Bottle standards | 5–100 |
| Baylis or St. Louis turbidimeter | 0–2 |

**Jackson Candle Turbidimeter.** The Jackson turbidimeter is the standard instrument for measuring turbidity. It consists of three essential parts: a calibrated glass tube, a holder, and a candle, as shown in Fig. 11-1. Details of its construction and operation are given in "Standard Methods." With the tube in place over the lighted candle, portions of the sample are added until the outline of the candle flame is no longer discernible. Readings in terms of turbidity are then made directly from the calibrated tube. A series of readings should be taken on each sample to obtain reliable results until the operator becomes highly proficient in its use.

The Jackson candle turbidimeter is considered a rather crude instrument in this day of modern instrumentation. Attempts are being made to replace it by a standard instrument with greater ease of operation and less dependence on the human eye.

**Bottle Standards.** Turbidity measurements in the range of 5 to 100 are usually made by reference to standard suspensions contained in glass bottles of similar size and color characteristics. Standard suspensions must be prepared by use of the Jackson turbidimeter. Usually a stock supply having a turbidity of 100 is prepared; then all suspensions of lower turbidity are prepared from it by dilution with distilled water. The standard suspensions must be replaced at frequent intervals because of changes in particle size and numbers that occur with time. Biological growths are controlled by use of mercuric chloride.

Measurement of turbidity is made by placing a suitable portion of the sample into a bottle of the same size and character as those used for the

Fig. 11-1. The Jackson candle turbidimeter showing short- and long-form tubes.

standards. Comparisons may be made by transmitted light or interference to visual perception. The latter is most common. Color of samples is often an interfering factor but most analysts of experience can compensate for it without recourse to the addition of color to the standards.

**Baylis or St. Louis Type of Turbidimeters.** The Baylis or St. Louis type of turbidimeter is designed to measure extremely low turbidities such as occur in the effluents of rapid sand filters; therefore their greatest use is in the operation of rapid sand filter plants. Figure 11-2 shows the detail of a Baylis turbidimeter. It consists of a light source and two glass tubes, one to hold a standard turbidity suspension and the other the sample.  The tubes are supported over a white glass plate which is lighted by blue light passing through a piece of cobalt glass.  The entire assembly is mounted within a case painted a dull black to eliminate

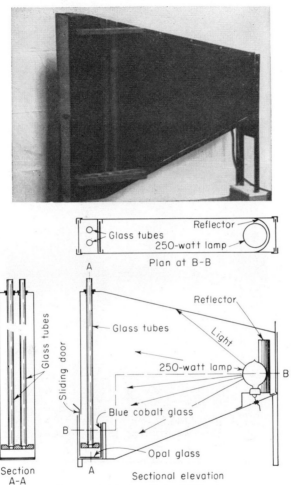

Fig. 11-2. The Baylis turbidimeter.

reflected light.  An observer looking down through a tube with turbidity-free water sees nothing but a blue background because light rays emanating from the light source pass through the tube and water at right angles to the line of vision of the observer.  If the water contains particles that cause turbidity, the light rays are scattered (Tyndall effect) and a whitish haze is produced against the blue background.  The degree of haziness is proportional to the turbidity.  By comparison with a series of standard suspensions, the turbidity of samples can be evaluated.

The standards for use in the Baylis or St. Louis type of turbidimeters must be prepared with a stock suspension that is standardized by means of the Jackson turbidimeter. Dilutions are made with turbidity-free water. A series containing 0.2, 0.4, 0.6, 0.8, and 1.0 unit of turbidity is

Fig. 11-3. The Hellige turbidimeter. (*Hellige, Inc.*)

usually sufficient, since well-operated rapid sand filters produce effluents with less than 0.5 unit of turbidity.

**Proprietary Devices.** A number of proprietary devices have been developed for measurement of turbidity. One which has been used rather widely is illustrated in Fig. 11-3. Some of the instruments depend upon visual comparisons and others depend upon the use of a photo-electric cell. Of the latter type, some employ systems which measure transmitted light while others employ the principles of nephelometry, as discussed in Sec. 4-6. None are accepted as standard methods, and all must be calibrated against standards prepared by use of the Jackson turbidimeter.

## 11-5. Application of Turbidity Data

Turbidity measurements are of particular importance in the field of water supply. They have limited use in the field of sewage and industrial waste treatment.

**Water Supply.** Knowledge of the turbidity variation in raw-water supplies is of prime importance to the sanitary engineer. He uses it in conjunction with other information to determine whether a supply requires special treatment by chemical coagulation and filtration before it may be used for a public water supply. Many large cities such as New York City, Boston, and Seattle have upland or mountain supplies whose turbidities are so low that treatment other than chlorination is not required.

Water supplies obtained from rivers usually require chemical flocculation because of high turbidity. Turbidity measurements are used to determine the effectiveness of the treatment produced with different chemicals and the dosages needed. Thus they aid in selection of the most effective and economical chemical to use. Such information is necessary to design facilities for feeding the chemicals and for their storage.

Turbidity measurements help to gauge the amount of chemicals needed from day to day in the operation of treatment works. This is particularly important on "flashy" rivers where no impoundment is provided. Measurement of turbidity in settled water prior to filtration is of aid in controlling chemical dosages so as to prevent excessive loading of rapid sand filters. Finally, turbidity measurements of the filtered water are needed to check on faulty filter operation.

**Sewage and Industrial Waste Treatment.** The suspended-solids determination is usually employed in waste treatment plants to determine the effectiveness of suspended-solids removal. The determination is slow and time-consuming, and, in plants employing chemical treatment, changes in chemical dosages have to be made rather frequently. Turbidity measurements can be used to advantage, because of the speed with which they can be made, to gain the necessary information. By their use, chemical dosages can be adjusted to use the minimum amount of chemical while producing a high-quality effluent.

# 12. Color

## 12-1. General Considerations

Many surface waters, particularly those emanating from swampy areas, are often colored to the extent that they are not acceptable for domestic or some industrial uses without treatment to remove the color. The coloring material results from contact of the water with organic debris, such as leaves, needles of conifers, and wood, all in various stages of decomposition. It consists of vegetable extracts of a considerable variety. Tannins, humic acid, and humates, from the decomposition of lignin, are considered to be the principal color bodies.[1] Iron is sometimes present as ferric humate and produces a color of high potency.

Natural color exists in water primarily as negatively charged colloidal particles.[2] Because of this fact, its removal can usually be readily accomplished by coagulation with the aid of a salt having a trivalent metallic ion, such as aluminum or iron.

Surface waters may appear highly colored, because of colored suspended matter, when in reality they are not. Rivers which drain areas of red clay soils, such as those in the Piedmont area of the South Atlantic states, become highly colored during times of flood. Color caused by suspended matter is referred to as *apparent color* and is differentiated from color due to vegetable or organic extracts that are colloidal and which is called *true color*. In water analysis it is important to differentiate between "apparent" and "true" color.

Surface waters may become colored by pollution with highly colored waste waters. Notable among these are wastes from dyeing operations in the textile industry and from pulping operations in the paper industry. Dye wastes may impart colors of wide variety that are readily recognized and traced. The pulping of wood produces considerable amounts of waste liquors containing lignin derivatives and other materials in dis-

[1] T. R. J. McCrea, *J. Am. Water Works Assoc.*, **25**, 931 (1933).
[2] T. Saville, *J. New Engl. Water Works Assoc.*, **31**, 78 (1917).

solved form.   The lignin derivatives are highly colored and quite resistant to biological attack.   Much of this material is disposed of into natural
watercourses, adding color which persists for great distances.   Considerable research is currently under way to find an economical way of removing color from pulp-mill wastes.

## 12-2. Sanitary Significance

Waters containing coloring matter derived from natural substances
undergoing decay in swamps and forests are not considered to possess
harmful or toxic properties.   The natural coloring materials, however,
give a yellow-brownish appearance to the water, somewhat like that of
urine, and there is a natural reluctance on the part of water consumers
to drink such waters because of the associations involved.

It is the responsibility of any water purveyor, public or private, to
produce a product that is hygienically safe.   Public health officials are
aware of the fact that consumers will seek other sources of drinking water
if the public water supply is not aesthetically acceptable, no matter how
safe it may be from the hygienic viewpoint.   Where waters are not aesthetically acceptable, consumers often shun safe domestic supplies and
use waters from uncontrolled springs or private wells which may serve as
foci for dissemination of pathogenic organisms.   For this reason, the
U.S. Public Health Service recommends that waters intended for human
use should not have a color exceeding 20 units.

## 12-3. Methods of Determination

Natural color, like turbidity, is due to a wide variety of substances,
and it has been necessary to adopt an arbitrary standard for its measurement.   This standard is employed directly and indirectly in the measurement of color.   Many samples require pretreatment to remove suspended
matter before true color can be determined.   The method of pretreatment must be carefully selected to avoid introduction of errors.

**Standard Color Solutions.**   Waters containing natural color are yellow-
brownish in appearance.   Through experience, it has been found that
solutions of potassium chloroplatinate ($K_2PtCl_6$) tinted with small
amounts of cobalt chloride yield colors that are very much like the natural
colors.   The shading of the color can be varied to match natural hues
very closely by increasing or decreasing the amount of cobalt chloride.

The color produced by 1 mg/l of platinum (as $K_2PtCl_6$) is taken as
the standard unit of color.   The usual procedure is to prepare a stock
solution of $K_2PtCl_6$ that contains 500 mg/l of platinum.   Cobalt chloride
is added to provide the proper tint.   The stock solution has a color of
500 units, and a series of working standards may be prepared from it

by dilution. Color-comparison tubes, commonly called Nessler tubes, as shown in Fig. 12-1, are usually used to contain the standards. A series ranging from 0 to 70 color units is employed and will serve for several months, provided that it is protected from dust and evaporation. The color-comparison tubes should be a matched set conforming to APHA standards as described in the introductory chapter of "Standard Methods."

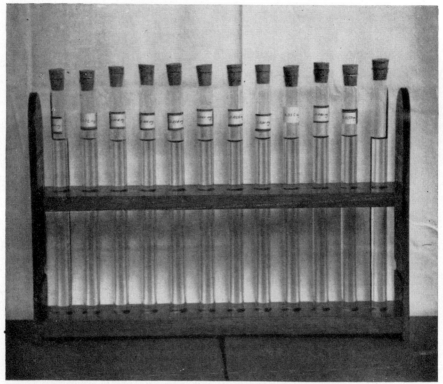

Fig. 12-1. Color-comparison tubes, commonly called Nessler tubes.

Samples subjected to analysis may contain suspended matter which will interfere with the measurement of true color. Apparent color is determined on the sample "as is." Suspended matter must be removed to enable determination of true color. This can usually be accomplished by centrifuging the sample to separate the suspended solids. Analysis is performed on the clarified liquor. Filtration is not recommended because of possible adsorption of color on the filtering medium.

Samples with color less than 70 units are tested by direct comparison with the prepared standards. For samples with a color greater than 70 units, a dilution is made with distilled water to bring the resulting color within the range of the standards, and calculation of color is made, using a correction factor for the dilution employed.

**Methods Employing Proprietary Devices.** A number of instruments have been developed for the measurement of color to eliminate the need

Fig. 12-2. The Hellige Aquatester. (*Hellige, Inc.*)

for renewing standard color solutions from time to time. Most of these instruments employ colored glass disks which simulate the various color standards when used in the particular instrument. One of the most popular is shown in Fig. 12-2.

The proprietary devices find their greatest use in water works laboratories where trained chemists are not employed. They are not accepted as a standard procedure for measuring color because of variations in the color of the glass disks and their tendency to change characteristics owing to finger prints, dust, etc. They should always be standardized against standard solutions of $K_2PtCl_6$ for highly important work.

Most of the proprietary devices suffer from the fact that replacement parts are rather expensive. This limits their use in laboratories designed for teaching, where breakage of glassware is normally rather great.

**Field Methods.** In some instances it becomes highly desirable to conduct color and other determinations in the field. The use of standard color solutions or of most proprietary devices is impractical because of possibilites of breakage, spillage, or lack of a suitable power source. The U.S. Geological Survey has developed a field kit. It employs aluminum tubes with glass windows on each end and a series of colored glass disks. Two tubes are used. One contains the sample and the other distilled water. The colored glass disks are placed over the end of the tube with distilled water until a combination is found that appears to have a color similar to that of the sample. The method is recognized as standard for field use.

**Methods Applicable to Sewage and Industrial Wastes.** Many industrial wastes are highly colored, and some contain colored substances that are quite resistant to biological destruction. Regulations concerning the color of effluents that may be discharged to streams are becoming more common. Evaluation of the color of yellow-brownish-hue wastes can be made by the standard procedures described above. Other systems of measurement have to be used to measure and describe colors that do not fall into this classification. A system adopted by the International Commission on Illumination utilizing characterization and measurement of color by spectrophotometric means is recommended in "Standard Methods." A discussion is beyond the scope of this book.

## 12-4. Interpretation and Application of Color Data

The color of surface waters utilized for domestic supplies is of major concern for reasons mentioned above. Many industrial processes also require the use of color-free water. Removal of color is an expensive matter when capital investment and operating costs are considered. Therefore the water engineer, when developing or looking for new supplies, is always searching for a suitable supply with a color low enough so that chemical treatment will not be required. His "prospecting" may or may not be successful. If it is, he will use color data as one of the parameters to satisfy his client that expensive chemical treatment is not necessary. If it is not successful, he will use color data along with other information to prove that expensive chemical coagulation and sand filtration are needed to produce an acceptable supply.

Before a chemical treatment plant is designed, research should be conducted to ascertain the best chemicals to use and amounts required. In dealing with colored waters, color determinations serve as the basis of the decisions. Such data must be obtained for proper selection of chemical feeding machinery and the design of storage space.

Once operation of the treatment facilities has begun, color determinations on the raw and finished waters serve to govern the dosages of chemicals used, to ensure economical operation, and to produce a low-color water that is well within the accepted limits established by the U.S. Public Health Service.

# 13. Standard Solutions

## 13-1. General Considerations

Chemists familiar with the analysis of water, sewage, and industrial wastes involving volumetric procedures have learned that the use of standard reagents of definite normality saves a great deal of time in calculating results in terms of milligrams per liter. The preparation of solutions of a definite normality is not a tedious procedure if a logical system is used. Two or three important steps are involved, depending upon the nature of the materials.

**Selection of the Proper Normality.** In sanitary analysis it is usually desirable to report results in terms of milligrams per liter of some particular ion, element, or compound. As a rule, it is most convenient to have the standard titrating agent of such strength that 1 ml is equivalent to 1 mg of the material being measured. Thus 1 liter of a standard solution is ordinarily equivalent to 1,000 mg or 1 g of the measured substance. The desired normality of the titrant is obtained by the relationship of 1 to the equivalent weight of the measured material. For example, the normality of acid solutions used to measure ammonia, ammonia nitrogen, and alkalinity (as $CaCO_3$) is as follows:

|  | *Ammonia* | *Ammonia nitrogen* | *Alkalinity (as $CaCO_3$)* |
|---|---|---|---|
| $\dfrac{1}{\text{eq. wt}}$ = | $1/17 = N/17$ | $1/14 = N/14$ | $1/50 = N/50$ |
|  | $= 0.0588\ N$ | $0.0715\ N$ | $0.02\ N$ |

The normality of basic solutions for measuring carbon dioxide (as $CO_2$) and mineral acidity (as $CaCO_3$) is

|  | $CO_2$ | *Acidity* (as $CaCO_3$) |
|---|---|---|
| $\dfrac{1}{\text{eq. wt}}$ = | $1/44 = N/44$ | $1/50 = N/50$ |
|  | $= 0.0288\ N$ | $0.02\ N$ |

The normality of silver nitrate solutions for measuring chlorides or sodium chloride is

Chlorides      Sodium chloride

$$\frac{1}{\text{eq. wt}} = 1/35.46 = N/35.46 \qquad\qquad 1/58.46 = N/58.46$$

The normality of reducing agents for measuring oxygen[1] is

Oxygen

$$\frac{1}{\text{eq. wt}} = 1/8 = N/8$$

The normality of oxidizing agents is obtained in a similar manner.

From the fact that standard solutions of titrating agents are of such strength that 1 ml is equivalent to 1 mg of the measured material, it will be readily apparent that when 1-liter samples are titrated the buret reading will give milligrams per liter directly. Usually it is inconvenient to use 1-liter samples, and calculations are easily made by the simple formula

$$\text{ml titrant used} \times \frac{1,000}{\text{ml sample}} = \text{mg/l}$$

In some instances, as in the determination of dissolved oxygen where a fixed sample size is used, the strength of the titrant is adjusted so that each milliliter of titrant is equivalent to 1 mg/l.

**Preparation of a Solution of Proper Normality.** In cases where a standard solution can be prepared from materials of known purity that can be accurately weighed on the analytical balance, the desired amount can be weighed, transferred to a volumetric flask, and diluted to the proper volume. Such solutions may be used without standardization against primary standards.

Many materials from which standard solutions are prepared are of such a character that their purity is not accurately known, or it may be impossible to weigh them exactly. In these cases, a solution is prepared that is known to be slightly stronger than desired, and it can be kept most conveniently in a graduated cylinder until standardization is completed. Standardization is accomplished by using a suitable primary standard.

**Standardization of Solutions with Primary Standards.** The procedure for standardizing solutions to an exact normality is somewhat peculiar to sanitary analysis and is not usually described in quantitative textbooks. Six fundamental steps are involved, as follows:

1. Calculate the weight of the primary standard that is exactly equivalent to 1 liter of the solution to be standardized.

---

[1] Actually a $N/40$ solution is used in practice for reasons given in Sec. 22-4.

2. Weigh three or four samples of the heat-dried primary standard that are sufficient to use about 20 ml of the solution. Weighings must be exact, and corrections must be made for per cent purity if it differs significantly from 100 per cent.

3. Calculate the volume of titrant of the desired normality needed to react with the corrected weight of each sample.

4. Add sufficient distilled water, and other reagents as needed, to each sample of primary standard to accomplish solution, and titrate two of them with the reagent to be standardized. The titrations should be less than the calculated amounts obtained in step 3. If so, the solution is stronger than desired, and the difference in titrations represents the deficiency of water.

5. Calculate the amount of water to be added to the remaining solution. Drain the contents of the buret into the stock supply in the graduated cylinder and measure the total volume remaining. The amount of water to be added may be calculated from the following expression:

$$\frac{\text{Volume remaining}}{\text{Actual titration}} (\text{calc. titration} - \text{actual titration}) = ml$$

Make separate calculations for each of the titrations and add the least amount of water indicated.[1] *Mix thoroughly after adding the water, rinse, and fill the buret with the new solution.*

6. Titrate additional samples of primary standard and repeat steps 4 and 5 until the proper strength has been reached as shown by a correlation of actual titrations with calculated values. The solution may then be considered to have the desired normality.

## 13-2. Preparation of $N/1$ and $N/50$ $H_2SO_4$ Solutions

Standard solutions of sulfuric acid are used for the determination of alkalinity which is normally expressed in terms of $CaCO_3$, with an equivalent weight of 50; therefore $N/50$ solutions are required. Because large amounts of this reagent are used, it is most convenient to prepare a stock solution of $N/1$ acid and prepare the $N/50$ solution from it by simple dilution.

The purity of sulfuric acid as purchased usually varies from about 96 to 98 per cent. In addition, it is very difficult to weigh accurately because of its hygroscopic properties. Solutions prepared from it must be standardized by means of some primary standard. Sodium carbonate is the primary standard usually used. The analytical grade is satisfactory provided that it has been dried for 1 hr at 140°C and kept in a desiccator prior to use.

---

[1] Beginners should add slightly less water to avoid overdilution.

**Calculation of Concentrated $H_2SO_4$ Needed.** In order to simplify calculations, they will be made on the basis of 1-liter amounts. By definition, 1 liter of $N/1$ acid contains 1.008 g of available hydrogen ion. Calculations are as follows:

$$1 \text{ GMW or } 98 \text{ g pure } H_2SO_4 = 2.016 \text{ g } H^+$$

$$\frac{\text{GMW}}{2} \text{ or } 49 \text{ g pure } H_2SO_4 = 1.008 \text{ g } H^+$$

Assume that concentrated acid is 96 per cent pure.

Then,       $\dfrac{49}{0.96} = 51 \text{ g conc. acid} = 1.008 \text{ g } H^+$

It is desirable that the solution be slightly stronger than $N/1$. To be sure of this, take 5 per cent excess.

$$51 \times 1.05 = 53.5 \text{ g}$$

**Preparation of $N/1$ Acid Solution.** Weigh approximately 53 g, $\pm 1$ g, of concentrated acid into a small beaker on a trip balance. Place about 500 ml of distilled water in a 1-liter graduated cylinder and add the acid to it. Rinse the contents of the beaker into the cylinder with distilled water and add water to the 1-liter mark. Mix thoroughly by stirring or pouring back and forth from the cylinder into a large beaker. Cool to room temperature before use.

**Calculation of Primary Standard Needed.** Sodium carbonate is a convenient primary standard. It has a molecular weight of 106 and an equivalent weight of 53 when reacting with $H_2SO_4$ to a pH of 4.2 to 4.4, the methyl orange end point.

$$53 \text{ g } Na_2CO_3 \approx 1{,}000 \text{ ml } N/1 \text{ } H_2SO_4$$
or       $$1.06 \text{ g } Na_2CO_3 \approx 20 \text{ ml } N/1 \text{ } H_2SO_4$$

Weigh four samples of $Na_2CO_3$ ranging from 1.00 to 1.10 g and proceed as described in the third part of Sec. 13-1.

**Preparation of $N/50$ Acid Solution.** When a $N/1$ acid solution is available, solutions of any normality less than $N/1$ can be prepared from it by dilution, provided that proper care is used in measuring the amount of $N/1$ acid needed and dilutions are made in volumetric flasks. The amount of acid of any normality needed to make a definite volume of an acid of another normality may be calculated from the relationship

$$\text{ml} \times N = \text{ml} \times N$$

If it is desired to make 1 liter of $N/50$ acid from a stock supply of $N/1$ acid, the calculation is as follows:

$$\text{ml} \times 1.0 = 1{,}000 \times 0.02$$
$$\text{ml} = 20$$

Twenty milliliters of $N/1$ acid when diluted to 1,000 ml with distilled water and thoroughly mixed yields a $N/50$ solution that is satisfactory for most purposes. For referee work, it would be advisable to check the normality of the $N/50$ acid against weighed samples of a primary standard.

### 13-3. Preparation of $N/1$ and $N/50$ NaOH Solutions

Standard solutions of sodium hydroxide are used to measure carbon dioxide and mineral acidity. The equivalent weight of carbon dioxide when reacting with sodium hydroxide, to pH 8.2 or the phenolphthalein end point, is 44, as may be calculated from the equation

$$\underset{44}{CO_2} + Na^+ + \underset{17}{OH^-} \rightarrow Na^+ + HCO_3^- \qquad (13\text{-}1)$$

Therefore $N/44$ solutions of NaOH are best suited for determination of carbon dioxide. Mineral acidity is always expressed in terms of calcium carbonate which has an equivalent weight of 50, and $N/50$ solutions of bases are used for its determination.

In practice, it is most convenient to prepare a $N/1$ solution of NaOH as a stock supply and make solutions of lower normality by dilution, as with sulfuric acid. In some laboratories, so few determinations of carbon dioxide are made that it is impractical to keep a supply of both $N/44$ and $N/50$ solutions on hand. In such cases, the $N/50$ solution is used for both determinations, and a factor of 0.88 is applied to correct buret readings when carbon dioxide is measured.

Sodium hydroxide cannot be purchased in a pure form. It is always contaminated with sodium carbonate as a result of its reaction with carbon dioxide of the air during its manufacture. Even the so-called analytical reagent grade contains several per cent of sodium carbonate and is unfit for the preparation of standard solutions without purification. Several methods are used but only two are commonly used in sanitary engineering laboratories.

A primary standard is required in the preparation of standard solutions of sodium hydroxide. Potassium acid phthalate ($KHC_8H_4O_4$) is excellent because of its high equivalent weight and other desirable properties. It should be dried at 105 to 110°C for 1 hr and kept in a desiccator prior to use.

**Purification of NaOH.** All sodium hydroxide must be subjected to a purification process to free it of sodium carbonate which also has basic properties. Two methods will be described in order of their preference.

1. Sodium carbonate is relatively insoluble in concentrated (approximately 50 per cent or 18 $M$) solutions of sodium hydroxide. If 500 g of stick or pellet-form sodium hydroxide is added to 500 ml of distilled

water, the sodium hydroxide will dissolve, leaving the sodium carbonate undissolved. The resulting solution will be rather turbid because of the suspended sodium carbonate. On standing several days, the carbonate will float or settle and a clear solution will result that is sufficiently free of carbonate for the preparation of standard solutions. Siphon the purified 50 per cent solution into a pyrex bottle and use a rubber stopper to exclude the air. It is good practice to keep a considerable supply of purified 50 per cent sodium hydroxide on hand because of the time involved in its preparation.

2. Dilute solutions of sodium hydroxide may be freed of carbonate by precipitation with barium hydroxide.

$$2Na^+ + CO_3^= + Ba(OH)_2 \rightarrow \underline{BaCO_3\downarrow} + 2NaOH \qquad (13\text{-}2)$$

The resulting barium carbonate precipitate may be removed by filtration (if protected from carbon dioxide of air), or it may be allowed to settle and the clarified solution siphoned to another bottle. The purified solution must be standardized after this treatment, as barium hydroxide is used in excess and an amount of sodium hydroxide equivalent to the sodium carbonate originally present remains.

**Calculation of NaOH Needed.** For purposes of these calculations, it is assumed that a purified solution of sodium hydroxide, 50 per cent, is available and that approximately 1 liter of a $N/1$ solution is to be prepared. By definition, 1 liter of $N/1$ base contains the equivalent of 1.008 g of $H^+$ or 17 g of $OH^-$ per liter. Calculations are as follows:

$$1 \text{ GMW or } 40 \text{ g pure NaOH} = 17 \text{ g } OH^-$$

The stock solution of purified NaOH is 50 per cent strength. Therefore,

$$\frac{40}{0.5} = 80 \text{ g } 50\% \text{ NaOH} = 17 \text{ g } OH^-$$

Since the stock solution of NaOH may not contain exactly 50 per cent and it is desirable to prepare a solution which is slightly stronger than $N/1$, take 10 per cent excess.

$$80 \times 1.1 = 88 \text{ g}$$

**Preparation of $N/1$ NaOH Solution.** As rapidly as possible, so as to minimize adsorption of carbon dioxide from the air, weigh 88 g, $\pm 1$ g, of the purified 50 per cent sodium hydroxide solution into a small erlenmeyer flask on a trip balance. Place 500 ml of carbon-dioxide-free distilled water in a 1-liter graduated cylinder and add the sodium hydroxide solution. Rinse the erlenmeyer flask with carbon-dioxide-free water and add rinsings to the cylinder. Dilute to approximately 1 liter with carbon-dioxide-free water and mix thoroughly with a plunger-type stirrer to minimize contact with the air. Protect the solution from the air by keeping an inverted beaker or some other form of cap over the top of the cylinder until standardization is completed.

**Calculation of Primary Standard Needed.** Potassium acid phthalate is an excellent primary standard. It may be obtained in essentially 100 per cent pure form. Its equivalent weight is equal to its molecular weight, which is 204.

$$204 \text{ g KHC}_8\text{H}_4\text{O}_4 \approx 1,000 \text{ ml } N/1 \text{ NaOH}$$
or
$$2.04 \text{ g KHC}_8\text{H}_4\text{O}_4 \approx 10 \text{ ml } N/1 \text{ NaOH}$$

Weigh four samples of $KHC_8H_4O_4$ ranging from 2.0 to 2.2 g and proceed as described in the third part of Sec. 13-1. When standardization is completed, the $N/1$ solution should be stored in a pyrex bottle fitted with a rubber stopper to exclude air.

**Preparation of $N/50$ NaOH Solution.** Proceed in a manner similar to the instructions for preparing $N/50$ acid. The $N/1$ hydroxide should be diluted with carbon-dioxide-free water, stored in a pyrex bottle, and protected from the carbon dioxide of the atmosphere.

**Standardization with Secondary Standards.** The $N/1$ and $N/50$ solutions of sodium hydroxide may be standardized against corresponding solutions of sulfuric acid. The acid solutions serve as secondary standards, and any error made in their preparation will be reflected in the hydroxide solutions. Methyl orange must be used as the indicator, and whether the acid or the hydroxide is used as the titrant is optional. It is usually most convenient to use the acid.

# 14. pH

## 14-1. General Considerations

pH is a term used rather universally to express the intensity of the acid or alkaline condition of a solution. More exactly, it is a way of expressing the hydrogen-ion concentration. It is of importance in practically every phase of sanitary engineering practice. In the field of water supplies, it is a factor that must be considered in chemical coagulation, disinfection, water softening, and corrosion control. In sewage and industrial waste treatment employing biological processes, pH must be controlled within a range favorable to the particular organisms involved. Chemical processes used to coagulate sewage or industrial wastes, dewater sludges, or oxidize certain substances, such as cyanide ion, require that the pH be controlled within rather narrow limits. For these reasons and because of the fundamental relationships that exist between pH, acidity, and alkalinity, it is very important to understand the theoretical as well as the practical aspects of pH.

## 14-2. Theoretical Considerations

The concept of pH evolved from a series of developments that led to a fuller understanding of acids and bases. Acids and bases were originally distinguished by their difference in taste and later by the manner in which they affected certain materials that came to be known as indicators. With the discovery of hydrogen by Cavendish in 1766, it soon became apparent that all acids contained the element hydrogen. Chemists soon found that neutralization reactions between acids and bases always produced water. From this and other related information, it was concluded that bases contained hydroxyl groups.

In 1887, Arrhenius announced his theory of ionization. Since that time acids have been considered to be substances that dissociate to yield hydrogen ions, and bases have been considered to be substances that dissociate to yield hydroxyl ions. According to the concepts of Arrhenius, strong acids and bases are highly ionized and weak acids and bases are poorly ionized in aqueous solution. Proof of these claims had to await the development of suitable devices for the measurement of hydrogen-ion concentration.

**Measurement of Hydrogen-ion Concentration.** The hydrogen electrode (Sec. 6-14) was found to be a very suitable device for measuring hydrogen-ion concentration. With its use, it was found that pure water dissociates to yield a concentration of hydrogen ions equal to $10^{-7}$ mole/l.

$$H_2O \rightleftharpoons H^+ + OH^- \tag{14-1}$$

Since water dissociates to produce one hydroxyl ion for each hydrogen ion, it is obvious that $10^{-7}$ mole of hydroxyl ion is produced simultaneously. By substitution into the mass action equation, we obtain

$$\frac{[H^+][OH^-]}{[H_2O]} = K \tag{14-2}$$

but, since the concentration of water is so extremely large and is diminished so very little by the slight degree of ionization, it may be considered as constant and Eq. (14-2) may be written

$$[H^+][OH^-] = K_w \tag{14-3}$$

and for pure water at about 25°C

$$[H^+][OH^-] = 10^{-7} \times 10^{-7} = 10^{-14} \tag{14-4}$$

This is known as the ion product or ionization constant for water.

When an acid is added to water, it ionizes in the water and the hydrogen-ion concentration increases; consequently the hydroxyl-ion concentration must decrease in conformity with the ionization constant. For example, if acid is added to increase the $[H^+]$ to $10^{-1}$, the $[OH^-]$ must decrease to $10^{-13}$.

$$10^{-1} \times 10^{-13} = 10^{-14}$$

Likewise, if a base is added to water to increase the $[OH^-]$ to $10^{-3}$, the $[H^+]$ decreases to $10^{-11}$. It is important to remember that the $[OH^-]$ or the $[H^+]$ can never be reduced to zero, no matter how acidic or basic the solution may be.

**The pH Concept.** Expression of hydrogen-ion concentrations in terms of molar concentrations is rather cumbersome. In order to overcome this difficulty, Sorenson (1909) proposed to express such values in terms of their negative logarithms and designated such values as $p_H^+$. His symbol has been superseded by the simple designation pH. The term may be represented by

$$pH = -\log [H^+] \quad \text{or} \quad pH = \log \frac{1}{[H^+]} \quad (14\text{-}5)$$

and the pH scale is usually represented as ranging from 0 to 14, with pH 7 representing absolute neutrality.

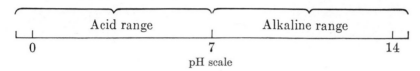

pH scale

Acid conditions increase as pH values decrease and alkaline conditions increase as the pH values increase. pH 7 has little significance as a reference point in water chemistry and therefore is of little importance in sanitary engineering practice.

## 14-3. Measurement of pH

The hydrogen electrode is the absolute standard for the measurement of pH. It is rather cumbersome and not well adapted for universal use, particularly in field studies or in solutions containing materials that are adsorbed on the platinum black. A wide variety of indicators were calibrated with the hydrogen electrode to determine their color characteristics at various pH levels. From these studies it became possible to determine pH values fairly accurately by choosing an indicator that exhibited significant color changes in the particular range involved. With the use of about six to eight indicators it is possible to determine pH values in the range of interest to sanitary engineers.

About 1925, it was discovered that an electrode could be constructed of glass (Sec. 6-14) which would develop a potential related to the hydrogen-ion concentration without interference from most other ions. Its use has become the standard method of measuring pH.

**Colorimetric Measurement.** A wide variety of indicators have been used for measurement of pH. To be of real value they must show distinct color changes over a pH range of about one pH unit. A list of some of the indicators commonly used and the range of their usefulness are given in Table 14-1. As a general rule, they are quite unreliable for measuring pH values below 3 and above 10. Determinations can be made quite accurately, $\pm 0.1$ pH unit, in colorless turbidity-free samples that are well buffered, provided that care is taken to add the proper amount of indicator and a reliable set of color standards is available. Their reliability on turbid, highly colored, or poorly buffered samples is very poor, and they are quite inconvenient to use unless the pH range

TABLE 14-1. COMMON INDICATORS USED TO MEASURE pH

| Indicator | pH range | Color change |
|---|---|---|
| Bromophenol blue | 3.0– 4.6 | Yellow-blue-violet |
| Methyl orange* | 3.1– 4.4 | Red-orange |
| Brom cresol green | 3.8– 5.4 | Yellow-blue |
| Methyl red* | 4.4– 6.2 | Red-yellow |
| Chlor phenol red | 5.4– 6.8 | Yellow-red |
| Brom thymol blue | 6.2– 7.6 | Yellow-blue |
| Phenol red | 6.4– 8.0 | Yellow-red |
| Cresol red | 7.2– 8.8 | Yellow-red |
| Thymol blue | 8.0– 9.6 | Yellow-blue |
| Phenolphthalein* | 8.2–10.0 | Colorless-red |
| Thymolphthalein | 9.3–10.5 | Colorless-blue |

* Principal use is as indicators in acidimetry and alkalimetry.

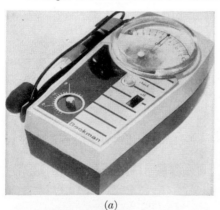

(a)

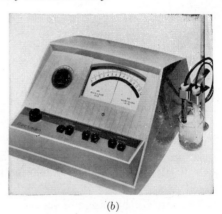

(b)

(c)

FIG. 14-1. Commercial models of pH meters. (a) Battery-operated portable model. (b) Line-operated laboratory model. (c) Battery-operated laboratory model. (*Beckman Scientific Instruments.*)

of the sample is known in advance. For these reasons, the glass electrode has become the generally accepted method of determining pH.

**Measurement with the Glass Electrode.** pH meters employing the glass electrode are manufactured by many concerns. They range from portable battery-operated units selling for about one hundred dollars to highly precise instruments selling for several hundred dollars. Units that can be operated on 110-volt alternating current were developed about 1940 and are highly satisfactory for most routine laboratory purposes, being capable of measuring pH within a $\pm 0.1$ pH unit. The small portable battery-operated units are most suitable for field work. Figure 14-1 shows examples of the three types of instruments available in the United States. Figure 14-2 is a simplified diagram of a pH meter circuit.

pH measurements can be made in a wide variety of materials and under extreme conditions provided that attention is paid to the type of

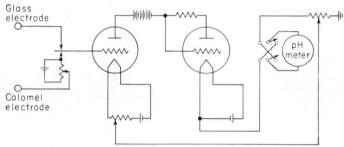

FIG. 14-2. Simplified diagram of a pH meter circuit.

electrode used. Measurement of pH values above 10 and at high temperatures is best made with special glass electrodes designed for such service. The pH of semisolid substances can be made with a spear-type electrode. The instruments are normally standardized with buffer solutions of known pH values.

## 14-4. Interpretation of pH Data

pH data should always be interpreted in terms of hydrogen-ion concentration which, of course, is a measure of the intensity of acid or basic conditions. For all practical purposes the conversion is very simple.

$$\text{at pH 2} \qquad [\text{H}^+] = 10^{-2}$$
$$\text{at pH 10} \qquad [\text{H}^+] = 10^{-10}$$
$$\text{at pH 4.5} \qquad [\text{H}^+] = 10^{-4.5}$$
$$\text{etc.}$$

pH does not measure total acidity or total alkalinity. This can be illustrated by comparing the pH of $N/10$ solutions of sulfuric acid and acetic acids, which have the same neutralizing value. The pH of the former is approximately 1 because of its high degree of ionization, and the pH of the latter is about 3 because of its low degree of ionization.

In some instances the pOH, or hydroxyl-ion concentration, of a solution is of major interest. It is customary to calculate pOH from pH values, using the relationship given in Eq. (14-3). Approximations are often made from the relationship

$$pH + pOH = 14 \qquad\qquad (14\text{-}6)$$
$$\text{or} \qquad\qquad pOH = 14 - pH \qquad\qquad (14\text{-}7)$$

It is just as important for the sanitary engineer to remember that the $[OH^-]$ of a solution can never be reduced to zero, no matter how acid the solution is, as it is for him to remember that the $[H^+]$ can never be reduced to zero, no matter how alkaline a solution becomes.

Concepts of pOH, or hydroxyl-ion concentration, are of particular importance in precipitation reactions involving formation of hydroxides. Examples are the precipitation of $Mg^{++}$ in softening of water with lime and in chemical coagulation processes employing iron and aluminum salts.

# 15. Acidity

## 15-1. General Considerations

Most natural waters, domestic sewage, and many industrial wastes are buffered principally by a carbon dioxide–bicarbonate system.  By reference to Fig. 4-4, which shows titration curves for several weak acids, it will be noted from the curve for carbonic acid that the stoichiometric end point is not reached until the pH has been raised to about 8.5.  On the basis of this information, it is customary to consider that all waters

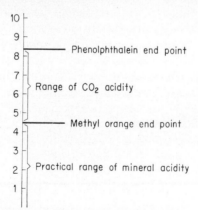

FIG. 15-1. Types of acidity of importance in ordinary sanitary analysis and the pH ranges in which they are significant.

having a pH lower than 8.5 contain acidity.  Usually the phenolphthalein end point at pH 8.2 to 8.4 is taken as the reference point.  Inspection of the curve for carbonic acid in Fig. 4-4 shows that at pH 7.0 considerable carbon dioxide remains to be neutralized.  It also shows that carbon dioxide (carbonic acid) alone will not depress the pH below a value of about 4.5.

Figure 4-3 shows a titration curve for a strong acid, and, from the

211

nature of the curve, it may be concluded that neutralization of the acid is essentially complete at pH 4.5.   Thus, from the nature of the titration curves for carbonic acid and for strong acids, it becomes obvious that the acidity of natural waters is caused by carbon dioxide or by strong mineral acids, the former being the effective agent in waters having pH values greater than 4.5 and the latter the effective agent in waters with pH values less than 4.5, as shown in Fig. 15-1.

## 15-2. Sources and Nature of Acidity

Carbon dioxide is a normal component of all natural waters.   It may enter surface waters by absorption from the atmosphere but only when the partial pressure of carbon dioxide in the water is less than the partial pressure of the carbon dioxide in the atmosphere, in accordance with Henry's law.   Carbon dioxide may also be produced in waters through biological oxidation of organic matter, particularly in polluted water. In such cases, if photosynthetic activity is limited, the partial pressure of carbon dioxide in the water may exceed that of the atmosphere and carbon dioxide will escape from the liquid.   Thus it may be concluded that surface waters are constantly absorbing or giving up carbon dioxide to maintain an equilibrium with that of the atmosphere.   The amount that can exist at equilibrium is very small because of the low partial pressure of carbon dioxide in the atmosphere.

Ground waters and waters from the hypolimnion of stratified lakes and reservoirs often contain considerable amounts of carbon dioxide.   This concentration results from bacterial oxidation of organic matter with which the water has been in contact, and, under the conditions, the carbon dioxide is not free to escape to the atmosphere.   Carbon dioxide is an end product of both aerobic and anaerobic bacterial oxidation; therefore its concentration is not limited by the amount of dissolved oxygen originally present.   It is not uncommon to encounter ground waters with 30 to 50 mg/l of carbon dioxide.   This is particularly true of waters that have percolated through soils that do not contain enough calcium or magnesium carbonate to neutralize the carbon dioxide through formation of bicarbonates.

$$CO_2 + CaCO_3 + H_2O \rightarrow Ca(HCO_3)_2 \qquad (15\text{-}1)$$

Mineral acidity is present in many industrial wastes, particularly those of the metallurgical industry and some from the production of synthetic organic materials.   Certain natural waters may also contain mineral acidity.   The drainage from abandoned mines, lean ore dumps, and "gob" piles will contain significant amounts of sulfuric acid or salts of sulfuric acid if sulfur, sulfides, or iron pyrites are present.   Conversion of these materials to sulfuric acid and sulfates is brought about by sulfur-oxidizing bacteria under aerobic conditions.

$$2S + 3O_2 + 2H_2O \xrightarrow{\text{bact.}} 2H_2SO_4 \qquad (15\text{-}2)$$

$$FeS_2 + 3\tfrac{1}{2}O_2 + H_2O \xrightarrow{\text{bact.}} FeSO_4 + H_2SO_4 \qquad (15\text{-}3)$$

Salts of heavy metals, particularly those with trivalent metal ions such as $Fe^{3+}$ and $Al^{3+}$, hydrolyze in water to release mineral acidity.

$$FeCl_3 + 3H_2O \rightleftharpoons Fe(OH)_3 + 3H^+ + 3Cl^- \qquad (15\text{-}4)$$

Their presence is indicated by the formation of a precipitate as the pH of solutions containing them is increased during neutralization.

Many industrial wastes contain organic acids. Their presence and nature can be determined best by use of electrometric titration curves.

## 15-3. Significance of Carbon Dioxide and Mineral Acidity

Acidity is of little concern from a sanitary or public health viewpoint. Carbon dioxide is present in malt and carbonated beverages in concentrations greatly in excess of any concentrations known in natural waters, and no deleterious effects due to the carbon dioxide have been recognized. Waters that contain mineral acidity are usually so unpalatable that problems related to human consumption are nonexistent.

Acid waters are of concern to sanitary engineers because of their corrosive characteristics and the expense involved in removing or controlling the corrosion-producing substances. The corrosive factor in most waters is carbon dioxide, but in many industrial wastes it is mineral acidity. Carbon dioxide must be reckoned with in water-softening problems where the lime or lime-soda ash method is employed.

Where biological processes of treatment are used, the pH must ordinarily be maintained within the range of 6 to 9.5. This criterion often requires adjustment of pH to favorable levels, and calculation of the amount of chemicals needed is based upon acidity values in most cases.

## 15-4. Method of Measurement

Both carbon dioxide and mineral acidity can be measured by means of standard solutions of alkaline reagents. In the past, solutions of sodium hydroxide have been used: $N/44$ for carbon dioxide and $N/50$ for mineral acidity, as discussed in Sec. 13-3. The ninth edition of "Standard Methods" recommended the use of $N/50$ sodium hydroxide solution for both and the application of a correction factor of 0.88 to the titration values obtained when measuring carbon dioxide. Because of the inability of some analysts to obtain reliable results for carbon dioxide when using the titration procedure, the titration method was eliminated in the tenth edition of "Standard Methods," and a method of calculation based upon pH and alkalinity measurements became standard.   This change left the profession without a field method of measurement, which is needed greatly.   Indications are that the titration method, in a somewhat modified form, will be reinstated in future editions of "Standard Methods."

**Carbon Dioxide.**   If reliable results are to be obtained, special precautions must be taken during the collection, handling, and analysis of samples for carbon dioxide, regardless of the method used.   In waters where carbon dioxide is an important consideration, its partial pressure is greatly in excess of that in the atmosphere; therefore exposure to the air must be avoided or kept at a minimum.   For this reason analysis can be accomplished to best advantage at the point of collection where exposure to the air and temperature change can be avoided.

The sample should be collected in the same manner that is used to obtain a sample for dissolved oxygen, i.e., by using a submerged tube or pipe inlet, to exclude air bubbles, and allowing the container to overflow in order to displace any water that has come in contact with the air. If the sample must be transported to the laboratory for analysis, the bottle should be filled completely and capped or stoppered so as to leave no air pocket.   The temperature should be kept as near that at which it was collected as possible.

*Titration Method.*   In order to minimize contact with the air, it is best to collect and titrate the sample in a graduated cylinder or a color-comparison tube.   The tube or cylinder should be filled to overflowing and the excess siphoned off or removed with a pipet to get the proper sample size.   After addition of the proper amount of phenolphthalein indicator, the titration is conducted in a manner to minimize loss of carbon dioxide.   Ordinarily, appreciable amounts of carbon dioxide will be lost in the first titration because of the excessive stirring needed. Reliable results may be obtained by taking a second sample and adding the indicated amount of titrant to it before stirring.   The titration may then be completed without significant loss of carbon dioxide.   The final end point is reached somewhat slowly, and so it is recommended that the titration not be considered complete until a pinkish color persists for 30 sec.

When sodium hydroxide is used as the standard reagent, it is important that it be free of sodium carbonate.   The reaction involved in the neutralization may be considered to occur in two steps,

$$2NaOH + CO_2 \rightarrow Na_2CO_3 + H_2O \qquad (15\text{-}5)$$
$$Na_2CO_3 + CO_2 + H_2O \rightarrow 2NaHCO_3 \qquad (15\text{-}6)$$

and, from Eq. (15-6), it should be obvious that if sodium carbonate is originally present in the sodium hydroxide, it will cause erroneous results.

In order to overcome this problem, the use of sodium carbonate solutions is being recommended for the standard titrant in carbon dioxide measurements. Sodium carbonate can be used in this capacity since it reacts quantitatively with carbon dioxide, as shown in Eq. (15-6). It has a definite advantage in that it may be purchased in analytical-grade form.

*Calculation from pH and Alkalinity.* Theoretically, it should be possible to calculate the amount of carbonic acid present in a water whose pH is less than 8 from the mathematical expression for the primary ionization constant of carbonic acid, provided that the hydrogen-ion and bicarbonate-ion concentrations and the value for $K_1$ are known.

$$\frac{[H^+][HCO_3^-]}{[H_2CO_3]} = K_1 \qquad (15\text{-}7)$$

From this equation it may be concluded that the relationship between bicarbonate ion and carbonic acid is a constant at any given pH. However, carbonic acid exists in equilibrium with carbon dioxide and water, and the total amount of free carbon dioxide is not represented in a linear manner by carbonic acid, particularly at low alkalinity values. In addition, the value of $K_1$ varies somewhat with temperature and the concentration of other ions in solution. Calculation of free carbon dioxide by mathematical means is a complicated process; therefore a nomographic chart is included in "Standard Methods" to facilitate the determination of free carbon dioxide from pH and alkalinity measurements.

Determination of carbon dioxide from pH and alkalinity measurements can result in highly accurate results but not necessarily so. The method suffers from the fact that a knowledge of total solids must be known. This usually requires a separate determination by gravimetric methods. The pH must be measured very accurately, as small variations can introduce serious errors. An appreciation of the need for precise pH measurements can be obtained from an inspection of the titration curve for carbonic acid in Fig. 4-4. In the pH range of 6.5 to 7.5, appreciable amounts of alkali must be added to change the pH significantly. If this is true, the amount of free carbon dioxide must change accordingly.

It is questionable whether results obtained by this method under ordinary laboratory conditions are more reliable than results obtained by the titration procedure, if proper attention is paid to details described above in the titration method.

*Field Method.* The titration procedure has many advantages and is sufficiently accurate for all practical purposes.

**Mineral Acidity.** All natural waters and most industrial wastes that have a pH below 4 contain mineral acidity. Since mineral acids are essentially neutralized by the time the pH has been raised to about 4.5 (see Fig. 4-3), it is customary to use methyl orange as the indicator.

$N/50$ NaOH is used as the titrating agent.    Results are reported in terms of mineral acidity expressed as $CaCO_3$.

## 15-5. Application of Acidity Data

Carbon dioxide determinations are particularly important in the field of public water supplies.    In the development of new supplies, it is an important factor that must be considered in the treatment method and the facilities needed.    Many underground supplies require treatment to overcome corrosive characteristics resulting from carbon dioxide.    The amount present is an important factor in determining whether removal by aeration or simple neutralization with lime or sodium hydroxide will be chosen as the treatment method.    The size of equipment, chemical requirements, storage space, and cost of treatment all depend upon amounts of carbon dioxide present.    Carbon dioxide is an important consideration in estimating chemical requirements for lime or lime–soda ash softening.

Most industrial wastes containing mineral acidity must be neutralized before they may be discharged to rivers or sewers or subjected to treatment of any kind.    Quantities of chemicals, size of chemical feeders, storage space, and costs are determined from laboratory data on acidity.

# 16. Alkalinity

## 16-1. General Considerations

The *alkalinity* of natural waters is due to the presence of salts of weak acids. Bicarbonates represent the major form of alkalinity since they are formed in considerable amounts from the action of carbon dioxide upon basic materials in the soil, as shown in Eq. (15-1). Other salts of weak acids, such as borates, silicates, and phosphates, may be present in small amounts. A few organic acids that are quite resistant to biological oxidation, for example, humic acid, form salts that add to the alkalinity of natural waters.

Under certain conditions natural waters may contain appreciable amounts of carbonate and hydroxide alkalinity. This condition is particularly true in surface waters where algae are flourishing. The algae remove carbon dioxide, free and combined, from the water to such an extent that pH values of 9 to 10 are often obtained. The chemistry involved is discussed in Sec. 16-7. Boiler waters always contain carbonate and hydroxide alkalinity. Chemically treated waters, particularly those produced in lime or lime–soda ash softening of water, contain carbonates and excess hydroxide.

From the discussion above, it should be obvious that alkalinity is caused by three major classes of materials which may be ranked in order of their effect on pH as follows: (1) hydroxides, (2) carbonates, and (3) bicarbonates and other salts of weak acids.

Since the alkalinity of natural waters is due principally to the salts of weak acids, such substances act as buffers, as discussed in Sec. 8-6. For this reason, alkalinity may be interpreted directly in terms of buffer capacity. It is used in this sense to a great extent in sewage and industrial waste treatment practice.

## 16-2. Sanitary Significance

As far as is known, the alkalinity of a water has little sanitary significance. Highly alkaline waters are usually unpalatable, and consumers

217

tend to seek other supplies.   Chemically treated waters sometimes have rather high pH values which have met with some objection on the part of consumers.   For these reasons, the U.S. Public Health Service has established standards on chemically treated waters.   These standards, relating to phenolphthalein and total and excess alkalinity, are too detailed to summarize here.

## 16-3. Method of Determining Alkalinity

Alkalinity is measured volumetrically by titration with $N/50$ $H_2SO_4$ and is reported in terms of equivalent $CaCO_3$.   For samples whose initial pH is above 8.3, the titration is made in two steps.   In the first step the titration is conducted until phenolphthalein indicator turns from pink to colorless.   The second phase of the titration is conducted with the aid of methyl orange or some other indicator to a pH of about 4.5. When the pH of a sample is less than 8.3, a single titration is made, using methyl orange as the indicator.

Alkalinity measurements can be made most satisfactorily by electrometric means, employing the glass-electrode pH meter.   This allows titration without use of internal indicators and makes it possible to terminate the titration at any desired pH, as discussed below in Sec. 16-4.

## 16-4. Methods of Expressing Alkalinity

Alkalinity measurements are made on a wide variety of materials. These range from relatively pure waters through polluted waters, such as sewage and industrial wastes, to digesting sludges.   The method of expressing alkalinity values varies considerably; therefore it is necessary to explain the methods in some detail and to indicate the areas where the various methods are employed.

**Phenolphthalein and Total Alkalinity.**   Inspection of the titration curves for a strong base (hydroxide alkalinity), shown in Fig. 4-3, and for sodium carbonate, in Fig. 4-5, shows that essentially all the hydroxide has been neutralized by the time the pH has been decreased to 10 and that the carbonate has been converted to bicarbonate by the time the pH has been lowered to about 8.3.   In a mixture containing both hydroxide and carbonate, the carbonate modifies the titration curve to the extent that only the inflection at pH 8.3 occurs, as shown in Fig. 16-1. Because of this, it has become common practice to express the alkalinity measured to the phenolphthalein end point as *phenolphthalein alkalinity*. This term is quite widely used at the present time in the field of sewage and industrial waste treatment and is still used to some extent in the area of water analysis.

If the titration of a sample that originally contained both carbonate and hydroxide alkalinity is continued beyond the phenolphthalein end point, the bicarbonates react with the acid and are converted to carbonic acid.   The reaction is essentially complete when the pH has been lowered to about 4.5.   See Fig. 16-1.   The amount of acid required to react with the hydroxide, carbonate, and bicarbonate represents the *total alkalinity*.

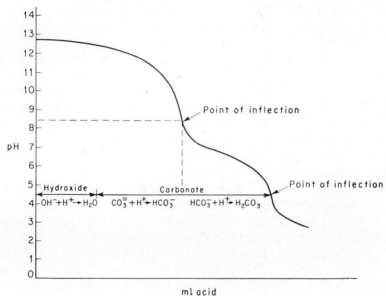

FIG. 16-1. Titration curve for a hydroxide-carbonate mixture.

It is customary to express alkalinity in terms of $CaCO_3$; therefore $N/50$ $H_2SO_4$ is used in its measurement.   Calculations are made as follows:

$$\text{Phenol. alk.} = (\text{ml } N/50 \text{ } H_2SO_4 \text{ to pH } 8.3) \frac{1{,}000}{\text{ml sample}} \qquad (16\text{-}1)$$

$$\text{Total alk.} = \text{total ml } N/50 \text{ } H_2SO_4 \text{ to pH} \begin{cases} 5.0 \\ 4.8 \\ 4.6 \\ 4.0 \end{cases} \times \frac{1{,}000}{\text{ml sample}} \qquad (16\text{-}2)$$

In the determination of total alkalinity, the pH at the stoichiometric end point is a function of the amount of carbonic acid produced in the reaction $H^+ + HCO_3^- \rightarrow H_2CO_3 \rightleftharpoons H_2O + CO_2$ and is directly related to the amount of carbonate alkalinity originally present in the sample.   The theoretical aspects are presented in Sec. 16-6.

**Hydroxide, Carbonate, and Bicarbonate Alkalinity.**   In water analysis it is often desirable to know the kinds and amounts of the various forms of alkalinity present.   This information is especially needed in water-softening processes and in boiler-water analysis.   It is customary to calculate hydroxide, carbonate, and bicarbonate alkalinities from the fundamental information given by the titration curves for strong bases and sodium carbonate.   See Figs. 4-3 and 4-5.   Formulas have been developed for the calculation of the various forms of alkalinity from phenolphthalein and total alkalinities.   They are intended for the use of technicians and others who do not have a knowledge of the fundamental chemistry involved.   It seems important that sanitary engineers as well as chemists understand the basis of these formulas.   If the fundamental chemistry is understood, there is no need to remember the formulas.

Early concepts concerning alkalinity held that five possible situations could be present, which were as follows: (1) hydroxide only, (2) carbonate only, (3) hydroxide plus carbonate, (4) carbonate plus bicarbonate, and (5) bicarbonate only.   Reference to Figs. 4-3 and 4-5 will demonstrate that neutralization of hydroxides is complete by the time enough acid has been added to decrease the pH to 8.3 and that a carbonate is exactly one-half neutralized when its pH has been decreased to the same degree. Upon continuation of the titration to reach a pH of about 4.5, a negligible amount of acid is needed in the case of the hydroxide and an amount exactly equal to that needed to reach pH 8.3 is required for the carbonate. This is the fundamental information needed to determine which forms of alkalinity are present and the amounts of each.   A graphical representation of typical titrations obtained with the various combinations of alkalinity is shown in Fig. 16-2.

*Hydroxide Only.*   Samples containing only hydroxide alkalinity have a high pH, usually well above 10.   Titration is essentially complete at the phenolphthalein end point.   In this case hydroxide alkalinity is equal to the phenolphthalein alkalinity.

*Carbonate Only.*   Samples containing only carbonate alkalinity have a pH of 9.5 or higher.   The titration to the phenolphthalein end point is exactly equal to one-half of the total titration.   In this case carbonate alkalinity is equal to the total alkalinity.

*Hydroxide-Carbonate.*   Samples containing hydroxide and carbonate alkalinity have a high pH, usually well above 10.   The titration from the phenolphthalein to the methyl orange end point represents one-half of the carbonate alkalinity.   Therefore carbonate alkalinity may be calculated as follows:

$$\text{Carbonate alk.} = 2 \text{ (titration from phenol. to methyl orange)} \times \frac{1,000}{\text{ml sample}}$$

and          Hydroxide alk. = total alk. − carbonate alk.

*Carbonate-Bicarbonate.*   Samples containing carbonate and bicarbonate alkalinity have a pH > 8.3 and usually less than 11.   The titration to the phenolphthalein end point represents one-half of the carbonate. Carbonate alkalinity may be calculated as follows:

$$\text{Carbonate alk.} = 2 \text{ (titration to phenol end point)} \times \frac{1,000}{\text{ml sample}}$$

and                    Bicarbonate alk. = total alk. − carbonate alk.

*Bicarbonate Only.* Samples containing only bicarbonate alkalinity have a pH of 8.3 or less, usually less. In this case bicarbonate alkalinity is equal to the total alkalinity.

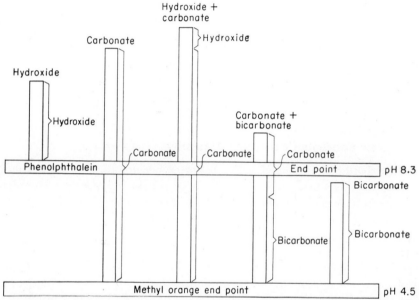

Fig. 16-2. Graphical representation of titration of samples containing various forms of alkalinity.

The foregoing methods of approximate calculation have been superseded by the more precise formulas described in Sec. 16-6.

## 16-5. Application of Alkalinity Data

Information concerning alkalinity is used in a variety of ways in sanitary engineering practice.

**Chemical Coagulation.** Chemicals used for coagulation of water, sewage, and industrial wastes react with water to form insoluble hydroxide precipitates. The hydrogen ions released react with the alkalinity of the water. Thus the alkalinity acts to buffer the water in a pH range where the coagulant can be effective. Alkalinity must be present in excess of that destroyed by the acid released by the coagulant for effective and complete coagulation to occur.

**Water Softening.**   Alkalinity is a major item that must be considered in calculating the lime and soda-ash requirements in softening of water by precipitation methods.   The alkalinity of softened water is a consideration as to whether such waters meet U.S. Public Health Service Standards.

**Corrosion Control.**   Alkalinity is an important parameter involved in corrosion control.   It must be known in order to calculate the Langelier saturation index.

**Buffer Capacity.**   Alkalinity measurements are made as a means of evaluating the buffering capacity of sewage, industrial wastes, and sludges.

**Industrial Wastes.**   Many regulatory agencies prohibit the discharge of wastes containing caustic (hydroxide) alkalinity to receiving waters. Municipal authorities usually prohibit the discharge of wastes containing caustic alkalinity to sewers.   Alkalinity as well as pH is an important factor in determining the amenability of waste waters to biological treatment.

## 16-6. New Concepts Concerning Alkalinity

With the development of ionic theory, it became obvious that some of the original concepts concerning alkalinity relationships were incomplete. For example, when sodium carbonate is dissolved in distilled water, the resulting solution normally has a pH of about 11.   In light of modern theory, this means that the resulting solution has a $[H^+] = 10^{-11}$ or a $[OH^-]$ of $10^{-3}$.   Obviously, the hydroxyl ions have to come from the water, and the hydrogen ions released in their formation have to disappear in some manner.   The modern conception of what happens is that the carbonate ion combines with the hydrogen ions of water,

$$CO_3^= + H_2O \rightleftharpoons HCO_3^- + OH^- \qquad (16\text{-}3)$$

to form bicarbonate ion in conformance with the second ionization constant of carbonic acid.   As the hydrogen-ion concentration is reduced in amount,

$$\frac{[H^+][CO_3^=]}{[HCO_3^-]} = K_2 = 10^{-11} \qquad (16\text{-}4)$$

more water must dissociate to maintain $K_w = 10^{-14}$.   This dissociation results in an increase of the hydroxyl-ion concentration.   The net result of the action of the carbonate ion is to produce a solution of high pH value.

From Eq. (16-3), it is obvious that any solution containing carbonate ion must also contain significant amounts of hydroxyl and bicarbonate ion.   It may be argued that the total alkalinity is the same and equal to the carbonate alkalinity. As far as considerations of alkalinity are concerned, there is little reason to worry how the carbonate ion behaves in water. However, water chemists and engineers concerned with water softening, corrosion control, and prevention of scaling at elevated pH levels are vitally concerned with ionic species and concentrations. For these reasons it has become necessary to be able to calculate hydroxyl-, carbonate-, and bicarbonate-ion concentrations at all pH levels with considerable accuracy. This is usually done from pH and alkalinity data.

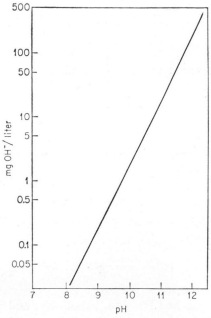

### Calculation of Hydroxyl-, Carbonate-, and Bicarbonate-ion Concentrations from pH and Alkalinity Data.[1]

These calculations apply in systems with pH levels above 8.0 where all three ions coexist and occur in significant amounts.

*Hydroxide.* The hydroxyl-ion concentration can be calculated directly from pH values, provided that the temperature is known so that the proper $K_w$ for water can be used.

FIG. 16-3. Relationship between hydroxyl-ion concentration and pH at 25°C.

$$[OH^-] = \frac{K_w}{[H^+]}$$

$$OH^- \text{ (in mg/l)} = [OH^-] \times 17{,}000 \qquad (16\text{-}5)$$

Figure 16-3 shows the relationship between pH and milligrams of hydroxyl ion per liter at 25°C. It will be noted that a pH of 9.5 must be reached before the hydroxyl-ion concentration reaches 0.5 mg/l.

*Carbonate and Bicarbonate.* The concentration of carbonate ion in terms of milligrams per liter can be calculated from the equation

$$CO_3^= \text{ (in mg/l)} = \frac{3.37 \times 10^{-6}}{[H^+]} \frac{\left( \dfrac{\text{alkalinity}}{50{,}000} + [H^+] - \dfrac{K_w}{[H^+]} \right)}{1 + \dfrac{11.22 \times 10^{-11}}{[H^+]}} \qquad (16\text{-}6)$$

and the concentration of bicarbonate ion in milligrams per liter can be

[1] E. W. Moore, *J. Am. Water Works Assoc.*, **31**, 51 (1939).

calculated from the equation

$$HCO_3^- \text{ (in mg/l)} = \frac{61,000 \left[ \dfrac{\text{alkalinity}}{50,000} + [H^+] - \dfrac{K_w}{[H^+]} \right]}{1 + \dfrac{11.22 \times 10^{-11}}{[H^+]}} \quad (16\text{-}7)$$

Since the value of $K_w$ varies quite radically with temperature and ionic concentration, it is important to use values corrected to the conditions involved. These corrections are rather tedious; consequently "Standard Methods" presents nomographs for the evaluation of carbonate and bicarbonate. The nomographs yield results in terms of alkalinity expressed as $CaCO_3$. Conversions to milligrams per liter of $CO_3^=$ or $HCO_3^-$ are as follows:

$$\text{mg/l } CO_3^= = \text{mg/l carbonate alk.} \times 0.6 \quad (16\text{-}8)$$
$$\text{mg/l } HCO_3^- = \text{mg/l bicarbonate alk.} \times 1.22 \quad (16\text{-}9)$$

Molar concentrations may be obtained by dividing milligrams per liter by the mole ionic weight in milligrams.

$$\frac{\text{mg/l } CO_3^=}{60,000} \quad \text{and} \quad \frac{\text{mg/l } HCO_3^-}{61,000}$$

**Carbon Dioxide, Alkalinity, and pH Relationships in Natural Waters.** From the equations

$$CO_2 + H_2O \rightleftharpoons H_2CO_3 \rightleftharpoons HCO_3^- + H^+ \quad (16\text{-}10)$$
$$M(HCO_3)_2 \rightleftharpoons M^{++} + 2HCO_3^- \quad (16\text{-}11)$$
$$HCO_3^- \rightleftharpoons CO_3^= + H^+ \quad (16\text{-}12)$$
$$CO_3^= + H_2O \rightleftharpoons HCO_3^- + OH^- \quad (16\text{-}3)$$

it is obvious that carbon dioxide and the three forms of alkalinity are all part of one system that exists in equilibrium, since all equations involve $HCO_3^-$. A change in concentration of any one member of the system will, of course, cause a shift in the equilibrium, alter the concentration of the other ions, and result in a change of pH. Conversely, a change in pH will shift the relationships. Figure 16-4 shows the relationship between carbon dioxide and the three forms of alkalinity in a water with 100 mg/l of total alkalinity, over the pH range of importance in sanitary engineering practice. The information given in Fig. 16-4 is for illustrative purposes only, as the relationships differ with total alkalinity, temperature, etc.

**Measurement of Total Alkalinity.** In Sec. 4-4, the fundamentals were developed for the selection of indicators in acidimetry and alkalimetry. The point was made that the indicator must show when the stoichiometric end point has been reached. In the measurement of total alkalinity, the final stage of the titration is

$$H^+ + HCO_3^- \rightarrow H_2CO_3 \tag{16-13}$$

Thus the indicator used must not be affected by the acid titrant until all bicarbonate ion can be considered to be converted to carbonic acid. The pH at which this occurs varies with the amount of bicarbonate ion present since

$$K_1 = \frac{[H^+][HCO_3^-]}{[H_2CO_3]} \tag{16-14}$$

The value for $K_1$ is about $4.3 \times 10^{-7}$ at normal laboratory temperature.

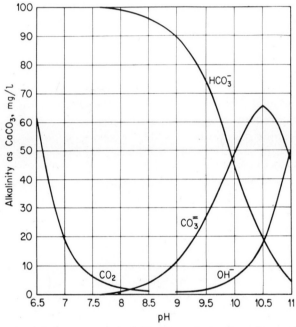

Fig. 16-4. Relationship between carbon dioxide and the three forms of alkalinity at various pH levels.   (Values calculated for a water with a total alkalinity of 100 mg/l at 25°C.)

The pH at the stoichiometric end point for any alkalinity can be determined by the equation

$$pH = \log \frac{1}{K_1} - \log \frac{[H_2CO_3]}{[HCO_3^-]} \tag{16-15}$$

but evaluation of the molar concentrations of carbonic acid and bicarbonate ion at the equivalence point is difficult to assess and becomes a matter of personal choice.   For this reason, the considerations above are largely of theoretical interest.

The actual pH of the stoichiometric end point in alkalinity determinations can be best determined by electrometric titration. This fact is particularly important in natural waters where the total alkalinity is a summation of the effects resulting from salts of weak acids of which bicarbonates are only one. The pH at which the inflection in the titration curve occurs (see Fig. 16-1) is taken as the true end point. The pH values given for the equivalence points for various alkalinities in "Standard Methods" hold only for essentially pure bicarbonate solutions and should not be applied indiscriminately to sewage, industrial wastes, or even natural waters.

### 16-7. Other Considerations of Interest to Sanitary Engineers

The sanitary engineer encounters a number of situations in practice which involve carbon dioxide–alkalinity–pH relationships that often require explanation.

**pH Changes during Aeration of Water.** It is common practice to aerate water to remove carbon dioxide. On the basis of Eq. (16-10) it would be predicted that relatively pure water with a pH of about 7 would result. This prediction is true if distilled water is involved. In natural waters containing bicarbonate salts, however, removal of free carbon dioxide results in a water that is buffered by bicarbonates at a pH of about 8.3, as shown in Fig. 16-4.

**pH Changes in the Presence of Algal Blooms.** Many surface waters support extensive algal blooms. pH values as high as 10 have been observed in areas where algae are growing rapidly, particularly in shallow water. Since algae use carbon dioxide in their photosynthetic activity, removal of carbon dioxide must be responsible for the development of such high pH conditions. We have seen above that removal of free carbon dioxide allows the pH to increase to about 8.3. For higher pH levels to develop it is necessary for carbon dioxide to be abstracted from the bicarbonates present.

In natural waters containing bicarbonates the following equilibrium exists:

$$M^{++} + [2HCO_3^- \rightleftharpoons CO_2 + CO_3^= + H_2O] \qquad (16\text{-}16)$$

The carbon dioxide existing in this equilibrium is available to the algae. As it is removed, the carbonate-ion concentration increases. This produces two effects. The carbonate ion, of course, is always in equilibrium with the bicarbonate ion and hydroxyl ion, as shown in Eq. (16-3).

$$CO_3^= + H_2O \rightleftharpoons HCO_3^- + OH^- \qquad (16\text{-}3)$$

An increase in carbonate ion results in an increased hydroxyl-ion concentration and, therefore, an increase in pH. In natural waters containing appreciable amounts of $Ca^{++}$, calcium carbonate precipitates when the carbonate-ion concentration becomes great enough to exceed its solubility product.

$$Ca^{++} + CO_3^= \rightarrow \underline{CaCO_3} \qquad (16\text{-}17)$$

This precipitation usually happens before pH levels have exceeded 10, and it places a ceiling over the pH values obtainable. The calcium carbonate precipitated as a result of removal of carbon dioxide through algal action produces the marl deposits in our lakes. Marl deposits are the precursors of limestone.

**Alkalinity of Boiler Waters.** Boiler waters contain both carbonate and hydroxide alkalinity. Both are derived from bicarbonates in the feed water. Simple boiling of natural waters results in removal of carbon dioxide with the steam and the bicarbonate is converted completely to carbonate because the carbon dioxide is lost from the sphere of the reaction.

$$M^{++} + 2HCO_3^- \rightarrow M^{++} + CO_3^= + CO_2\uparrow + H_2O \qquad (16\text{-}18)$$

The carbonate ion, of course, exists in equilibrium with bicarbonate and hydroxyl ions [Eq. (16-3)]. Under the high temperatures that prevail in most boilers, significant amounts of carbon dioxide are removed from the bicarbonates involved in the latter equilibrium. As a result, part of the carbonate alkalinity is converted to hydroxide alkalinity. Complete conversion is prevented by high pH levels which often exceed 11.0.

# 17. Chemical Coagulation of Water

## 17-1. General Considerations

Chemical coagulation is an important process applied extensively in water treatment practice, particularly where surface supplies are involved. It is used to some extent in sewage and industrial waste treatment also. Although chemical coagulation cannot be classed as an analytical procedure, laboratory studies employing it provide an excellent opportunity to practice color, turbidity, pH, carbon dioxide, and alkalinity measurements which have been the object of attention up to this point. Furthermore, it provides an opportunity for students to become familiar with an important process which they may miss unless they pursue more advanced courses in sanitary engineering.

## 17-2. Purposes of Chemical Coagulation

Chemical coagulation of waters is performed for several reasons. The major ones are removal of (1) turbidity, inorganic and organic; (2) color, true and apparent; (3) harmful bacteria and other pathogens; (4) algae and other plankton organisms; and (5) taste- and odor-producing substances. Removal of these materials produces a water that is aesthetically acceptable and that can be disinfected properly. In addition, the clarified water is rendered much more amenable to filtration through sand filters.

## 17-3. Nature of Suspended Matter in Water

Much of the suspended matter in water is colloidal in nature. This is particularly true of substances that cause color and turbidity. The colloidal materials are negatively charged and for this reason the salts of trivalent metals, usually iron and aluminum, are used to coagulate them. The sulfates are normally used to provide a divalent negative ion for reasons discussed in Sec. 7-2.

### 17-4. Fundamental Reactions Involved in Chemical Coagulation

The reactions involved in chemical coagulation are essentially the same for both ferric and aluminum sulfates. Since aluminum sulfate, usually called filter alum [$Al_2(SO_4)_3 \cdot 14H_2O$],[1] is most commonly used, its action will be discussed.

**Flash Mix.** When aluminum sulfate solutions are added to water, the molecules dissociate to yield $Al^{3+}$ and $SO_4^=$. The $Al^{3+}$ may combine with negatively charged colloids to neutralize part of the charge on the colloidal particle,

$$Al^{3+} + {}^-\overline{(colloid)}^- \longrightarrow Al\overline{(colloid)}^- \qquad (17\text{-}1)$$

thereby reducing the zeta potential to a value where agglomeration of the colloidal particles can occur. The $Al^{3+}$ may also combine with $OH^-$ in the water to form aluminum hydroxide.

$$Al^{3+} + 3OH^- \rightarrow Al(OH)_3 \qquad (17\text{-}2)$$

and $$Al(OH)_3 + \text{positive ions} \rightarrow [Al(OH)_3]^+ \qquad (17\text{-}3)$$

The aluminum hydroxide as formed is colloidal in character; hence it adsorbs positive ions from solution to form a positively charged sol. The aluminum hydroxide sol, being positively charged, is active in neutralizing the charge on negative colloids and aids in completing the agglomeration of the negative colloids.

$$[Al(OH)_3]^+ + {}^-\overline{(colloid)}^= \longrightarrow Al(OH)_3\overline{(colloid)}^= \qquad (17\text{-}4)$$

An excess of the aluminum hydroxide sol is always formed, and its destruction and eventual precipitation are brought about by the sulfate ions and other negative ions in the water.

$$[Al(OH)_3]^+ + SO_4^= \rightarrow \underline{Al(OH)_3} + \text{adsorbed sulfates} \qquad (17\text{-}5)$$

Since the trivalent aluminum ion is much more effective than the $[Al(OH)_3]^+$ sol in reducing the zeta potential on negative colloids and because $[Al(OH)_3]^+$ sol is best formed in very dilute solution, it is important that the aluminum sulfate be distributed rapidly throughout the mass of water in order that contact can be made with all the colloidal particles before other less desirable changes occur. This distribution is accomplished by means of a flash mix which is designed to give good

---

[1] Actually filter alum is a dehydrated form of $Al_2(SO_4)_3 \cdot 18H_2O$ and has water of hydration corresponding to about 14.3 moles. Its molecular weight is usually given a value of 600.

distribution of the coagulant and should be accomplished as rapidly as possible, in a period not to exceed 10 sec.

**Flocculation.**    During the flocculation period, which usually lasts 20 to 30 min, agglomeration of colloidal materials is completed and they become incorporated in the mass of precipitated floc.    During the sedimentation period, the entire floc settles to leave a clarified liquid.

**Chemistry.**    The discussion above describes the physical aspects of coagulation but does not indicate in a quantitative way the changes that occur with regard to pH, alkalinity, etc.    The changes can be best illustrated by considering certain equations.    When aluminum sulfate is added to water, it combines with the hydroxyl ions of water to form poorly ionized $Al(OH)_3$, hydrogen, and sulfate ions.

$$Al_2(SO_4)_3 + 6H_2O \rightarrow 2Al(OH)_3 + 6H^+ + 3SO_4^= \qquad (17\text{-}6)$$

The hydrogen ions depress the pH to such an extent that further formation of $Al(OH)_3$ is prevented unless they are removed from the solution.    The bicarbonates present in natural waters serve as buffers and act in this capacity as follows:

$$HCO_3^- + H^+ \rightarrow H_2CO_3 \rightleftharpoons CO_2 + H_2O \qquad (17\text{-}7)$$

In order to develop the quantitative aspects, it is best to write the equations in molecular form as follows:

$$Al_2(SO_4)_3 + 6H_2O \rightarrow 2\underline{Al(OH)_3} + 3H_2SO_4 \qquad (17\text{-}6)$$
$$\underline{3Ca(HCO_3)_2 + 3H_2SO_4 \rightarrow 3CaSO_4 + 6CO_2 + 6H_2O} \qquad (17\text{-}8)$$
$$Al_2(SO_4)_3 + 3Ca(HCO_3)_2 \rightarrow 2\underline{Al(OH)_3} + 3CaSO_4 + 6CO_2 \qquad (17\text{-}9)$$

Addition of Eqs. (17-6) and (17-8) yields Eq. (17-9) which is the well-known equation given in most textbooks on water treatment.    For weight relationships Eq. (17-9) should be written

$$\underset{600}{Al_2(SO_4)_3 \cdot 14H_2O} + \underset{3 \times 100 \,=\, 300}{3Ca(HCO_3)_2}$$
$$\rightarrow \underline{Al(OH)_3} + 3CaSO_4 + \underset{6 \times 44 \,=\, 264}{6CO_2} \qquad (17\text{-}10)$$

The molecular weight of filter alum is approximately 600.    Calcium bicarbonate represents alkalinity, which is always expressed as $CaCO_3$ with a molecular weight of 100.    From these weight relationships, it will be seen that

> 600 parts of alum will destroy 300 parts of alkalinity, or
> 1 mg/l of alum will destroy 0.5 mg/l of alkalinity, and
> 600 parts of alum will produce 264 parts of $CO_2$, or
> 1 mg/l of alum will produce 0.44 mg/l of $CO_2$

Inspection of Eq. (17-10) shows that calcium bicarbonate is converted to calcium sulfate; thus some carbonate hardness is changed to noncarbonate hardness during chemical coagulation and represents a definite disadvantage.

## 17-5. Optimum pH for Chemical Coagulation

The optimum pH for removal of negative colloids varies somewhat with the nature of the water but usually falls in the range of pH 5.0 to 6.5. The solubility product of $Fe(OH)_3$ is $1.1 \times 10^{-36}$ and that for $Al(OH)_3$ is $1.9 \times 10^{-33}$; consequently both are quite completely precipitated at pH levels as low as 5, and very little $Fe^{3+}$ or $Al^{3+}$ remains in the coagulated water. The solubility curves for ferric and aluminum hydroxides are shown in Fig. 17-1. From them it will be noted that at pH levels below

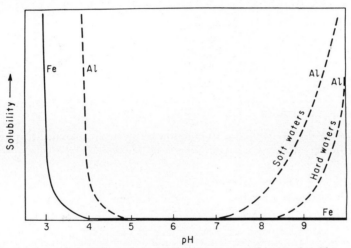

FIG. 17-1. Solubility curves for ferric and aluminum hydroxides.

4 the $[OH^-]$ is insufficient to precipitate $Fe^{3+}$ completely. $Al^{3+}$ is incompletely precipitated at pH levels below 5 for the same reason. These facts indicate why it is essential to have a residual alkalinity during chemical coagulation. The residual alkalinity serves to buffer the system at pH levels above 5 and ensures complete precipitation of the coagulating ions.

It will be noted that the solubility curve for $Al(OH)_3$ trends upward at pH levels of 7 to 9. This is because it is amphoteric in character and tends to form aluminate ion at high pH values. A discussion of amphoteric hydroxides is presented in Sec. 3-5.

## 17-6. Significance of Laboratory Studies on Chemical Coagulation

Laboratory studies of chemical coagulation are often required to determine the best chemical or combination of chemicals and amounts needed to accomplish a desired objective in water, sewage, and industrial waste treatment practice.   The results obtained serve as a basis of design and of operation of treatment facilities.   A recommended laboratory procedure is as follows:

1. Place a series of 1- or 2-liter samples in beakers or preferably in square glass jars.

2. Prepare a solution of the coagulant of such strength that 1 ml contains 10 mg of coagulant.

3. Add the desired amount of coagulant to each sample while stirring the sample vigorously.   Continue the flash mix for 10 sec.

4. Flocculate the samples for 20 to 30 min on a paddle stirrer operating at 30 to 40 rpm.

5. Let the samples stand for 30 min; then siphon the clarified water into clean containers for analysis.

6. Analyze for pH, color, turbidity, alkalinity, $CO_2$, and other information that is pertinent.   Residual turbidity sometimes interferes with the determination of color.   Filtration through a sand filter is recommended to remove the turbidity in such cases.

## 17-7. Coagulant Aids

Many waters are difficult to coagulate by the simple addition of aluminum or ferric salts.   Activated silica, and more recently certain materials called polyelectrolytes, are added to stimulate floc formation.   Activated silica is a negatively charged sol and acts to aid in flocculation of the positively charged metallic hydroxide sol formed by the metallic salt.

Polyelectrolytes are water-soluble high-molecular-weight polymers that contain groups capable of undergoing electrolytic dissociation to give large highly charged ions.   Polymers that dissociate to form negatively charged polymeric ions, such as those with carboxylic groups, are called *anionic* polymers.   Polymers having amino groups that dissociate to form positively charged ions are called *cationic* polymers.   Some polymers dissociate to yield both large positive ions and large negative ions.   These are erroneously referred to as nonionic polymers.

The polyelectrolytes when serving as coagulant aids undoubtedly act to reduce the stability of colloidal systems and to facilitate their coagulation.   The use of polyelectrolytes as coagulant aids has not been reduced to an exact science.   This shortcoming may be attributed to the fact that they are of three widely differing classes.   Furthermore, they are applied to a wide variety of materials possessing markedly different characteristics.

# 18. Hardness

## 18-1. General Considerations

*Hard waters* are generally considered to be those waters that require considerable amounts of soap to produce a foam or lather and that also produce scale in hot-water pipes, heaters, boilers, and other units in which the temperature of water is increased materially. To the layman, the soap-consuming capacity is most important because of economic aspects and because of the difficulty encountered in obtaining suitable conditions for optimum cleansing; to the engineer, the scaling problem is the most challenging.

With the advent of synthetic detergents, many of the disadvantages of hard waters for household use have been diminished. However, soap is preferred for some types of laundering and for personal hygiene, and hard waters remain as objectionable as ever for these purposes. The scaling problem continues to be a consideration in spite of advances in our knowledge of water chemistry and the development of many proprietary devices which are claimed to prevent scaling through the application of principles not fully explainable.

Although there is less demand today, from the general public, for the removal of hardness through water-softening processes, the need is still great. The trend is toward private and industrial installations in preference to municipal softening plants, except where hardness is considered unreasonably high.

The hardness of waters varies considerably from place to place. In general, surface waters are softer than ground waters. The hardness of water reflects the nature of the geological formations with which it has been in contact. Figure 18-1 shows the general character of the water supplies in the United States. The softest waters are found in the New England, South Atlantic, and Pacific Northwest states. Iowa, Illinois, Indiana, Arizona, New Mexico, and the Great Plains states have the hardest waters.

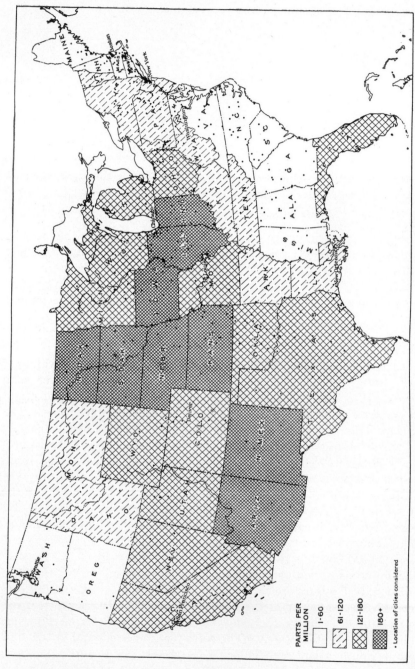

FIG. 18-1. Hardness characteristics of U.S. water supplies. *(From U.S. Geol. Survey Paper 658.)*

Waters are commonly classified in terms of the degree of hardness, as follows:

| | |
|---|---|
| 0– 75 mg/l | Soft |
| 75–150 mg/l | Moderately hard |
| 150–300 mg/l | Hard |
| 300 up  mg/l | Very hard |

## 18-2. Cause and Source of Hardness

*Hardness* is caused by divalent metallic ions that are capable of reacting with soap to form precipitates and with certain anions present in the water to form scale.   The principal divalent cations are calcium, magnesium, strontium, ferrous iron, and manganous ion.   These ions, plus the most important anions, are shown in Table 18-1 in the order of their relative abundance in natural waters.   Aluminum and ferric ions are sometimes considered as contributing to the hardness of water.   Their solubility is so limited at the pH values of natural waters that ionic concentrations are negligible.

TABLE 18-1. PRINCIPAL CATIONS CAUSING HARDNESS IN WATER AND THE
MAJOR ANIONS ASSOCIATED WITH THEM

| Cations causing hardness | Anions |
|---|---|
| $Ca^{++}$ | $HCO_3^-$ |
| $Mg^{++}$ | $SO_4^=$ |
| $Sr^{++}$ | $Cl^-$ |
| $Fe^{++}$ | $NO_3^-$ |
| $Mn^{++}$ | $SiO_3^=$ |

The hardness in water is derived largely from contact with the soil and rock formations.   Rain water as it falls upon the earth is incapable of dissolving the tremendous amounts of solids found in many natural waters.   The ability to dissolve is gained in the soil where carbon dioxide is released by bacterial action.   The soil water becomes highly charged with carbon dioxide which, of course, exists in equilibrium with carbonic acid.   Under the low pH conditions that develop, basic materials, particularly limestone formations, are dissolved.   Figure 18-2 shows where the carbon dioxide originates and how it attacks the insoluble carbonates in the soil and in limestone formations to convert them to soluble bicarbonates.   Since limestone is not pure carbonate but includes impurities such as sulfates, chlorides, silicates, etc., these materials become exposed to the solvent action of the water as the carbonates are dissolved and they pass into solution also.

In general, hard waters originate in areas where the topsoil is thick and limestone formations are present.   Soft waters originate in areas where the topsoil is thin and limestone formations are sparse or absent.

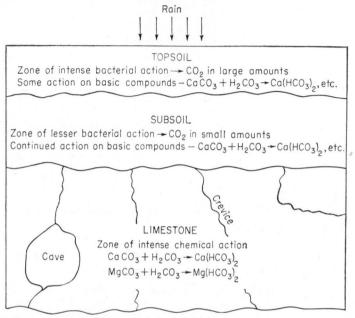

FIG. 18-2. Source of carbon dioxide and the solution of substances causing hardness.

## 18-3. Sanitary Significance

Hard waters are as satisfactory for human consumption as soft waters. Because of their adverse action with soap, their use for cleansing purposes is quite unsatisfactory, unless soap costs are disregarded.

## 18-4. Methods of Determination

Hardness is normally expressed in terms of $CaCO_3$. Many methods of determination have been proposed over the course of the years. Three are presently used.

**Calculation Method.** Perhaps the most accurate method of determining hardness is by calculation based upon the divalent ions found by a complete analysis. This method is to be preferred where complete analyses are available, but unfortunately such analyses are not made routinely. Seldom are complete analyses made except in exploratory work.

Recently it has been shown that some hard waters contain appreciable amounts of strontium. Unless it is analyzed for separately, it will be measured as calcium, and calculations of hardness based upon such limited analysis may be in considerable error.

Calculation of the hardness caused by each ion is performed by use of the general formula

$$\text{Hardness (in mg/l) as } CaCO_3 = M^{++} \text{ (in mg/l)} \times \frac{50}{\text{eq. wt of } M^{++}} \quad (18\text{-}1)$$

where $M^{++}$ represents any divalent metallic ion.

**Soap Method.** The soap method is one of the oldest ways of determining hardness. In reality, it is a measure of the soap-consuming power of a water, or, more exactly, a measure of the power of the water to precipitate soap. The reactions involved may be represented in general as follows:

$$M^{++} + 2Na \text{ soap} \rightarrow \underline{M(\text{soap})_2} + 2Na^+ \quad (18\text{-}2)$$

Although ordinary sodium soaps are a mixture of the salts of several fatty acids, sodium palmitate will serve more exactly to illustrate the action between metallic ions causing hardness and soap.

$$M^{++} + 2C_{15}H_{31}COONa \rightarrow \underline{M(C_{15}H_{31}COO)_2} + 2Na^+ \quad (18\text{-}3)$$

The soap method of determining hardness is empirical in nature. In spite of this, it is capable of producing reasonably accurate results in the hands of experienced analysts. It has been replaced largely by a compleximetric method where precise determinations are required, but it is still used for routine control work and as a field method. The accuracy of the results obtained by this method may be increased to a maximum by attention to several details which include (1) use of a pure castile soap, (2) careful determination of the lather factor, (3) use of a standard hardness solution that contains calcium and magnesium ions in about the same ratio as the water to be tested, (4) adjustment of the pH of samples in the range of 8 to 8.5, and (5) limitation of titrations to 5 ml.

**Compleximetric, or EDTA, Method.** The compleximetric method involves the use of solutions of ethylenediaminetetraacetic acid (EDTA) or its sodium salt as the titrating agent.

HOOC—CH₂            CH₂COOH

          H  H

      N—C—C—N

          H  H

HOOC—CH₂            CH₂COOH

Acid

NaOOC—CH₂          CH₂—COONa

          H  H

      N—C—C—N

          H  H

NaOOC—CH₂          CH₂—COONA

Sodium salt

These compounds, usually represented by EDTA, are chelating agents and form extremely stable complex ions with $Ca^{++}$, $Mg^{++}$, and other divalent ions causing hardness, as shown in the equation

$$M^{++} + EDTA \rightarrow [M \cdot EDTA]_{complex} \tag{18-4}$$

The successful use of EDTA for determining hardness depends upon having an indicator present to show when EDTA is present in excess, or when all the ions causing hardness have been complexed.

The dye known as Chrome Black T serves as an excellent indicator to show when all the hardness ions have been complexed. When a small amount of Chrome Black T, having a blue color, is added to a hard water, it combines with a few of the $Ca^{++}$ and $Mg^{++}$ ions to form a weak complex ion which is wine red in color, as shown in the equation

$$M^{++} + \text{Chrome Black T} \rightarrow (\text{M Chrome Black T}) \tag{18-5}$$
$$\text{Wine red complex}$$

During the titration with EDTA, all free hardness ions are complexed according to Eq. (18-4). Finally the EDTA disrupts the red (M Chrome Black T) complex because it is capable of forming a more stable complex with the hardness ions. This action frees the Chrome Black T indicator, and the wine red color changes to a distinct blue color, heralding the end of the titration.

Although the EDTA method is subject to certain interferences, most of them can be overcome by proper modifications. The method yields very precise and accurate results. It is the method of choice in most laboratories at the present time.

## 18-5. Types of Hardness

In addition to total hardness, it is desirable and sometimes necessary to know the types of hardness present. Hardness is classified in two ways: (1) with respect to the metallic ion and (2) with respect to the anions associated with the metallic ions.

**Calcium and Magnesium Hardness.** In some considerations it is important to know the amounts of calcium and magnesium hardness in water. For example, it is necessary to know the magnesium hardness or the amount of $Mg^{++}$ in order to calculate lime requirements in lime–soda ash softening. The calcium and magnesium hardness may be calculated from the complete chemical analysis, as discussed in Sec. 18-4. Such information is not always available, and recourse is made to some method of analysis that allows separate measurement of calcium or magnesium hardness. If calcium hardness is determined, magnesium hardness is obtained by subtracting calcium hardness from total hardness, as follows:

$$\text{Total hardness} - \text{calcium hardness} = \text{magnesium hardness} \tag{18-6}$$

This procedure yields reasonably reliable results because most of the hardness in natural waters is due to these two cations.   Any method for measuring calcium hardness will also include strontium hardness.

**Carbonate and Noncarbonate Hardness.**   The part of the total hardness that is chemically equivalent to the bicarbonates present in a water is considered to be *carbonate hardness*.   Since bicarbonate is usually measured as alkalinity and expressed in terms of $CaCO_3$, the alkalinity of most natural waters is considered to be equal to the carbonate hardness.

$$\text{Alkalinity (in mg/l)} = \text{carbonate hardness (in mg/l)} \qquad (18\text{-}7)$$

The bicarbonates are singled out for special recognition because they serve as a source of carbonate ions to precipitate $Ca^{++}$ as $CaCO_3$ at elevated temperatures such as occur in boilers or during the softening process with lime.

$$Ca^{++} + 2HCO_3^- \overset{\Delta}{\rightarrow} \underline{CaCO_3} + CO_2\uparrow + H_2O \qquad (18\text{-}8)$$

$$Ca^{++} + 2HCO_3^- + Ca(OH)_2 \rightarrow 2\underline{CaCO_3} + 2H_2O \qquad (18\text{-}9)$$

It may also be considered as that part of the total hardness that originates from the action of carbonic acid on limestone, as illustrated in Fig. 18-2.   Carbonate hardness was formerly called *temporary hardness* because it can be caused to precipitate by prolonged boiling [see Eq. (18-8)].

All hardness not chemically related to bicarbonates is *noncarbonate hardness*.   It is generally considered to be due to sulfates, chlorides, nitrates, etc., of the metallic ions causing hardness.   The amount of noncarbonate hardness is normally calculated by subtracting the alkalinity from the total hardness.

$$\text{Total hardness} - \text{alkalinity} = \text{noncarbonate hardness (NCH)} \qquad (18\text{-}10)$$

Since both are expressed in terms of $CaCO_3$, the subtraction can be made directly.   This is an excellent example of the reason why alkalinity is normally expressed in terms of $CaCO_3$.   Noncarbonate hardness was formerly called *permanent hardness* because it cannot be removed or precipitated by boiling.

**Negative Noncarbonate Hardness.**   Certain natural waters, particularly alkali waters, contain alkalinity in excess of the total hardness, and when a calculation is made according to Eq. (18-10) a negative value is obtained.   The result is termed *negative noncarbonate hardness*.   This means that more bicarbonate ions are present than are needed to satisfy the divalent metallic ions present.   The excess bicarbonate ions are related to monovalent metallic ions such as $Na^+$ and $K^+$.

**Pseudo-hardness.**  Sea, brackish, and other waters that contain appreciable amounts of $Na^+$ interfere with the normal behavior of soap because of the common ion effect.  This effect is said to be due to *pseudo-hardness*.

## 18-6.  Application of Hardness Data in Sanitary Engineering Practice

Hardness of a water is an important consideration in determining the suitability of a water for domestic and industrial uses.  The engineer uses it as a basis of recommending the need for softening processes.  The relative amounts of carbonate and noncarbonate hardness present in a water are a factor in determining the most economical type of softening process to use and become an important consideration in design.  Determinations of hardness serve as a basis for routine control of softening processes.

# 19. Water Softening

## 19-1. General Considerations

Experience with water softening is an important aspect of the training of sanitary engineers. The emphasis it receives usually varies in direct proportion to the hardness of the water in the area where the engineer receives his training. It seems pertinent to include procedures for water softening in a course in water, sewage, and industrial waste analysis for the same reasons advanced in Chap. 17 to justify inclusion of procedures for chemical coagulation.

Water softening is an expensive process from the standpoint of capital investment and daily operating costs. An engineer who recommends or opposes such expenditures must be well prepared to defend his position. Firsthand knowledge concerning water softening is a great asset.

## 19-2. Methods of Softening

Softening of domestic water supplies is accomplished by either of two methods or a combination of them.

**Precipitation Method.** The common precipitation method employs calcium hydroxide or calcium hydroxide plus sodium carbonate, depending upon the nature of the water. By the use of these chemicals, an attempt is made to reverse the processes through which the hardness ions were able to pass into solution and thereby cause them to precipitate.

In Sec. 18-2 it was shown that carbonate hardness gains entrance to water by the action of carbon dioxide upon deposits of calcium and magnesium carbonates in the soil by conversion of carbonate ion to bicarbonate ion, as shown in Fig. 18-2. Addition of a basic material such as hydroxide should, therefore, reverse this process, forming carbonate ion again. Hard waters always contain some free carbon dioxide, and this must be destroyed also. Lime $(CaO)$ or hydrated lime $[Ca(OH)_2]$ is used to supply the necessary hydroxyl ions, because of its low cost. Lime must be hydrated or slaked before it is satisfactory for use.

241

The reactions involved in lime softening may be represented as follows:

$$CO_2 + Ca(OH)_2 \rightarrow \underline{CaCO_3} + H_2O \tag{19-1}$$

$$Ca(HCO_3)_2 + Ca(OH)_2 \rightarrow 2\underline{CaCO_3} + 2H_2O \tag{19-2}$$

$$Mg(HCO_3)_2 + Ca(OH)_2 \rightarrow \underline{CaCO_3} + MgCO_3 + 2H_2O \tag{19-3}$$

From these equations it will be seen that free carbon dioxide and bicarbonate ions are converted to carbonate ions by the hydroxyl ions. Under the conditions,

$$[Ca^{++}][CO_3^=] > K_{sp} \text{ of } CaCO_3 \tag{19-4}$$

and $CaCO_3$ precipitates; however, the solubility product of $MgCO_3$ is not exceeded because of its high solubility. Fortunately, magnesium hydroxide is quite insoluble, and, by adding sufficient lime to produce an appreciable $[OH^-]$, magnesium ion is precipitated as the hydroxide. A pH of about 10.8 is required. The reactions involved in precipitation of magnesium may be represented by

$$MgCO_3 + Ca(OH)_2 \rightarrow \underline{Mg(OH)_2} + \underline{CaCO_3} \tag{19-5}$$

$$Mg^{++} + SO_4^= + Ca(OH)_2 \rightarrow \underline{Mg(OH)_2} + Ca^{++} + SO_4^= \tag{19-6}$$

From these equations it will be seen that lime added to precipitate $Mg^{++}$ occurring as carbonate hardness is precipitated as $CaCO_3$ simultaneously, but the lime added to precipitate $Mg^{++}$ occurring as noncarbonate hardness leaves $Ca^{++}$ in solution in an amount equivalent to the magnesium removed. Thus, no net softening effect is produced in the latter case unless provision is made to remove the calcium ions by use of soda ash.

After the removal of $Mg^{++}$, all noncarbonate hardness occurs as $Ca^{++}$. The cheapest way of precipitating it is by supplying $CO_3^=$ from an outside source. Soda ash ($Na_2CO_3$) is the cheapest source of $CO_3^=$.

$$Ca^{++} + SO_4^= + Na_2CO_3 \rightarrow \underline{CaCO_3} + 2Na^+ + SO_4^= \tag{19-7}$$

The lime required for softening is related to free carbon dioxide, carbonate hardness, and the $Mg^{++}$ content. Since carbonate hardness and alkalinity are numerically equal when expressed as $CaCO_3$, calculations of lime requirements can be simplified as follows:

| *Reactants* | *Calculations* |
|---|---|
| $\underset{44}{CO_2} + \underset{56}{CaO} \rightarrow$ | $CO_2 \text{ (in mg/l)} \times \dfrac{56}{44} = CaO \text{ (in mg/l)}$ |
| $\underset{100}{Alkalinity} + \underset{56}{CaO} \rightarrow$ | $Alk. \text{ (in mg/l)} \times \dfrac{56}{100} = CaO \text{ (in mg/l)}$ |
| $\underset{24.3}{Mg^{++}} + \underset{56}{CaO} \rightarrow$ | $Mg^{++} \text{ (in mg/l)} \times \dfrac{56}{24.3} = CaO \text{ (in mg/l)}$ |
| | $Total = \overline{CaO \text{ (in mg/l)}}$ |

The amount of hydrated lime may be calculated by substituting 74 for 56 in the above equations. Calculations give the theoretical amount of pure chemical required. Corrections should be made for per cent purity. Because of the high pH conditions necessary to precipitate $Mg^{++}$ as $Mg(OH)_2$ (pH of about 10.8), it is necessary to use lime in excess of the theoretical amounts. It is customary to use about 35 mg/l of CaO or 50 mg/l of $Ca(OH)_2$, and provision must be made to remove the excess during recarbonation.

The amount of soda ash required for softening is related to the amount of noncarbonate hardness (NCH). This is usually calculated as follows:

| *Reactants* | *Calculation* |
|---|---|
| $\underset{100}{NCH} + \underset{106}{Na_2CO_3} \rightarrow$ | $NCH \text{ (in mg/l)} \times \dfrac{106}{100} = Na_2CO_3 \text{ (in mg/l)}$ |

Because soda ash is a relatively expensive chemical and waters with less than 50 mg/l of residual hardness can seldom be produced by the lime–soda ash softening process, it is customary to leave about two-thirds of the residual hardness in the form of noncarbonate hardness, and the soda ash requirement may be calculated as follows:

$$\left(NCH - \frac{2}{3} \text{ expected residual hardness}\right) \times \frac{106}{100} = Na_2CO_3 \text{ (in mg/l)}$$

Soda ash normally has a purity of at least 98 per cent; therefore it is not necessary to compensate for the per cent purity.

It is impossible to produce waters free of hardness by the lime or lime–soda ash method of softening because of the natural solubilities of $Mg(OH)_2$ and $CaCO_3$. The former is soluble to the extent of about 9 mg/l and the latter to the extent of about 17 mg/l. Thus it is theoretically impossible to produce a water with less than about 25 mg/l of hardness. In addition, both $Mg(OH)_2$ and $CaCO_3$ tend to form supersaturated solutions that do not approach saturation rapidly even in the presence of precipitated material. In practice it is impractical to allow detention times that will permit complete precipitation; consequently waters softened by the lime or lime–soda ash processes usually have from 50 to 80 mg/l of residual hardness.

Because excess lime is used in lime or lime–soda ash softening when magnesium has to be removed, the softened water contains excess calcium and hydroxide ions. The excess calcium ions defeat the purpose of softening, and the hydroxyl ions result in hydroxide alkalinity. Both are normally decreased by addition of carbon dioxide, a treatment known as recarbonation.

$$CO_2 + 2OH^- \rightarrow CO_3^= + H_2O \qquad\qquad (19\text{-}8)$$
$$CO_3^= + Ca^{++} \rightarrow \underline{CaCO_3} \qquad\qquad (19\text{-}9)$$

Care must be exercised in adding the carbon dioxide to prevent the pH from falling below pH 9.5; otherwise significant amounts of the $CO_3^=$ will be converted to $HCO_3^-$ (see Fig. 16-4) and the excess $Ca^{++}$ will not be precipitated as $CaCO_3$ as desired.   A flocculation period should follow recarbonation to allow contact with precipitated material and hasten precipitation.   Following sedimentation, a water having a hardness value of 50 to 80 mg/l should be obtainable.

The softened water obtained in lime or soda ash softening is normally supersaturated with $CaCO_3$ to some degree.   It will continue to precipitate as scale on sand grains in filters and in pipelines unless the supersaturation is relieved.   This may be accomplished by a second stage of carbonation.

$$CO_2 + CO_3^= + H_2O \rightarrow 2HCO_3^- \qquad (19\text{-}10)$$

In this step the object is to convert a sufficient amount of the $CO_3^=$ to $HCO_3^-$ so as to reduce the $[CO_3^=]$ to a point where

$$[Ca^{++}][CO_3^=] < K_{sp} \text{ of } CaCO_3 \qquad (19\text{-}11)$$

and no further precipitation can occur.

In order to produce waters of maximum softness, recarbonation must occur in two steps when excess lime treatment is used.   If excess lime is not used, recarbonation can be accomplished in one step.

**Zeolite or Base Exchange Softening.**   A wide variety of materials, including soils, have the ability to exchange cations.   Glauconite, a natural green sand, has exceptional exchange capacity and has been widely used for water softening.   It is a complex sodium aluminum silicate and belongs to a class of compounds known as *zeolites*.   Synthetic zeolites and organic exchange resins of much higher exchange capacity have largely replaced the natural zeolites in water-softening practice.

The zeolites and other materials possessing cation exchange properties have a natural preference for multivalent ions because of the more stable compounds that they form with these ions.   As a result they tend to give up monovalent cations and take on divalent cations.

$$M^{++} + Na_2Ze \rightleftharpoons MZe + 2Na^+ \qquad (19\text{-}12)$$

Equation (19-12) represents the reaction by which softening of water is accomplished with exchange minerals or resins.   Although the reaction is reversible, the equilibrium is greatly in favor of the reaction proceeding to the right.   However, it is possible to reverse the reaction by increasing the concentration of monovalent cations.   This characteristic provides a means for regeneration of minerals or resins by reversing the reaction by mass action.   It also explains why it is impossible to soften brackish waters by the zeolite process.

The reactions involved in zeolite softening may be summarized as follows:

*Carbonate hardness:*

$$M(HCO_3)_2 + Na_2Ze \rightarrow MZe + 2Na^+ + 2HCO_3^- \qquad (19\text{-}13)$$

*Noncarbonate hardness:*

$$MSO_4 + Na_2Ze \rightarrow MZe + 2Na^+ + SO_4^= \qquad (19\text{-}14)$$

from which it will be observed that the only significant change is a conversion of salts of divalent metals to sodium salts. The alkalinity remains the same.

Regeneration of exchange minerals or resins is accomplished by treating them with a brine solution made from NaCl. Through mass action the sodium salt of the exchange mineral is re-formed.

$$MZe + [NaCl]_{brine} \rightarrow Na_2Ze + M^{++} + 2Cl^- + [NaCl]_{brine} \qquad (19\text{-}15)$$

When the excess brine containing the displaced divalent ions is washed away by rinsing, the regenerated mineral is ready to perform its normal function again. Approximately 3 mg of NaCl is needed to displace each milligram of hardness removed.

## 19-3. Significance of Laboratory Studies

Laboratory studies of water softening provide a means of evaluating the degree of softening that can be obtained by the various methods, and the results serve as a basis of selection for design purposes, particularly where waters of unusual character are involved. The studies with lime or lime–soda ash treatment are especially valuable in the training of students since the treated waters furnish samples for the measurement of caustic (hydroxide) alkalinity as well as the other forms of alkalinity.

# 20. Residual Chlorine and Chlorine Demand

## 20-1. General Considerations

The prime purpose of chlorinating public water supplies is to prevent the spread of water-borne diseases. The practice of chlorination has become so widespread and generally accepted that the real reason is frequently taken very much for granted. It seems important that sanitary engineers should be familiar with the history of the great plagues that have afflicted mankind and the developments that led to the proof that water is the major vehicle of transmission for some diseases. It is impossible to go into great detail here concerning the historical aspects that led to the practice of chlorination; hence supplementary reading is highly recommended.[1,2]

**Early History of Diseases.** Communicable diseases have been a curse of mankind since time immemorial. The intensity of the problem appears to have been magnified as the density of the population increased. During the fourteenth century a plague known as the "Black Death" swept over Europe, leaving about 25 per cent of the people dead in its wake. An epidemic in London in the winter of 1664–1665 caused 70,000 deaths, equal to 14 per cent of the population.

With the development of the industrial revolution, which attracted people to urban areas and caused them to live under more crowded conditions, the frequency of epidemics increased. Up until 1854, there had been a great deal of theorizing concerning the causes and modes of transmission of disease but no one had been able to prove his case. The science of bacteriology, upon which definite proof depended, was still unborn.

In 1854 a localized epidemic of Asiatic cholera broke out in London. Through the careful investigations of two men, John Snow and John

[1] M. J. Rosenau, "Preventive Medicine and Hygiene," Appleton-Century-Crofts, New York, 1935.

[2] S. C. Prescott and M. P. Horwood, "Sedgwick's Principles of Sanitary Science and Public Health," The Macmillan Company, New York, 1946.

York, it was demonstrated, as well as could be by the means available at that time, that the source of infection was water from the Broad Street Pump. It was further demonstrated that the well was contaminated by sewage from a damaged sewer nearby and that the sewer carried sewage from a home housing one suffering from the disease. The Broad Street Pump epidemic is a milestone in public health engineering practice for it established without doubt that water was a major vehicle for the spread of Asiatic cholera, one of the greatest plagues of mankind. This discovery stimulated and gave real purpose to the practice of slow sand filtration which had been initiated about 1830.

The science of bacteriology is considered to have originated about 1870. Robert Koch, in 1875, was successful in growing a pure culture of the bacterium causing anthrax. This was another event of great significance, for within a few years the causative organisms of typhoid (1884), Asiatic cholera (1883), and many other diseases were grown in pure culture. These developments provided the means for absolute proof that water can serve as a major vehicle for disease transmission.

The cholera epidemic in Hamburg, Germany, in 1892 served as another milestone in the knowledge concerning water-borne disease. During the epidemic, cholera organisms were actually found in the river waters used for the water supply. In addition, the efficacy of slow sand filters for removing disease organisms was demonstrated.

The typhoid epidemic at Lausen, Switzerland, in 1872 was caused by contamination of a spring water supply. It is noteworthy because of the remoteness of the point of contamination and the considerable distance the water traveled underground without freeing itself of the disease organisms. This characteristic has been shown to be particularly true in limestone areas where cracks and crevices occur.

**History of Chlorination Practice.** Chlorination of water supplies on an emergency basis has been practiced since about 1850. With definite evidence at hand that certain diseases were transmitted by water, emergency treatment with hypochlorites became quite common during periods of epidemics.

It was not until 1904 that continuous chlorination of a public water supply was attempted in England. Shortly thereafter, in 1908, George A. Johnson initiated treatment with calcium hypochlorite of the water at the Bubbly Creek filter plant of the Union Stock Yards in Chicago. In 1909, Jersey City, New Jersey, started hypochlorite treatment of its Boonton supply. This was the first attempt to chlorinate a public water supply in the United States and led to a celebrated court case in which a wise judge upheld the right of the city to chlorinate the water supply in the best interests of public health. From that day, chlorination of public water supplies has spread so that today it is almost routine practice.

The practice of chlorinating public water supplies did not spread rapidly at first because of the instability during storage of the calcium hypochlorites then available. The development of facilities for feeding gaseous chlorine occurred about 1912, and from that time chlorination practice has grown rapidly. With the increased use of chlorine for disinfecting purposes, there has been a corresponding decrease in the incidence of water-borne disease. The gross effect that modern sanitation practices, of which chlorination of water supplies and pasteurization of milk are major ones, have had upon the typhoid death rate in the United States is shown in Fig. 20-1.

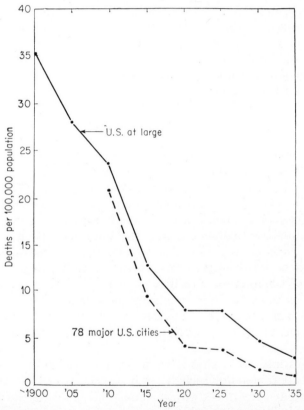

FIG. 20-1. Typhoid and paratyphoid death rate in the United States and in 78 major U.S. cities. (*A. E. Gorman* and *A. Wolman, J. Am. Water Works Assoc., February*, 1939.)

## 20-2. Chemistry of Chlorination

Chlorine is used in the form of free chlorine or as hypochlorites. In either form it acts as a potent oxidizing agent and often dissipates itself in side reactions so rapidly that little disinfection is accomplished until amounts in excess of the chlorine demand have been added.

**Reactions with Water.**   Chlorine combines with water to form hypochlorous and hydrochloric acids.

$$Cl_2 + H_2O \rightleftharpoons HOCl + H^+ + Cl^- \qquad (20\text{-}1)$$

The former, being a weak acid ($K = 2.8 \times 10^{-8}$), is very poorly dissociated at pH levels below 6.   In dilute solution and at pH levels above 4, the equilibrium shown above is displaced greatly to the right and very little $Cl_2$ exists as such in solution.

Hypochlorites are used largely in the form of modern-day high-test calcium hypochlorites.   When such compounds are dissolved in water, they ionize to yield hypochlorite ion.

$$Ca(OCl)_2 + H_2O \rightleftharpoons Ca^{++} + H_2O + 2OCl^- \qquad (20\text{-}2)$$

This ion, of course, establishes an equilibrium with hydrogen ions in accordance with the equation

$$OCl^- + H^+ \rightleftharpoons HOCl \qquad (20\text{-}3)$$

The amounts of $OCl^-$ ion and HOCl in the solution depend upon the pH, as shown in Fig. 20-2.   Natural waters always contain some chloride ions, and so the hypochlorous acid and chloride and hydrogen ions present in the water exist in equilibrium with free chlorine, as shown in Eq. (20-1). Thus it may be concluded that the same equilibria are established in water regardless of whether chlorine or hypochlorites are added.   The significant difference would be in pH effects and its influence on the relative amounts of $OCl^-$ and HOCl at equilibrium.   Chlorine tends to decrease the pH whereas hypochlorites tend to increase the pH.

**Reactions with Impurities in Water.**   Chlorine and hypochlorous acid react with a wide variety of substances, including ammonia.

*Reactions with Ammonia.*   Ammonium ion exists in equilibrium with ammonia and hydrogen ion [Eq. (2-23)].   The ammonia reacts with chlorine or hypochlorous acid to form monochloramines, dichloramines, and trichloramines, depending upon the relative amounts of each and to some extent upon the pH, as follows:

$$NH_3 + HOCl \rightarrow NH_2Cl + H_2O \qquad \text{monochloramine} \quad (20\text{-}4)$$
$$NH_3 + 2HOCl \rightarrow NHCl_2 + 2H_2O \qquad \text{dichloramine} \quad (20\text{-}5)$$
$$NH_3 + 3HOCl \rightarrow NCl_3 + 3H_2O \qquad \text{trichloramine} \quad (20\text{-}6)$$

The mono- and dichloramines have significant disinfecting power and are, therefore, of interest in the measurement of chlorine residuals.

*Extraneous Reactions.*   Chlorine combines with a wide variety of materials, particularly reducing agents.   Many of the reactions are very rapid while others are much slower.    These side reactions complicate the use of chlorine for disinfecting purposes.    Their demand for chlorine must be satisfied before chlorine becomes available to accomplish disinfection.

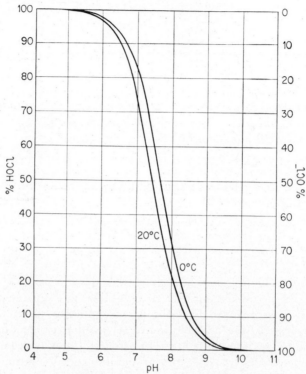

FIG. 20-2. Effect of pH on the distribution of hypochlorous acid and hypochlorite ion in water.

The reaction between hydrogen sulfide and chlorine will serve to illustrate the type of reaction that occurs with reducing agents.

$$H_2S + 4Cl_2 + 4H_2O \rightarrow H_2SO_4 + 8HCl \tag{20-7}$$

$Fe^{++}$, $Mn^{++}$, and $NO_2^-$ are examples of other inorganic reducing agents present in water supplies.    A few organic reducing agents may be present but their concentrations are very low in potable waters.

Organic compounds that possess unsaturated linkages will also add chlorine and increase the chlorine demand.

$$\begin{array}{c} \quad\quad\quad\quad Cl\ \ Cl \\ -C\!\!=\!\!C- + Cl_2 \rightarrow -C\!-\!C- \\ \ \ H\ \ H \quad\quad\quad\quad H\ \ H \end{array} \tag{20-8}$$

## 20-3. Sanitary Significance of Chlorine Residuals

Disinfection is a process designed to kill harmful organisms, and it does not ordinarily produce a sterile water. These generalizations hold for disinfection with chlorine also. Two factors are extremely important in disinfection: time of contact and concentration of the disinfecting agent. Where other factors are constant, the disinfecting action may be represented by

$$\text{Kill} \propto C \times t \qquad (20\text{-}9)$$

The important point is that with long contact times a low concentration of disinfectant suffices, whereas short contact times require high concentration to accomplish equivalent kills. Furthermore, research has shown that a greater concentration of chloramines than of hypochlorous acid is required to accomplish a given kill in a specified time. For these reasons it is important to know both the concentration and the kind of residual chlorine acting.

From the considerations mentioned above, it has become common practice to refer to chlorine, hypochlorous acid, and hypochlorite ion as *free chlorine residuals*, and the chloramines are called *combined chlorine residuals*.

The rate of the reaction between ammonia and hypochlorous acid varies considerably, depending upon the pH and temperature. The reaction rate is most rapid at pH 8.3 and decreases rapidly as the pH is decreased or increased. For this reason, it is common to find free chlorine and combined chlorine residuals coexisting after contact periods of 10, 15, or even 60 min.

The action of excess chlorine on waters containing ammonia merits special consideration. With mole ratios of chlorine to ammonia up to 1:1, both monochloramine and dichloramine are formed, the relative amounts of each being a function of the pH. Further increases in the mole ratio of chlorine to ammonia result in formation of some trichloramine and oxidation of part of the ammonia to nitrogen gas. These reactions are essentially complete when 2 moles of chlorine has been added for each mole of ammonia nitrogen originally present in the water. Chloramine residuals usually reach a maximum when 1 mole of chlorine has been added for each mole of ammonia and then decline to a minimum value at a chlorine-to-ammonia ratio of 2:1. Further additions of chlorine produce free chlorine residuals. Chlorination of a water to the extent that all the ammonia is converted to trichloramine or oxidized to free nitrogen or other gases is referred to as "break-point chlorination" because of the peculiar character of the chlorine residual curve, as illustrated in Fig. 20-3.

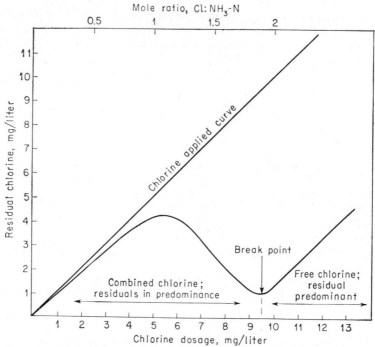

Fɪɢ. 20-3. A residual-chlorine curve showing a typical break point. Ammonia-nitrogen content of water, 1.0 mg/l.

Theoretically, it should require 3 moles of chlorine for the complete conversion of 1 mole of ammonia to nitrogen trichloride (trichloramine). The fact that only 2 moles of chlorine is required to reach the break point indicates that some unusual reactions occur. Nitrous oxide, nitrogen, and nitrogen trichloride have been identified among the gaseous products of the break-point reaction. The presence of nitrous oxide could be accounted for by the following reaction:

$$NH_2Cl + NHCl_2 + HOCl \rightarrow N_2O + 4HCl \qquad (20\text{-}10)$$

The total chlorine required for formation of the monochloramine, dichloramine, and the hypochlorous acid for the final oxidation step corresponds to 2 moles for each mole of ammonia. This would indicate that nitrous oxide is the major end product when ammonia is oxidized by chlorine in dilute solutions.

## 20-4. Methods of Determination

It was not until about 1940 that the difference in disinfecting power of chloramine and free chlorine residuals was demonstrated. Prior to that time no attempt had been made to develop analytical procedures for differentiation.   Therefore methods for measuring chlorine residuals may be classed into old methods that measure total chlorine and new methods that allow measurement of free and combined forms.

**Total Chlorine Residual.**   All common methods of measuring chlorine residuals depend upon their oxidizing power; consequently any other oxidizing agents present may interfere with the test.   Manganese in valences above 2 and nitrites are the most common interferences.

*Starch-Iodide Method.*   The starch-iodide method is of interest, historically, because it served as the basis of controlling chlorination until about 1913 when the orthotolidine test was developed.   The method depends upon the oxidizing power of free and combined chlorine residuals to convert iodide ion to free iodine, the reactions being represented as

$$Cl_2^\circ + 2I^- \rightarrow I_2^\circ + 2Cl^- \tag{20-11}$$
$$I_2 + starch \rightarrow blue\ color \qquad (qualitative\ test) \tag{20-12}$$

In the presence of starch, the iodine produced a blue color which was accepted as evidence of the presence of residual chlorine but, of course, did not indicate the amount of residual present, except as people were able to judge the intensity of the blue color.

The starch-iodide method provides a means of quantitative measurement of total residual if the iodine released is titrated with a standard solution of a reducing agent.   The usual reagent is sodium thiosulfate and the end point is indicated by the disappearance of the blue color.

$$I_2 + 2Na_2S_2O_3 \rightarrow Na_2S_4O_6 + 2NaI \tag{20-13}$$
or
$$I_2 + 2S_2O_3^= \rightarrow S_4O_6^= + 2I^- \tag{20-14}$$

*Orthotolidine Method.*   In 1909 Phelps proposed the use of orthotolidine as a colorimetric indicator for chlorine residuals.   Ellms and Hauser (1913) incorporated the use of color standards and, thereby, made the test quantitative.   Shortly thereafter, proprietary devices employing colored glass disks or sealed colored liquid standards, suitable for field as well as laboratory use, were developed.   An instrument commonly used is shown in Fig. 20-4.   The introduction of a simple testing procedure, which allowed close control of chlorination, was an important factor in the widespread acceptance of chlorination of public water supplies.   It made chlorination a practical method of disinfection on even the smallest supplies because of the simplicity of the test.

Orthotolidine is an aromatic organic compound that is oxidized in acid solution by chlorine, chloramines, and other oxidizing agents to produce a yellow-colored compound.   The reaction is represented as follows:

$$CH_3 \qquad\qquad CH_3$$

$$H_2N - \langle\ \rangle - \langle\ \rangle - NH_2 + Cl_2 \xrightarrow{H^+}$$

Orthotolidine

$$CH_3 \qquad\qquad\qquad CH_3 \qquad (20\text{-}15)$$

$$\begin{array}{cc} H \\ Cl\ \ N = \langle\ \rangle = \langle\ \rangle = N\ \ Cl \\ H \end{array}$$

A holoquinone (yellow)

The holoquinone produced is yellow at pH values less than 1.8, and the intensity of the yellow color is proportional to the amount present. It meets the requirements of Beer's law (Sec. 4-5) and is suitable for quantitative measurement.

Fig. 20-4. A residual chlorine comparator.    (*Wallace & Tiernan Incorporated.*)

Nitrites and oxidized forms of manganese both oxidize orthotolidine to produce holoquinones, thus producing false indications of chlorine residuals. Separate tests should be made on unchlorinated samples of water to measure the extent of the interference and the corrections that must be made. The reaction between orthotolidine and chloramines is slow. For this reason it is recommended that the sample be warmed to 20°C and a contact period of 3 to 5 min provided before reading the residual chlorine. In some instances, particularly in sewage, considerable fading may occur before 3 min have elapsed.    The reading at maximum color should be recorded as the chlorine residual.

**Free and Combined Chlorine Residuals.**    With the development of knowledge concerning the relative disinfecting powers of free and combined chlorine residuals, it became important to have ways of differentiating and measuring them.    Two methods are commonly used.

*Orthotolidine-Arsenite (OTA) Method.*    The OTA method of measuring free and combined chlorine residuals is based upon the fact that free chlorine residuals react instantaneously with orthotolidine to produce the yellow holoquinone, whereas chloramines react much more slowly.    In the simplest form of the determination, two tests are performed.    Total residual is measured in the usual way with readings made after 5 min have elapsed.    A second test is made in which a reducing agent (sodium arsenite solution) is added within 5 sec after the orthotolidine is added. This allows time for the free chlorine to oxidize the orthotolidine and allows only a small amount of the combined chlorine to act before the arsenite is added.    The arsenite, being a much stronger reducing agent than orthotolidine, reduces the chloramines instantaneously, stopping further action with the orthotolidine.    The yellow color developed in this case is due principally to free chlorine residual.    If the results of the second test are subtracted from the first test,

$$\text{Total residual} - \text{free residual} = \text{combined residual} \quad (20\text{-}16)$$

a reasonable measure of the combined chlorine residual is obtained.    The results are always in error to some degree because the values of free chlorine residual are higher than they should be by the amount of action occurring between chloramines and orthotolidine in the 5-sec period which elapses before the arsenite is added.

In cases where interferences are present, they are measured separately and proper corrections made to the total and free residual values used in Eq. (20-16).

*Amperometric Titration Method.*    The most accurate method of measuring free and combined chlorine residuals is through oxidation-reduction titration procedures.    Such methods require the use of internal indicators or electrometric devices employing a suitable electrode system to show when reactions are completed.    Amperometric titrators employing rotating platinum electrodes have been developed for such purposes.    Figure 4-6 shows an instrument that is widely used in the United States.

Phenylarseneoxide ($C_6H_5AsO$) is the reducing agent normally used as the titrating agent.    It reacts with free chlorine residuals at pH 6.5 to 7.5 in a quantitative manner.    It reduces chloramines at pH levels below 6.0 provided that iodide ion is present.    Presumably, the chloramines oxidize iodide ion to free iodine and the phenylarseneoxide reduces the free iodine, thereby measuring the amount of chloramines present. By conducting a two-stage titration, with the pH adjusted at about 7 and then at about 4, it is possible to measure separately free chlorine residuals and combined chlorine residuals. Interferences from nitrites and oxidized forms of manganese are eliminated by conducting the titrations at pH levels above 3.5.

## 20-5. Measurement of Chlorine Demand

The *chlorine demand* of a water is the amount of chlorine that must be applied to leave a desired free, combined, or total residual after a specified contact period. The nature and amount of the residual, as well as the contact time, depend upon local circumstances. The test should be conducted with chlorine or with hypochlorites, depending upon the form that will be used in practice.

Measurement of chlorine demand can be readily made by treating a series of samples of the water in question with known but varying dosages of chlorine or hypochlorite. The water samples should be at a temperature within the range of interest, and, after the desired contact period, determination of residual chlorine in the samples will demonstrate which dosage satisfied the requirements of the chlorine demand.

## 20-6. Application of Chlorine Demand and Chlorine Residual Data

Determination of the chlorine demand of a water, sewage, or industrial waste is an important consideration in design. It serves as the basis for determining the number and capacity of chlorinators required, the amount of chlorine needed, the type of shipping containers, and all appurtenances required for handling and storage.

Chlorine residuals are used universally in disinfection practice to control addition of chlorine so as to ensure effective disinfection without waste of chlorine. They are also used to control chlorination of sewage and industrial wastes and usually are the sole criteria immediately available to determine whether or not desired objectives are being maintained.

# 21. Chlorides

## 21-1. General Considerations

Chlorides occur in all natural waters in widely varying concentration. The chloride content normally increases as the mineral content increases. Upland and mountain supplies usually are quite low in chlorides whereas river and ground waters usually have a considerable amount. Sea and ocean waters represent the residues resulting from partial evaporation of natural waters that flow into them, and chloride levels are very high.

Chlorides gain access to natural waters in many ways. The solvent power of water dissolves chlorides from topsoil and deeper formations. Spray from the ocean is carried inland as droplets or as minute salt crystals, which result from evaporation of the water in the droplets. These sources constantly replenish the chlorides in inland areas where they fall. Ocean and sea waters invade the rivers that drain into them, particularly the deeper rivers. The salt water, being more dense, flows upstream under the fresh water which is flowing downstream. There is a constant intermixing of the salt water with the fresh water above. In the case of the Hudson River, which has a deep channel and rather slight gradient, sea water invades for a distance of about 50 miles upstream. This invasion has been a major factor in preventing New York City from developing the Hudson River as a source of water supply. Ground waters in areas adjacent to the ocean are in hydrostatic balance with sea water. Over-pumping of ground waters produces a difference in hydrostatic head in favor of the sea water and it intrudes into the fresh-water area. Such intrusion has occurred at many locations in Florida and in southern California.

Human excreta, particularly the urine, contain chloride in an amount about equal to the chlorides consumed with food and water. This amount averages about 6 g of chlorides per person per day and increases the amount of $Cl^-$ in sewage about 15 mg/l above that of the carriage water. Thus sewage effluents add considerable chlorides to receiving streams. Many industrial wastes contain appreciable amounts of chlorides. Control of contamination of surface waters by chlorides contained

257

in industrial wastes is a major consideration in the Ohio River valley and in all areas where oil-field brines and other salt brines are allowed to reach receiving streams.

## 21-2. Sanitary Significance of Chlorides

Chlorides in reasonable concentrations are not harmful to humans. At concentrations above 250 mg/l they give a salty taste to water which is objectionable to many people.    For this reason, the U.S. Public Health Service recommends that chlorides be limited to 250 mg/l in supplies intended for public use.    In many areas of the world where water supplies are scarce, sources containing as much as 2,000 mg/l are used for domestic purposes without the development of adverse effects, once the human system becomes adapted to the water.

Before the development of bacteriological testing procedures, chemical tests for chloride and for nitrogen, in its various forms, served as the basis of detecting contamination of ground waters by sewage.    The chloride test was of special value in areas where the level of chlorides was low. In Massachusetts, for example, a survey of the chloride content of ground waters was made and maps prepared showing normal levels.    Locations with similar chloride levels were connected by lines and a map with chloride contours (isochlors) was obtained.    Such maps provided reference information of considerable value in sanitary surveys where sewage contamination was suspected.    A great deal of judgment and caution was needed for proper interpretation.    The chemical tests have been largely replaced by the more sensitive bacteriological tests used today.

Chlorides are used to some extent as tracers in sanitary engineering practice.    They are inconvenient to use in many instances because of the quantities required to produce significant increases in chloride level and because of their tendency to produce density currents.    Their use as tracers has been superseded to a great extent by dyes, nitrites, and radioactive materials.

## 21-3. Methods of Determination

Chlorides may be readily measured by means of volumetric procedures employing internal indicators.    For most purposes the Mohr method employing silver nitrate as the titrant and potassium chromate as the indicator is satisfactory.    A new method using mercuric nitrate as the titrant and diphenycarbazone as the indicator promises to replace the Mohr method because of certain inherent advantages.

**Mohr Method.**    The Mohr method employs a solution of silver nitrate for titration, and "Standard Methods" recommends the use of a 0.0141 $N$ solution.    This corresponds to a $N/71$ solution or one in which each milliliter is equivalent to 0.5 mg of chloride ion.    The silver nitrate solution can be standardized against standard chloride solutions prepared

from pure sodium chloride.    In the titration the chloride ion is precipitated as white silver chloride.

$$Ag^+ + Cl^- \rightarrow AgCl \tag{21-1}$$

The end point cannot be detected by eye unless an indicator capable of
demonstrating the presence of excess $Ag^+$ is present.    The indicator normally used is potassium chromate which supplies chromate ions.    As the
concentration of chloride ions approaches extinction, the silver-ion concentration increases to a level where the solubility product of silver
chromate is exceeded and it begins to form a reddish-brown precipitate.

$$2Ag^+ + CrO_4^= \rightarrow Ag_2CrO_4 \tag{21-2}$$

This is taken as evidence that all the chloride has been precipitated.
Since an excess of $Ag^+$ is needed to produce a visible amount of $Ag_2CrO_4$,
the indicator error or blank must be determined and subtracted from all
titrations.

Several precautions must be observed in this determination if accurate
results are to be obtained:

1. A uniform sample size must be used, preferably 100 ml, so that
ionic concentrations needed to indicate the end point will be constant.

2. The pH must be in the range of 7 to 8 because $Ag^+$ is precipitated
as AgOH at high pH levels and the $CrO_4^=$ is converted to $Cr_2O_7^=$ at low
pH levels.

3. A definite amount of indicator must be used to provide a certain
concentration of $CrO_4^=$; otherwise $Ag_2CrO_4$ may form too soon or not
soon enough.

The indicator error or blank varies somewhat with the ability of indi-
viduals to detect a noticeable color change.    The usual range is 0.2 to
0.4 ml of titrant.

If the silver nitrate solution used for titration is exactly 0.0141 $N$,
the calculation for chlorides as given in "Standard Methods" may be
simplified as

$$Cl^- \text{ (in mg/l)} = \frac{(\text{ml AgNO}_3 - \text{blank}) \times 0.5 \times 1{,}000}{\text{ml sample}} \tag{21-3}$$

since $0.0141 \times 35.46 = 0.5$.

For routine control work, it is most convenient to prepare a $N/35.46$
(0.0282 $N$) silver nitrate solution of which each milliliter is equivalent to
1.0 mg of $Cl^-$ and the factor 0.5 can be eliminated from the calculation.

**Mercuric Nitrate Method.**    The mercuric nitrate method of determining chlorides is much less subject to interferences than the Mohr method
because the titration is performed in a sample whose pH is adjusted to a
value of about 3.    Under these conditions, $Hg^{++}$ ion combines with $Cl^-$
to form poorly ionized $HgCl_2$ ($K = 2.6 \times 10^{-15}$).

$$Hg^{++} + 2Cl^- \rightarrow HgCl_2 \quad \text{(poorly ionized)} \tag{21-4}$$

As the $Cl^-$ concentration approaches zero, the $Hg^{++}$ concentration increases to a level where it becomes significant as the mercuric nitrate is added.

Diphenylcarbazone is the indicator used to show the presence of excess $Hg^{++}$ ions. It combines with them to form a distinct violet color. The indicator is very sensitive and is affected by one drop, 0.05 ml, of the titrating solution; therefore a blank correction is not needed.

"Standard Methods" recommends that a 0.0141 $N$ solution of mercuric nitrate be used as the titrant in determining chlorides. Each milliliter of such a solution is equivalent to 0.5 mg of $Cl^-$ and, therefore, the comments made above concerning calculations with similar strength solutions of $AgNO_3$ also apply in this case.

The use of $N/35.46$ (0.0282 $N$) solutions of the mercuric nitrate titrant is more convenient for routine determinations since each milliliter is equivalent to 1.0 mg of $Cl^-$.

## 21-4. Application of Chloride Data

In many areas the level of chlorides in natural waters is an important consideration in the selection of supplies for human use. Where brackish waters must be used for domestic purposes, the amount of chlorides present is an important factor in determining the type of desalting apparatus to be used. The chloride determination is used to control pumping of ground water from locations where intrusion of sea water is a problem.

In areas where the discharge of salt-water brines and industrial wastes containing high concentrations of chlorides must be controlled to safeguard receiving waters, the chloride determination serves to excellent advantage for regulatory purposes.

Chlorides interfere in the determination of nitrates and chemical oxygen demand (COD). In the former case, they must be removed by precipitation, and in the latter case, a correction is made based upon the amounts present.

Sodium chloride has a considerable history as a tracer. One of its principal applications has been in tracing pollution of wells. It is admirably suited for such purposes for five reasons:

1. Its presence is not detectable by eye. This permits secrecy.
2. It is a normal constituent of water and has no toxic effects.
3. The chloride ion is not adsorbed by soil formations.
4. It is not altered or changed in amount by biological processes.
5. The chloride ion is easily measured.

It is to be expected that chlorides will continue in limited use as tracers where other methods are not applicable.

# 22. Dissolved Oxygen

## 22-1. General Considerations

All living organisms are dependent upon oxygen in one form or another to maintain the metabolic processes that produce energy for growth and reproduction. Aerobic processes are the subject of greatest interest because of their need for free oxygen. Man is vitally concerned with the oxygen content of the air that he breathes, since he knows from experience that an appreciable reduction in oxygen content will lead to discomfort and, possibly, death. For this reason, he is careful to restrict the number of occupants within enclosures to the ventilating capacity.

The sanitary engineer is, of course, interested in atmospheric conditions in relation to man, but, in addition, he is vitally concerned with the "atmospheric conditions" that exist in liquids, water being the liquid in greatest abundance and importance.

All the gases of the atmosphere are soluble in water to some degree. Both nitrogen and oxygen are classed as poorly soluble and, since they do not react with water chemically, their solubility is directly proportional to their partial pressures. Hence, Boyle's law may be used to calculate the amounts present at saturation at any given temperature. The solubility of both nitrogen and oxygen varies greatly with the temperature over the range of interest to sanitary engineers. Figure 22-1 shows solubility curves for the two gases in distilled or low-solids-content water in equilibrium with air at 760-mm pressure. It will be noted that, under the partial-pressure conditions that exist in the atmosphere, more nitrogen than oxygen dissolves in water. At saturation, the dissolved gases contain about 38 per cent oxygen, or nearly twice as much oxygen as in the normal atmosphere.

The solubility of atmospheric oxygen in fresh waters ranges from 14.6 mg/l at 0°C to about 7 mg/l at 35°C under 1 atm of pressure. Since it is a poorly soluble gas, its solubility varies directly with the atmospheric pressure at any given temperature. This is an important

261

consideration at high altitudes. Because rates of biological oxidation increase with temperature and oxygen demand increases accordingly, high-temperature conditions, where dissolved oxygen is least soluble, are of greatest concern to sanitary engineers. Most of the critical conditions related to dissolved-oxygen deficiency in sanitary engineering practice occur during the summer months when temperatures are high and solubility of oxygen is at a minimum. For this reason it is customary to think of dissolved-oxygen levels of about 8 mg/l as being the maximum available under critical conditions.

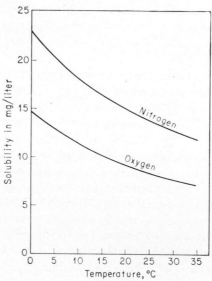

Fig. 22-1. Solubility of oxygen and nitrogen in water saturated with air at 760 mm Hg.

The low solubility of oxygen is the major factor that limits the purification capacity of natural waters and necessitates treatment of wastes to remove pollutional matter before discharge to receiving streams. In aerobic biological treatment processes, the limited solubility of oxygen is of great importance because it governs the rate at which oxygen will be absorbed by the medium and, therefore, the cost of aeration.

## 22-2. Sanitary Significance of Dissolved Oxygen

In liquid wastes, dissolved oxygen is the factor that determines whether the biological changes are brought about by aerobic or by anaerobic organisms. The former require free oxygen and produce innocuous end products, whereas the latter can utilize chemically bound oxygen, such as that from sulfates, and the end products are often very obnoxious.

Since both types of organisms are ubiquitous in nature, it is highly important that conditions favorable to the aerobic organisms (aerobic conditions) be maintained; otherwise the anaerobic organisms will take over and development of nuisance conditions will result. Thus dissolved-oxygen measurements are vital for maintaining aerobic conditions in natural waters that receive pollutional matter and in aerobic treatment processes intended to purify sewage and industrial wastes.

Dissolved-oxygen determinations are used for a wide variety of other purposes. It is one of the most important single tests that the sanitary engineer uses. In most instances involving the control of stream pollution, it is desirable to maintain conditions favorable for the growth and reproduction of a normal population of fish and other aquatic organisms. This condition requires the maintenance of dissolved-oxygen levels that will support the desired aquatic life in a healthy condition at all times.

Determinations of dissolved oxygen serve as the basis of the BOD test; thus they are the foundation of the most important determination used to evaluate the pollutional strength of sewages and industrial wastes. The rate of biochemical oxidation can be measured by determining residual dissolved oxygen in a system at various intervals of time.

All aerobic treatment processes depend upon the presence of dissolved oxygen, and tests for it are indispensable as a means of controlling the rate of aeration to make sure that adequate amounts of air are supplied to maintain aerobic conditions and, also, to prevent excessive use of air.

Oxygen is a significant factor in the corrosion of iron and steel, particularly in water distribution systems and in steam boilers. Removal of oxygen from boiler-feed waters by physical and chemical means is common practice in the power industry. The dissolved-oxygen test serves as the means of control.

## 22-3. Collection of Samples for Determination of Dissolved Oxygen

A certain amount of care must be exercised in the collection of samples to be used for dissolved-oxygen determinations. In most cases of interest, the dissolved-oxygen level will be below saturation, and exposure to the air will result in obtaining erroneous results. For this reason, a special sampling device similar to the one described in "Standard Methods" is needed. All such instruments are designed on the principle that contact with air cannot be avoided during the time the sample bottles are being filled. However, if space is available to allow the bottles to overflow, a sample of water that is representative of the mixture being sampled can be obtained. Most samplers are designed to provide an overflow of two or three times the bottle volume to ensure collection of representative samples.

Most samples for dissolved oxygen are collected in the "field" where it is not convenient to perform the entire determination. Since oxygen values may change radically with time because of biological activity, it is customary to "fix" the samples immediately after collection. The usual procedure is to treat the samples with the conventional reagents used in the dissolved-oxygen test and then perform the titration when the samples are brought to the laboratory. The chemical treatment employed in "fixing" the samples is radical enough to arrest all biological action, and the final titration may be delayed several hours.

### 22-4. Choice of Standard Reagent for Measuring Dissolved Oxygen

All modern methods of determining dissolved oxygen depend upon reactions that release an amount of iodine equivalent to the amount of oxygen originally present, with subsequent measurement of the amount of iodine released by means of a standard solution of a reducing agent. Sodium thiosulfate is the reducing agent normally used and starch solution is used to determine the end point. All reactions in the determination of oxygen involve oxidation and reduction. The starch indicator, however, acts in the capacity of an adsorption indicator. It adsorbs iodine from dilute solutions to produce a brilliant blue color and returns to a colorless form when the iodine is all reduced to iodide ion.

**Selection of $N/40$ Thiosulfate Solution.** The equivalent weight of oxygen is 8. Since the normality of most titrating agents used in sanitary analysis is adjusted so that each milliliter is equivalent to 1.0 mg of the measured material, it would follow that a $N/8$ solution of thiosulfate should be used. However, such a solution is too concentrated to allow accurate determinations of dissolved oxygen unless unreasonably large samples are titrated. It has become standard practice to use 200-ml samples for titration. This is one-fifth of a liter. By using a titrating agent which is one-fifth as strong as conventionally used, the results obtained on 200-ml samples, in terms of milliliters of titrant used, are the same as if 1-liter samples had been treated with the $N/8$ reagent. Thus when a $N/40$ ($N/8 \times \frac{1}{5}$) solution of thiosulfate solution is used to titrate 200-ml samples, dissolved-oxygen values in milligrams per liter are equal to the titration. This eliminates the need for calculations.

**Preparation and Standardization of $N/40$ (0.025 $N$) Thiosulfate.** Sodium thiosulfate ($Na_2S_2O_3 \cdot 5H_2O$) can be obtained in relatively pure form. However, because of its water of hydration, it cannot be dried to a compound of definite composition and even loses water at room temperature under conditions of low humidity. It is necessary, therefore, to prepare solutions that are slightly stronger than desired and to standardize them against a primary standard.

The equivalent weight of sodium thiosulfate cannot be calculated from its formula and anticipated valence change, as is the case with most reducing agents (see Table 4-1). Rather, it must be calculated from its reaction with the oxidizing agent, in this case iodine.

$$2Na_2S_2O_3 \cdot 5H_2O + I_2^\circ \rightarrow Na_2S_4O_6 + 2NaI + 10H_2O \qquad (22\text{-}1)$$

From Eq. (22-1), it may be concluded that each molecule of sodium thiosulfate is equivalent to one atom of iodine. Since each atom of iodine gains one electron in the conversion to iodide ion, it is obvious that each molecule of thiosulfate supplies one electron when oxidized to the tetrathionate, or

$$2S_2O_3^= + I_2^\circ \rightarrow S_4O_6^= + 2I^- \qquad (22\text{-}2)$$

From these considerations, it may be concluded that the equivalent weight of sodium thiosulfate is equal to the molecular weight, and something in excess of one-fortieth of the molecular weight, 6.205 g, should be taken to prepare 1 liter of a solution that is slightly stronger than $N/40$. Usually 6.5 g is sufficient.

The thiosulfate solution may be standardized with either of two primary standards, potassium dichromate or potassium bi-iodate. Both can be obtained in essentially 100 per cent pure form. It is customary to prepare $N/40$ solutions of either, by weighing out exact amounts on the analytical balance and diluting to the proper volume in volumetric flasks. Both primary standards react with iodide ion in acid solution to release free iodine:

$$Cr_2O_7^= + 6I^- + 14H^+ \rightarrow 2Cr^{3+} + 3I_2^\circ + 7H_2O \qquad (22\text{-}3)$$
$$2IO_3^- + 10I^- + 12H^+ \rightarrow 6I_2^\circ + 6H_2O \qquad (22\text{-}4)$$

The iodine released is chemically equivalent to the oxidizing agent used. Thus if 20 ml of $N/40$ $K_2Cr_2O_7$ or $N/40$ $KIO_3 \cdot HIO_3$ is used in the standardization procedure, exactly 20 ml of $N/40$ thiosulfate solution should be used in the titration. If the solution of thiosulfate is stronger than desired, it may be brought to proper strength by diluting with water in accordance with the principles set forth in Sec. 13-1.

The reaction between $Cr_2O_7^=$ and $I^-$ is not instantaneous under the conditions prescribed for the determination. Five minutes are normally needed for completion. The $Cr^{3+}$ produces a greenish-blue color which interferes slightly with the normal starch end point. This difficulty may be overcome to a considerable extent by dilution before titration. Standardization with potassium bi-iodate is usually preferred because it does not suffer from these limitations.

Thiosulfate solutions are subject to attack by bacterial action and by carbon dioxide. Sulfur bacteria oxidize thiosulfates to sulfates under aerobic conditions, and carbon dioxide can depress the pH sufficiently to cause the thiosulfate ion to decompose into $SO_3^=$ and $S°$. The $SO_3^=$ is converted to $SO_4^=$ by dissolved oxygen. Thiosulfate solutions may be protected from bacterial and $CO_2$ attack by adding 0.4 g of NaOH per liter. The resulting high pH prevents bacterial growth and keeps the pH from falling as a result of small amounts of carbon dioxide that may gain access to the solution. Chloroform may be used as a preservative, but it does not protect the solution from carbon dioxide that may be absorbed from the air. In addition, solutions preserved with it tend to dissolve stopcock lubricant.

## 22-5. Methods of Determining Dissolved Oxygen

Originally, measurement of dissolved oxygen was made by heating samples to drive out the dissolved gases and analyzing the collected gases for oxygen by methods applied in gas analysis. Such methods require large samples and are very cumbersome and time-consuming.

The Winkler method or its modifications are the standard procedures for determining dissolved oxygen at the present time. The test depends upon the fact that oxygen oxidizes $Mn^{++}$ to a higher state of valence under alkaline conditions and that manganese in higher states of valence is capable of oxidizing $I^-$ to free $I_2^o$ under acid conditions. Thus the amount of free iodine released is equivalent to the dissolved oxygen originally present. The iodine is measured with standard sodium thiosulfate solution and interpreted in terms of dissolved oxygen.

**The Winkler Method.** The unmodified Winkler method is subject to interference from a great many substances. Certain oxidizing agents such as nitrite and $Fe^{3+}$ are capable of oxidizing $I^-$ to $I_2^o$ and produce results that are too high. Reducing agents such as $Fe^{++}$, $SO_3^=$, $S^=$, polythionates, etc., reduce $I_2^o$ to $I^-$ and produce results that are too low. The unmodified Winkler method is applicable only to relatively pure waters.

The reactions involved in the Winkler procedure are as follows:

$$Mn^{++} + 2OH^- \rightarrow \underline{Mn(OH)_2} \quad \text{white precipitate} \quad (22\text{-}5)$$

If no oxygen is present, a pure white precipitate of $Mn(OH)_2$ forms when $MnSO_4$ and the alkaline iodide reagent (NaOH + KI) are added to the sample. If oxygen is present in the sample, then some of the $Mn^{++}$ is oxidized to a higher valence and precipitates as a brown hydrated oxide. The reaction is usually represented as follows:

$$Mn^{++} + 2OH^- + O \rightarrow MnO_2 + H_2O \quad (22\text{-}6)$$
$$\text{or} \qquad Mn(OH)_2 + O \rightarrow MnO_2 + H_2O \quad (22\text{-}7)$$

The oxidation of $Mn^{++}$ to $MnO_2$, sometimes called fixation of the oxygen, occurs slowly, particularly at low temperatures. Furthermore, it is necessary to move the flocculated material throughout the solution to enable all the oxygen to react. Vigorous shaking of the samples for at least 20 sec is needed. In the case of brackish or sea waters, much longer contact times are required.

After shaking the samples for a time sufficient to allow all oxygen to react, the floc is allowed to settle so as to leave at least 2 in. of clear liquid below the stopper; then sulfuric acid is added. Under the low pH conditions that result, the $MnO_2$ oxidizes $I^-$ to produce free $I_2^\circ$.

$$MnO_2 + 2I^- + 4H^+ \rightarrow Mn^{++} + I_2^\circ + 2H_2O \qquad (22\text{-}8)$$

The sample should be stoppered and shaken for at least 10 sec to allow the reaction to go to completion and to distribute the iodine uniformly throughout the sample.

The sample is now ready for titration with $N/40$ thiosulfate. The use of $N/40$ thiosulfate is based upon the premise that a 200-ml sample will be used for titration. In adding the reagents used for the Winkler test, a certain amount of dilution of the sample occurs; therefore it is necessary to take a sample somewhat greater than 200 ml for the titration. When 300-ml bottles are used in the test, 2 ml of $MnSO_4$ and 2 ml of alkaline-KI solutions are used. These are added in such a manner as to displace approximately 4 ml of sample from the bottle, and a correction should be made. When the 2 ml of acid is added, none of the oxidized floc is displaced; thus no correction need be made for its addition. The correction for the first two reagents may be made as shown in "Standard Methods."

Titration of a sample of a size equivalent to 200 ml of the original sample with $N/40$ thiosulfate solution yields results in milliliters which can be interpreted directly in terms of milligrams per liter of dissolved oxygen.

**The Azide Modification of the Winkler Method.** The nitrite ion is one of the most frequent interferences encountered in the dissolved-oxygen determination. It occurs principally in effluents from sewage treatment plants employing biological processes and in river waters. It does not oxidize $Mn^{++}$ but does oxidize $I^-$ to free $I_2^\circ$ under acid conditions. It is particularly obnoxious because its reduced form, $N_2O_2$, is oxidized by oxygen, which enters the sample during the titration procedure, and is converted to $NO_2^-$ again, establishing a cyclic reaction that can lead to erroneously high results, far in excess of amounts that would be expected. The reactions involved may be represented as follows:

$$2NO_2^- + 2I^- + 4H^+ \rightarrow I_2^\circ + N_2O_2 + 2H_2O \qquad (22\text{-}9)$$

and
$$N_2O_2 + O + H_2O \rightarrow 2NO_2^- + 2H^+ \qquad (22\text{-}10)$$

When interference from nitrites is present, it is impossible to obtain a permanent end point. As soon as the blue color of the starch indicator has been discharged, the nitrites formed by the reaction in Eq. (22-10) will react with more $I^-$ to produce free $I_2^0$ and the blue color of the starch indicator will return.

Nitrite interference may be easily overcome by the use of sodium azide ($NaN_3$). It is most convenient to incorporate the azide in the alkaline-KI reagent. When sulfuric acid is added, the following reactions occur and the $NO_2^-$ is destroyed.

$$NaN_3 + H^+ \rightarrow HN_3 + Na^+ \tag{22-11}$$
$$HN_3 + NO_2^- + H^+ \rightarrow N_2 + N_2O + H_2O \tag{22-12}$$

By this procedure, nitrite interference is eliminated and the method of determination retains the simplicity of the original Winkler procedure.

**Rideal-Stewart Modification of the Winkler Method.** The Rideal-Stewart modification is designed to overcome the effects of a wide variety of interferences caused by reducing substances, including nitrites. It involves pretreatment of the sample with potassium permanganate under acid conditions. The permanganate is added in excess and oxidizes the reducing agents present. The excess is destroyed by adding a reducing agent, potassium oxalate, which in slight excess does not react with free iodine. Some of the reactions involved are as follows:

$$5NO_2^- + 2MnO_4^- + 6H^+ \rightarrow 5NO_3^- + 2Mn^{++} + 3H_2O \tag{22-13}$$
$$5Fe^{++} + MnO_4^- + 8H^+ \rightarrow 5Fe^{3+} + Mn^{++} + 4H_2O \tag{22-14}$$
$$\text{Aldehydes} + MnO_4^- + H^+ \rightarrow \text{acids} + Mn^{++} + H_2O \tag{22-15}$$

$$\begin{array}{cc} H & H \\ | & | \\ \end{array}$$
$$-C{=}C- + MnO_4^- + H^+ \rightarrow \text{acids} + Mn^{++} + H_2O \tag{22-16}$$

The $NO_3^-$ formed in Eq. (22-13) does not oxidize $I^-$ under the conditions of the test. $Fe^{3+}$, in concentrations below 10 mg/l, does not interfere. At levels above 10 mg/l it must be treated to lower its ionic concentration to avoid interference. Potassium fluoride is usually added for this purpose since it supplies $F^-$ which combines with $Fe^{3+}$ to form poorly ionized $FeF_3$.

$$Fe^{3+} + 3F^- \rightarrow FeF_3 \tag{22-17}$$

Excess $KMnO_4$ is destroyed by adding potassium oxalate.

$$5(COO^-)_2 + 2MnO_4^- + 16H^+ \rightarrow 10CO_2 + 2Mn^{++} + 8H_2O \tag{22-18}$$

After the excess permanganate has been destroyed, the regular Winkler procedure is followed except that additional amounts of alkaline-KI are needed to overcome the effects of the acid added originally to facilitate the action of the permanganate. Proper corrections must be made for the volumes of reagents added, in order to calculate the volume of sample required for the titration with thiosulfate.

**The Alkaline-Hypochlorite Modification.** The alkaline-hypochlorite modification of the Winkler method is designed to overcome interferences due to complex sulfur compounds such as occur in certain industrial wastes. The wastes from the sulfite pulp industry and river waters polluted by such wastes are examples. Pretreatment of samples with alkaline-hypochlorite converts the polythionates to sulfates and free sulfur which do not interfere with the dissolved-oxygen test. Excess hypochlorite is destroyed by addition of KI, and the iodine released is destroyed with sodium sulfite. The test is difficult to perform, and results obtained are open to question.

## 22-6. Application of Dissolved-oxygen Data

Dissolved-oxygen data are used in a wide variety of applications. Many of these have been discussed under general considerations in Sec. 22-1.

# $23.$ Biochemical Oxygen Demand

## 23-1. General Considerations

*Biochemical oxygen demand* (BOD) is usually defined as the amount of oxygen required by bacteria while stabilizing decomposable organic matter under aerobic conditions. The term "decomposable" may be interpreted as meaning that the organic matter can serve as food for the bacteria, and energy is derived from its oxidation.

The BOD test is widely used to determine the pollutional strength of sewages and industrial wastes in terms of the oxygen that they will require if discharged into natural watercourses in which aerobic conditions exist. The test is one of the most important in stream-pollution-control activities. By its use, it is possible to determine the degree of pollution in streams at any time. This test is of prime importance in regulatory work and in studies designed to evaluate the purification capacity of receiving bodies of water.

The BOD test is essentially a bioassay procedure involving the measurement of oxygen consumed by living organisms (mainly bacteria) while utilizing the organic matter present in a waste, under conditions as similar as possible to those that occur in nature. In order to make the test quantitative, the samples must be protected from the air to prevent reaeration as the dissolved-oxygen level diminishes. In addition, because of the limited solubility of oxygen in water, about 9 mg/l at 20°C, strong wastes must be diluted to levels of demand in keeping with this value to ensure that dissolved oxygen will be present throughout the period of the test. Since this is a bioassay procedure, it is extremely important that environmental conditions be suitable for the living organisms to function in an unhindered manner at all times. This condition means that toxic substances must be absent and that all accessory nutrients needed for bacterial growth, such as nitrogen, phosphorus, and certain trace elements, must be present. Biological degradation of organic matter under natural conditions is brought about by a diverse group of organisms that carry the oxidation essentially to completion, i.e., almost entirely to carbon dioxide and water. Therefore it is important that a mixed group of organisms, commonly called "seed," be present in the test.

The BOD test may be considered as a wet oxidation procedure in which the living organisms serve as the medium for oxidation of the organic matter to carbon dioxide and water. Since quantitative relationships exist between the amount of oxygen required to convert a definite amount of any given organic compound to carbon dioxide and water, it is possible to interpret BOD data in terms of organic matter as well as the amount of oxygen used during its oxidation. This concept is fundamental to an understanding of the rate at which BOD is exerted.

The oxidative reactions involved in the BOD test are a result of biological activity, and the rate at which the reactions proceed is governed to a major extent by population numbers and temperature. Temperature effects are held constant by performing the test at 20°C which is, more or less, a median value as far as natural bodies of water are concerned. The predominant organisms responsible for the stabilization of organic matter in natural waters are forms native to the soil. The rate of their metabolic processes at 20°C is such that time must be reckoned in days. Theoretically, an infinite time is required for complete biological oxidation of organic matter but, for all practical purposes, the reaction may be considered complete in 20 days. However, a 20-day period is too long to wait for results in most instances. It has been found by experience that a reasonably large percentage of the total BOD is exerted in 5 days; consequently the test has been developed on the basis of a 5-day incubation period. It should be remembered, therefore, that 5-day BOD values represent only a portion of the total BOD. The exact percentage depends upon the character of the "seed" and the nature of the organic matter and can be determined only by experiment. In the case of domestic sewage and many industrial wastes, it has been found that the 5-day BOD value is about 70 to 80 per cent of the total BOD. This is a large enough percentage of the total so that 5-day values are used for many considerations.

## 23-2. The Nature of the BOD Reaction

Studies of the kinetics of BOD reactions have established that they resemble unimolecular reactions but are actually "first order" in character (see Sec. 6-12), or, in reality, the rate of the reaction is proportional to the amount of oxidizable organic matter remaining at any time, as modified by the population of active organisms. Once the population of organisms has reached a level where only minor variations occur, the reaction rate is controlled by the amount of food available to the organisms and may be expressed as follows:

$$\frac{-dC}{dt} \propto C \quad \text{or} \quad \frac{-dC}{dt} = kC \qquad (23\text{-}1)$$

where $C$ represents the concentration of oxidizable organic matter (pollutants) at the start of the time interval $t$, and $k$ is the rate constant for the reaction. This means that the rate of the reaction gradually decreases as the concentration $C$ of food or organic matter decreases.

In BOD considerations it is customary to use $L$ in place of $C$, where $L$ represents the ultimate demand, and the expression

$$\frac{-dL}{dt} = kL \qquad (23\text{-}2)$$

represents the rate at which organic polluting matter is destroyed. Since oxygen is used in stabilizing the organic matter in direct ratio to the amount of organic matter oxidized, it is possible to interpret $L$ in terms of organic polluting matter or in terms of oxygen used, as preferred.

Upon integration of Eq. (23-2), the expression

$$\frac{L_t}{L} = 10^{-kt} \qquad (23\text{-}3)$$

is obtained. This formula says that the amount of pollutants remaining after any time $t$ has elapsed is a fraction of $L$ corresponding to $10^{-kt}$, or the BOD that has not been exerted is a percentage of $L$ corresponding to $10^{-kt}$. This expression is used widely in engineering practice, particularly in stream-pollution-control studies.

In many cases the analyst and the sanitary engineer are interested in the BOD exerted. This value is usually determined by actual test through dissolved-oxygen measurements. Often it is desirable to translate 5-day results to total BOD ($L$) or the BOD at some other time. This is done by a modification of Eq. (23-3) to

$$y = L(1 - 10^{-kt}) \qquad (23\text{-}4)$$

In this expression $y =$ BOD at any time $t$, and $L$ is the total or ultimate BOD. The value of $k$ must be determined by experiment.

Since the BOD reaction is closely related to a unimolecular type of reaction, a plot of the amount of organic matter remaining versus time yields a parabolic curve similar to the decay curve for a radioactive element. Likewise, if a plot is made showing the amount of organic matter oxidized versus time, another parabolic curve is obtained that is the reciprocal of the first. Curves illustrating these changes are shown in Fig. 23-1.

Because oxygen is used in direct ratio to the amount of organic matter oxidized in biochemical oxidations, a plot of oxygen used versus time should produce a parabolic-type curve like the one for organic matter oxidized in Fig. 23-1.   A typical BOD or oxygen-used curve is shown in Fig. 23-2.   It will be noted that the curve has characteristics similar to

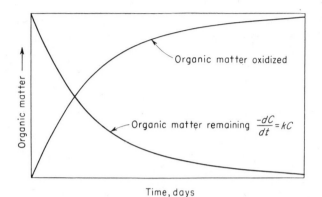

FIG. 23-1. Changes in organic matter during biological oxidation of polluted waters under aerobic conditions.

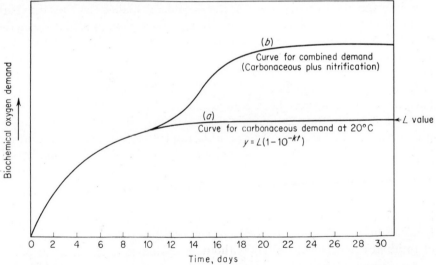

FIG. 23-2. The BOD curve. (*a*) Normal curve for oxidation of organic matter. (*b*) The influence of nitrification.

those for the curve for organic matter oxidized in Fig. 23-1 during the first 8 to 10 days.   Following that, the BOD curve digresses radically from the course it would be expected to follow as a unimolecular or first-order reaction.

The importance of having a mixed culture of organisms corresponding to those in the soil, for proper measurement of BOD, has been mentioned. Such cultures, when derived from the soil or domestic sewage, contain large numbers of saprophytic bacteria and other organisms that utilize the carbonaceous matter present in the samples subjected to BOD analysis and use oxygen in corresponding amount. In addition, they normally contain certain autotrophic bacteria, particularly nitrifying bacteria, which are capable of oxidizing noncarbonaceous matter. The nitrifying bacteria are usually present in relatively small numbers in untreated domestic sewage, and, fortunately, their reproductive rate at 20°C is such that their populations do not become sufficiently large to exert an appreciable demand for oxygen until about 8 to 10 days have elapsed in the regular BOD test. Once the organisms become established, they oxidize nitrogen in the form of ammonia to nitrous and nitric acids in amounts that introduce serious error into BOD work.

$$2NH_3 + 3O_2 \xrightarrow[\text{bacteria}]{\text{nitrite-forming}} 2NO_2^- + 2H^+ + 2H_2O \qquad (23\text{-}5)$$

$$2NO_2^- + O_2 + 2H^+ \xrightarrow[\text{bacteria}]{\text{nitrate-forming}} 2NO_3^- + 2H^+ \qquad (23\text{-}6)$$

The interference caused by nitrifying organisms makes the actual measurement of total carbonaceous BOD impossible unless provision is made to eliminate them. The interference caused by the nitrifying bacteria was a major reason for selecting a 5-day incubation period for the regular BOD test.

In cases where the effluents from biological treatment units, such as trickling filters and activated sludges, are to be analyzed for BOD, the effluents often contain populations of nitrifying organisms sufficient to utilize significant amounts of oxygen during the regular 5-day incubation period. It is important to know the amount of residual carbonaceous BOD in such cases in order to be able to measure plant efficiency.[1] The action of the nitrifying bacteria can be arrested by the use of specific inhibiting agents such as methylene blue, or the nitrifying populations can be reduced to insignificant levels by pretreatment of the sample by pasteurization, chlorination, or acid treatment, thus allowing measurement of residual carbonaceous BOD without interference from nitrification.

### 23-3. Method of Measuring BOD

The BOD test is based upon determinations of dissolved oxygen; consequently the accuracy of the results is influenced greatly by the care given to its measurement. BOD may be measured directly in a few samples but, in general, a dilution procedure is required.

[1] C. N. Sawyer and L. Bradney, *Sewage Works J.*, **18**, 1113 (1946).

**Direct Method.**  With samples whose 5-day BOD does not exceed 7 mg/l, it is not necessary to dilute them, provided that they are aerated to bring the dissolved-oxygen level nearly to saturation at the start of the test.  Many river waters fall into this category.

The usual procedure is to adjust the sample to about 20°C and aerate with diffused air to increase or decrease the dissolved gas content of the sample to near saturation.  Two or more BOD bottles are then filled with the sample; at least one is analyzed for dissolved oxygen immediately, and the others are incubated for 5 days at 20°C.  After 5 days, the amount of dissolved oxygen remaining in the incubated samples is determined, and the 5-day BOD is calculated by subtraction of the 5-day results from those obtained on 0 day.

The direct method of measuring BOD involves no modification of the sample and, therefore, produces results under conditions as nearly similar as possible to the natural environment.  Unfortunately, very few samples fall within the range of dissolved oxygen available in this test.

**Dilution Method.**  The dilution method of measuring BOD is based upon the fundamental concept that the rate of biochemical degradation of organic matter is directly proportional to the amount of unoxidized material existing at the time, as discussed in Sec. 23-2.  According to this concept, the rate at which oxygen is used in dilutions of the waste is in direct ratio to the per cent of waste in the dilution, provided that all other factors are equal.  For instance, a 10 per cent dilution uses oxygen at one-tenth the rate of a 100 per cent sample.  Experience has served as the basis for the mathematical development of the BOD reaction; therefore it is safe to assume the validity of the concept.

In any bioassay work, it is important to control all environmental and nutritional factors in a manner that will not interfere with the desired action.  In the BOD test, this means that everything influencing the rate at which organic matter is biologically stabilized must be kept under close control and highly reproducible from test to test.  The major items of importance are (1) freedom from toxic materials, (2) favorable pH and osmotic conditions, (3) presence of available accessory nutrient elements, (4) standard temperature, and (5) presence of a significant population of mixed organisms of soil origin.

A wide variety of waste materials are subject to the BOD test.  These range from industrial wastes that may be free of microorganisms to domestic sewage with an abundance of organisms.  Many industrial wastes have extremely high BOD values, and very high dilutions must be made to meet the requirements imposed by the limited solubility of oxygen.  Domestic sewage has an ample supply of accessory nutrient elements, such as nitrogen and phosphorus, but many industrial wastes are deficient in one and sometimes both of these elements.  Because of these limitations, the dilution water used in BOD work must compensate for the limitations imposed by any sample subjected to analysis.    Since these limitations are not always known, it is safe practice to use a dilution water that will provide for all contingencies.

*The Dilution Water.*    A wide variety of waters have been used for BOD work.    Natural surface waters would appear to be ideal but they have a number of disadvantages, including variable BOD, variable microorganism population (often including algae and significant populations of nitrifying bacteria), and variable mineral content.    Tap water has been used but it suffers from most of the limitations found in surface waters plus the possibility of toxicity from chlorine residuals.    Through long experience, it has been developed that a synthetic dilution water prepared from distilled water is best for BOD testing because most of the variables mentioned above can be kept under control.

The quality of the distilled water used for the preparation of dilution water is of prime importance.    It must be free from toxic substances. Chlorine or chloramines and copper are the two most commonly found. In many cases it is necessary to dechlorinate the water fed to the still to obtain a chlorine-free distillate.    Copper contamination is normally due to exposed copper in the condenser.    The BOD of distilled waters prepared from potable supplies is usually sufficiently low to allow use of the water without storage other than that needed to bring its temperature into a favorable range.

The pH of dilution water may range anywhere from 6.5 to 8.5 without affecting the action of the saprophytic bacteria.    It is customary to buffer the solution by means of a phosphate system at about pH 7.0.    The buffer is essential to maintain favorable pH conditions at all times.

The proper osmotic conditions are maintained by the potassium and sodium phosphates added to provide buffering capacity.    In addition, calcium and magnesium salts are added which contribute to the total salt content.

The potassium, sodium, calcium, and magnesium salts added to give buffering capacity and proper osmotic conditions also serve to provide the microorganisms with any of these elements that are needed in growth and metabolism.    Ferric chloride, magnesium sulfate, and ammonium chloride supply the requirements for iron, sulfur, and nitrogen.    The phosphate buffer furnishes any phosphorus that may be needed.

The dilution water now contains all the essential materials for the measurement of BOD except the necessary microorganisms.    A wide variety of materials have been used for "seeding" purposes.    Experience has shown that domestic sewage, particularly sewage from combined sewer systems, provides about as well balanced a population of mixed organisms as anything, and usually 2 ml of sewage per liter of dilution water is sufficient. Some river waters are satisfactory but care must be taken to avoid using waters that contain algae or nitrifying bacteria in significant amounts.

The dilution water should always be "seeded" with sewage or other material to ensure a uniform population of organisms in various dilutions and to provide an opportunity for any organic matter present in the dilution water to be exposed to the same type of organisms as are involved in the stabilization of the waste. The latter is a point that is often ignored; this has led to erroneously high results in many cases.

Finally, the dilution water should be aerated to saturate it with oxygen before use.

*The Need for Blanks.* In the determination of BOD by the dilution technique, it is safe to assume that the dilution water containing the "seeding" material will contain organic matter and that addition of the diluting water to the sample will increase the amount of oxidizable organic matter; therefore a correction must be applied. Usually the correction is made without special calculations by letting the 5-day dissolved-oxygen value of the blank represent the 0-day corrected value. It is not necessary to determine the dissolved oxygen of the dilution water on 0 day, unless it is desired to have some measure of the amount of organic matter in the dilution water.

At least three blanks should be included with each set of BOD samples. In any bioassay test there is a certain amount of biological variation. Since the blanks serve as the reference value from which all calculations of BOD are made, it is important that it have some statistical reliability. Usually three blanks provide such reliability, but each analyst should satisfy his particular requirements.

*Dilutions of Waste.* The analyst has a real responsibility in deciding what dilutions should be set for determination of BOD. Usually it is best to set three different dilutions. When the strength of a sample is known with some assurance, two dilutions may suffice. Where samples of unknown strength are involved, the dilutions should cover a considerable range, and in some instances it may be necessary to set as many as four dilutions. In any case there should be an overlapping of the BOD measurable by successive dilutions.

It has been demonstrated that BOD is not influenced by oxygen concentrations as low as 0.5 mg/l. It has also been learned that it is not statistically reliable to base BOD values upon dilutions that produce a depletion of oxygen less than 2 mg/l. Therefore it has become customary to base calculations of BOD on samples that produce a depletion of at least 2 mg/l and have at least 0.5 mg/l of dissolved oxygen remaining at the end of the incubation period. This restriction usually means a range of 2 to 7 mg/l. With this information at hand it is possible to construct a table showing the range of BOD measurable by various dilutions. Table 23-1 presents such information for dilutions prepared on a percentage basis and also for dilutions prepared by direct pipetting into bottles of about 300-ml capacity. It is customary to estimate the BOD of a sample and set one dilution based upon the estimate. Two other dilutions, one higher and one lower, are also set up. For example, a sample is estimated to have a BOD of 1,000 mg/l. Reference to Table 23-1 will show that a 0.5 per cent mixture should be used. If a 0.2 and a 1.0 per cent mixture are included, the range of measurable BOD is extended from 200 to 3,500 mg/l and should compensate for any errors in the original estimate.

TABLE 23-1. BOD MEASURABLE WITH VARIOUS DILUTIONS OF SAMPLES

| Using per cent mixtures | | By direct pipetting into 300-ml bottles | |
| --- | --- | --- | --- |
| % mixture | Range of BOD | ml | Range of BOD |
| 0.01 | 20,000–70,000 | 0.02 | 30,000–105,000 |
| 0.02 | 10,000–35,000 | 0.05 | 12,000– 42,000 |
| 0.05 | 4,000–14,000 | 0.10 | 6,000– 21,000 |
| 0.1 | 2,000– 7,000 | 0.20 | 3,000– 10,500 |
| 0.2 | 1,000– 3,500 | 0.50 | 1,200– 4,200 |
| 0.5 | 400– 1,400 | 1.0 | 600– 2,100 |
| 1.0 | 200– 700 | 2.0 | 300– 1,050 |
| 2.0 | 100– 350 | 5.0 | 120– 420 |
| 5.0 | 40– 140 | 10.0 | 60– 210 |
| 10.0 | 20– 70 | 20.0 | 30– 105 |
| 20.0 | 10– 35 | 50.0 | 12– 42 |
| 50.0 | 4– 14 | 100 | 6– 21 |
| 100 | 0– 7 | 300 | 0– 7 |

In the direct-pipetting technique, preliminary dilutions should be made of all samples that require less than 0.5 ml of the sample, so that amounts added to the bottles can be measured without serious error. The volumes of all bottles must be known in order to allow calculation of the BOD when this method is used.

*Incubation Bottles.* The bottles used for BOD analysis should be equipped with glass stoppers that are ground to a point to prevent trapping of air when the stopper is inserted. The bottles should be equipped with some form of water seal to prevent air entering the bottle during the incubation period.

It is extremely important that bottles used for BOD work be free of organic matter. Cleaning can be best accomplished by use of a chromic acid solution.[1] Care must be exercised to make sure that all chromic acid is removed from the bottle before use. This assurance can usually be accomplished by four rinses with tap water and a final rinse with distilled water.

*Initial Dissolved Oxygen.* With samples whose BOD is below 200 mg/l, it is necessary to use amounts of sample in excess of 1.0 per cent. Serious errors may be introduced in results if the dissolved oxygen of the sample differs materially from that of the dilution water and corrections are not made. In such cases, the dissolved oxygen of the sample should be determined separately. In most cases it is less laborious and time-consuming to adjust the samples to 20°C and aerate to saturation. This eliminates the need for measuring dissolved oxygen on the sample and also satisfies any immediate oxygen demand.

*Calculation of BOD.* For all practical purposes, the calculation of BOD by the dilution method can be made by the use of either of two simple formulas.

For per cent mixtures:

$$\text{BOD (in mg/l)} = \left[ (DO_b - DO_i) \frac{100}{\%} \right] - (DO_b - DO_s) \quad (23\text{-}7)$$

For direct pipetting:

$$\text{BOD (in mg/l)} = \left[ (DO_b - DO_i) \frac{\text{vol. of bottle}}{\text{ml sample}} \right] - (DO_b - DO_s) \quad (23\text{-}8)$$

In these calculations, $DO_b$ and $DO_i$ are the dissolved-oxygen values found in the blanks and the dilutions of the sample, respectively, at the end of the incubation period, and $DO_s$ is the dissolved oxygen originally present in the undiluted sample. From Eqs. (23-7) and (23-8), it becomes obvious that when $DO_s$ approaches the value of $DO_b$ it may be ignored. Further, it becomes unnecessary to correct for the dissolved oxygen of the sample when the BOD exceeds 200 mg/l because the value of $DO_b - DO_s$ seldom exceeds a value of 8. The BOD test is considered to have an accuracy of ±5 per cent, and 8 is within the expected error at and above such levels of BOD.

In BOD analysis it often happens that more than one dilution of the sample yield results that show a depletion of oxygen greater than 2 mg/l and have a residual of more than 0.5 mg/l. Thus it is possible to make more than one calculation of BOD. According to the fundamental concepts upon which the dilution method is based, the calculated values should check within the normal experimental variation of about ±5 per

[1] J. P. Mascarenhas and G. Klein, Evaluation of BOD Bottle Cleaning Techniques, *Sewage and Ind. Wastes*, **30**, 976 (1958).

cent.   This is not always the case, however.   When discrepancies occur, the question naturally arises as to which value is most reliable.   An answer can often be obtained by calculating a third value for BOD from the data available.   This situation can be best illustrated with an example.   Assume the following data have been accumulated at the end of the incubation period:

| Sample | DO | Depletion | BOD |
|---|---|---|---|
| Blanks | 8.2 | | |
| 1% Dilution | 5.5 | 2.7 | 270 |
| 2% Dilution | 3.3 | 4.9 | 245 |
| 4% Dilution | 0 | | |

The values of 245 and 270 do not check within the expected limits. Statistically, the chances are that one value is more reliable than the other; therefore it is not good practice to take the arithmetic average. A third value of BOD may be calculated by subtracting the residual dissolved oxygen of the 2 per cent mixture from that of the 1 per cent mixture.   The depletion of 2.2 mg/l obtained is due to the 1 per cent increment in the sample, and the calculated BOD would be 220.   This value indicates that the value of 245 is the more reliable.   If it had been near 270, it would have indicated that that value was more reliable.

It sometimes happens that all three dilutions used in BOD analysis yield depletions and residuals of dissolved oxygen that allow calculation of BOD.   Using the system of subtracting one dilution from another, it is possible to calculate six values of BOD from such a set of data.   By such a system, one can eliminate dependence upon blanks, if the analyst chooses to do so.   There is some hazard involved, however, since at least two dilutions must show significant residuals of dissolved oxygen.

## 23-4. Rate of Biochemical Oxidations

For a great many years the BOD reaction was considered to have a rate constant $k$ equal to 0.10 per day at 20°C.   This value was established by extensive studies on polluted river waters and domestic sewage in the United States and England.   As application of the BOD test spread to the analysis of industrial wastes and the use of synthetic dilution waters became established, it was soon noted that $k$ values considerably in excess of 0.10 per day were involved and that an appreciable variation occurred for different waste materials.   In addition, it was found that $k$ values for sewage varied considerably from day to day and averaged about 0.17 per day rather than 0.10 per day as originally determined.   The importance of the reaction rate $k$ with respect to the BOD developed at any time is shown in Table 23-2.

TABLE 23-2. SIGNIFICANCE OF REACTION RATE $k$ UPON BOD

| Time, days | Per cent of total BOD exerted | | | |
|---|---|---|---|---|
| | $k = 0.10$ | $k = 0.15$ | $k = 0.20$ | $k = 0.25$ |
| 1 | 20.6 | 29.2 | 36.9 | 43.8 |
| 2 | 37 | 50 | 60 | 68 |
| 3 | 50 | 64 | 75 | 82 |
| 4 | 60 | 75 | 84 | 90 |
| 5 | 68 | 82 | 90 | 94 |
| 6 | 75 | 87 | 94 | 97 |
| 7 | 80 | 91 | 96 | 98 |
| 10 | 90 | 97 | 99 | 99 |
| 20 | 99 | 99+ | 99+ | 99+ |

From the values shown in Table 23-2, it will be noted that the course of the BOD reaction varies greatly, depending upon the reaction rate. The 5-day BOD values represent about 68 per cent of the total BOD when $k = 0.1$ per day and as much as 94 per cent when $k = 0.25$ per day. From this it may be concluded that $k$ values must be known if a proper evaluation of ultimate BOD, or $L$, is to be calculated from 5-day values.

The significance of $k$ in determining the course of the BOD reaction is illustrated in Fig. 23-3. For a waste having a given $L$ value, the BOD

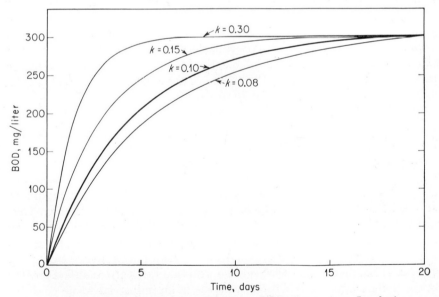

FIG. 23-3. Effect of velocity constant $k$ on BOD (for a given $L$ value).

values on any given day will vary widely until about 15 days have elapsed. In the past it was common practice to interpret 5-day BOD in terms of $L$ values by assuming a $k$ value of 0.10 per day. Figure 23-4 shows how the $L$ value of a sample with a 5-day BOD of 200 varies with the value of $k$.

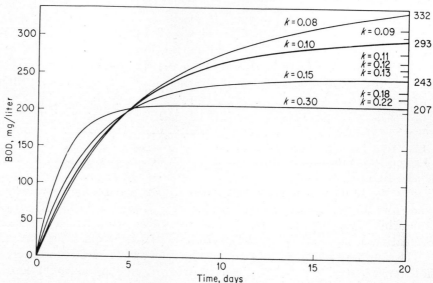

FIG. 23-4. Effect of velocity constant $k$ on total BOD $L$ (based on assumed 5-day BOD of 200 mg/l).

The variation in $k$ values leaves considerable room for speculation as to why such differences in rates of reaction occur. Two factors of major importance are involved: (1) the nature of the organic matter and (2) the ability of the organisms present to utilize the organic matter.

Organic matter occurring in sewage and industrial wastes varies greatly in chemical character and availability to microorganisms. That part which exists in true solution is readily available but that part which occurs in colloidal and coarse suspension must await hydrolytic action before it can diffuse into the bacterial cells where oxidation can occur. The rate of hydrolysis and diffusion are probably the most important factors in controlling the rate of the reaction. It is well known that simple substrates, such as glucose, are removed from solution at very rapid rates and $k$ values are correspondingly high. More complex materials are removed much more slowly and $k$ values are lower. In a complex material such as domestic sewage, reaction rates are modified greatly by the more complex substances, whereas in an industrial waste containing soluble compounds of simple character, the reaction rate is usually very rapid. Certain organic compounds, such as lignin, are very slowly attacked by bacteria. Some of the synthetic detergents also fall into this category.

A lag period is often noted in the BOD reaction with some industrial wastes, particularly those containing organic compounds of synthetic origin and of chemical structure not found in natural materials. The "seeding" organisms used in the BOD test may or may not have specific bacteria that can utilize the material as food. If not, the substance will not exert a BOD. Oftentimes only a few bacteria are present that can oxidize the substance, and the rate of oxidation is so slow for a period, possibly several days, that a measurable BOD cannot be detected. With sufficient time, however, the population of the specific bacteria will increase to levels where the oxidation progresses at normal rates. In cases of this kind, the lag period can usually be overcome by using for "seeding" purposes water from a river into which such wastes are discharged. The water should be taken well downstream from the point of discharge.

The phenomenon of the lag period is sometimes explained on the basis that the "seeding" organisms do not have the proper enzyme systems to utilize the organic matter. With time, however, they adapt themselves to the new food supply and furnish the necessary enzymes.

The rate of biochemical reactions, or rate constant $k$, can be evaluated in a number of ways. All are dependent upon making BOD observations at two or more time intervals so as to establish the "trajectory" of the reaction. A treatment of the various methods is beyond the scope of this discussion.

## 23-5. Discrepancy between $L$ Values and Theoretical Oxygen Demand Values

For many years the total BOD, or $L$, value of organic substances was considered to be equal to the theoretical oxygen demand as calculated from the chemical equation involved. For example, oxidation of glucose to carbon dioxide and water requires 192 g of oxygen per mole or 1.065 mg of oxygen per milligram of glucose.

$$\underset{180}{C_6H_{12}O_6} + \underset{192}{6O_2} \rightarrow 6CO_2 + 6H_2O \qquad (23\text{-}9)$$

A great deal of BOD work has been done with glucose solutions in a concentration of 300 mg/l. Such a solution has a theoretical oxygen demand of 320 mg/l. Actual BOD measurements made upon such solutions have yielded 20-day[1] and calculated $L$ values in the range of 250 to

[1] A. Q. Y. Tom, "Investigations on Improving the BOD Test," Sc.D. Thesis, Massachusetts Institute of Technology, 1951.

285.   Thus it is evident that all the glucose is not completely converted to carbon dioxide and water.   The explanation of the discrepancy involves an understanding of the transformations that organic matter undergoes when subjected to biological attack.

In order for organic matter to be oxidized by bacteria, it must serve as food material from which the organisms can derive energy for growth and reproduction.   This means that part of the organic matter is converted to cell tissue.   The part that is converted to cell tissue will remain unoxidized until such time as the organisms must draw upon cell tissue to derive energy to maintain life (endogenous respiration).   When bacteria die they become food material for other bacteria, and a further transformation to carbon dioxide, water, and cell tissue occurs.   Living bacteria, as well as dead ones, serve as food material for higher organisms such as protozoans.   In each transformation further oxidation occurs but in the final analysis there remains a certain amount of organic matter that is quite resistant to further biological attack.   This is commonly referred to as humus and represents an amount of organic matter corresponding to the discrepancy between the total BOD and the theoretical oxygen demand.

### 23-6. Application of BOD Data

BOD data have wide application in sanitary engineering practice.   It is the principal test applied to sewage and industrial wastes to determine strength in terms of oxygen required for stabilization.   It is the only test which is applied that gives a measure of the amount of biologically oxidizable organic matter present that can be used to determine the rates at which oxidation will occur, or BOD will be exerted, in receiving bodies of water.   BOD is, therefore, the major criterion used in stream pollution control where organic loading must be restricted to maintain desired dissolved-oxygen levels.   The determination is used in studies to measure the purification capacity of streams and serves regulatory authorities as a means of checking on the quality of effluents discharged to such waters.

Information concerning the BOD of wastes is an important consideration in the design of treatment facilities.   It is a factor in the choice of treatment method and is used to determine the size of certain units, particularly trickling filters and activated sludge units.   After treatment plants are placed in operation, the test is used to evaluate the efficiency of various units.

Many municipalities and sewer authorities finance sewage treatment operations through sewer rental charges.   BOD is one of the factors normally used in calculating such charges, particularly where secondary treatment employing biological processes is employed.

# $24.$ Chemical Oxygen Demand

## 24-1. General Considerations

The *chemical oxygen demand* (COD) test is widely used as a means of measuring the pollutional strength of sewages and industrial wastes. It is based upon the fact that all organic compounds, with a few exceptions, can be oxidized to carbon dioxide and water by the action of strong oxidizing agents under acid conditions.

During the determination of COD, organic matter is converted to carbon dioxide and water regardless of the biological assimilability of the substances. For example, glucose and lignin are both oxidized completely. As a result, COD values are greater than BOD values and may be much greater when significant amounts of biologically resistant organic matter is present. Wood-pulping wastes are excellent examples because of their high lignin content. For reasons presented in Sec. 23-5, the COD of materials such as glucose is always greater than the $L$ value.

One of the chief limitations of the COD test is its inability to differentiate between biologically oxidizable and biologically inert organic matter. In addition, it does not provide any evidence of the rate at which the biologically active material would be stabilized under conditions that exist in nature.

The major advantage of the COD test is the short time required for evaluation. The determination can be made in about 3 hr rather than the 5 days required for the measurement of BOD. For this reason it is used as a substitute for the BOD test in many instances. COD data can often be interpreted in terms of BOD values after sufficient experience has been accumulated to establish reliable correlation factors.

## 24-2. History of the COD Test

Chemical oxidizing agents have long been used for measuring the oxygen demand of sewage and polluted waters. Potassium permanganate solutions were used for many years, and the results were referred to as *oxygen consumed* from permanganate. The oxidation caused by permanganate was highly variable with respect to various types of compounds, and the degree of oxidation varied considerably with the strength of reagent used. Oxygen-consumed values were always considerably less than 5-day BOD values. This fact demonstrated the inability of permanganate to carry the oxidation to any particular end point.

Ceric sulfate, potassium iodate, and potassium dichromate are other oxidizing agents that have been studied extensively for the determination of chemical oxygen demand. Potassium dichromate has been found to be the most practical of all, since it is capable of oxidizing a wide variety of organic substances almost completely to carbon dioxide and water. Because all oxidizing agents must be used in excess, it is necessary to measure the amount of excess remaining at the end of the reaction period in order to calculate the amount actually used in the oxidation of the organic matter. It is relatively easy to measure any excess of potassium dichromate, an important point in its favor.

In order for potassium dichromate to oxidize organic matter completely, the solution must be strongly acidic and at an elevated temperature. As a result, volatile materials originally present and those formed during the digestion period are lost unless provision is made to prevent their escape. Reflux condensers are ordinarily used for this purpose and allow the sample to be boiled without significant loss of volatile organic compounds.

Certain organic compounds, particularly low-molecular-weight fatty acids, are not oxidized by dichromate unless a catalyst is present. It has been found that silver ion acts effectively in this capacity. Aromatic hydrocarbons and pyridine are not oxidized under any circumstances.

## 24-3. Chemical Oxygen Demand by Dichromate

Potassium dichromate is a relatively cheap compound which can be obtained in a high state of purity. The analytical-reagent grade, after drying at 103°C, can be used to prepare solutions of an exact normality by direct weighing and dilution to the proper volume. The dichromate ion is a very potent oxidizing agent in solutions that are strongly acid. The reaction involved may be represented in a general way as follows:

$$\text{Organic matter (CHO)} + Cr_2O_7^= + H^+ \rightarrow 2Cr^{3+} + CO_2 + H_2O \quad (24\text{-}1)$$

For these and other reasons mentioned previously dichromate approaches an ideal reagent for the measurement of COD.

**Selection of Normality.** COD results are reported in terms of milligrams of oxygen. Since the equivalent weight of oxygen is 8, it would seem logical to use a $N/8$ or $0.125\ N$ solution of oxidizing agent in the determination, so that results can be calculated in accordance with the general procedure described in Sec. 13-1. Experience with the test has shown that it has sufficient sensitivity to allow the use of a stronger solution of dichromate, and a $N/4$ or 0.25 $N$ solution is recommended. This allows the use of larger samples by doubling the range of COD that can be measured in the test procedure, since each milliliter of a 0.25 $N$ solution of dichromate is equivalent to 2 mg of oxygen.

**Measurement of Excess Oxidizing Agent.** In any method of measuring COD, an excess of oxidizing agent must be present to ensure that all organic matter is oxidized as completely as is within the power of the reagent. This requires that a reasonable excess be present in all samples. It is necessary, of course, to measure the excess in some manner so that the actual amount reduced can be determined. A solution of a reducing agent is ordinarily used.

Nearly all solutions of reducing agents are gradually oxidized by oxygen dissolved from the air unless special care is taken to protect them from oxygen. Ferrous ion is an excellent reducing agent for dichromate. Solutions of it can be best prepared from ferrous ammonium sulfate which is obtainable in rather pure and stable form. In solution, however, it is slowly oxidized by oxygen, and standardization is required each time the reagent is to be used. The standardization is made with the 0.25 $N$ solution of dichromate. The reaction between ferrous ammonium sulfate and dichromate may be represented as follows:

$$6Fe^{++} + Cr_2O_7^= + 14H^+ \rightarrow 6Fe^{3+} + 2Cr^{3+} + 7H_2O \qquad (24\text{-}2)$$

**Blanks.** Both the COD and BOD tests are designed to measure oxygen requirements by oxidation of organic matter present in the samples. It is important, therefore, that no organic matter from outside sources be present if a true measure of the amount present in the sample is to be obtained. Since it is impossible to exclude extraneous organic matter in the BOD test and it is impractical to do so in the COD test, blank samples are required in both determinations.

**Indicator.** A very marked change in oxidation-reduction potential (ORP) occurs at the end point of all oxidation-reduction reactions. Such changes may be readily detected by electrometric means if the necessary equipment is available. Oxidation-reduction indicators may also be used; Ferroin (ferrous 1, 10-phenanthroline sulfate) is an excellent one to indicate when all dichromate has been reduced by ferrous ion. It gives a very sharp color change that is easily detected in spite of the green color produced by the $Cr^{3+}$ formed on reduction of the dichromate.

**Calculations.** Although an oxidizing agent is used in the measurement of COD, it does not figure directly in the calculation of COD. This is because a solution of a reducing agent must be used to determine how much of the oxidizing agent was used, and it is simpler to relate everything to the reducing agent in this case, because its strength varies from day to day and its normality is seldom, if ever, exactly equal to 0.25 $N$.

## 24-4. Application of COD Data

The COD test is used extensively in the analysis of industrial wastes. It is particularly valuable in surveys designed to determine and control losses to sewer systems. Results may be obtained within a relatively short time and measures taken to correct errors on the day they occur. In conjunction with the BOD test, the COD test is helpful in indicating toxic conditions and the presence of biologically resistant organic substances. The test is widely used in the operation of treatment facilities because of the speed with which results can be obtained.

# $25.$ Nitrogen

## 25-1. General Considerations

The compounds of nitrogen are of great interest to sanitary engineers because of the importance of nitrogen in the life processes of all plants and animals. The chemistry of nitrogen is complex because of the several valence states that nitrogen can assume and the fact that changes in valence can be brought about by living organisms. To add even more interest, the valence changes wrought by bacteria can be either positive or negative, depending upon whether aerobic or anaerobic conditions prevail.

From the viewpoint of the inorganic chemist, nitrogen can exist in seven states of valence, and compounds in all valences are of interest to him.

$$\overset{3-}{NH_3} - \overset{1+}{N_2^o} - \overset{2+}{N_2O} - \overset{3+}{NO} - \overset{4+}{N_2O_3} - \overset{5+}{NO_2} - N_2O_5$$

As far as is known, compounds of nitrogen in $1+$, $2+$, and $4+$ valences have little, if any, significance in biological processes. All other forms are important, and the chemistry of nitrogen of interest to sanitary engineers may be summarized as follows:

$$\overset{3-}{NH_3} - \overset{3+}{N_2^o} - \overset{5+}{N_2O_3} - N_2O_5$$

Organic
derivatives

$N_2O_3$ and $N_2O_5$ are the acid anhydrides of nitrous and nitric acids.

The relationships that exist between the various forms of nitrogen compounds and the changes that can occur in nature are best illustrated by a diagram known as the nitrogen cycle, shown in Fig. 25-1. From it, it will be seen that the atmosphere serves as a reservoir from which nitrogen is constantly removed by the action of electrical discharge and nitrogen-fixing bacteria and algae. During electrical storms large amounts of nitrogen are oxidized to $N_2O_5$, and its union with water produces $HNO_3$

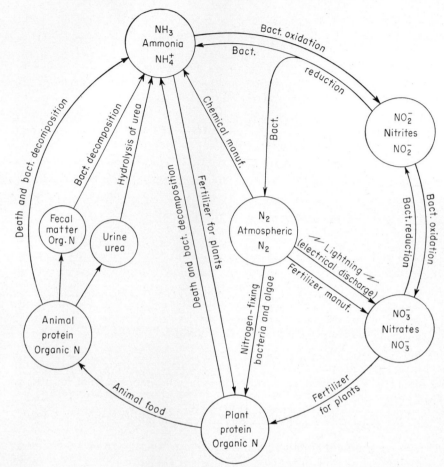

FIG. 25-1. The nitrogen cycle.

which is carried to the earth in the rain.   The nitrates serve to fertilize plant life and are converted to proteins.

$$NO_3^- + CO_2 + \text{green plants} + \text{sunlight} \rightarrow \text{protein} \qquad (25\text{-}1)$$

Atmospheric nitrogen is also converted to proteins by nitrogen-"fixing" bacteria and certain algae.

$$N_2 + \text{special bacteria or algae} \rightarrow \text{protein} \qquad (25\text{-}2)$$

In addition, ammonium compounds supply ammonia to plants for further production of proteins.

$$NH_3 + CO_2 + \text{green plants} + \text{sunlight} \rightarrow \text{protein} \qquad (25\text{-}3)$$

Animals and human beings are incapable of utilizing nitrogen from the atmosphere or from inorganic compounds to produce proteins. They are dependent upon plants, or other animals that feed upon plants, to provide protein. Within the animal body, protein matter is used largely for growth and repair of muscle tissue. Some may be used for energy purposes. In any event, nitrogen compounds are released in the waste products of the body during life. At death the proteins stored in the body become waste matter for disposal. The urine contains the nitrogen resulting from the metabolic breakdown of proteins. The nitrogen exists in urine principally as urea which is hydrolyzed rather rapidly by the enzyme urease to ammonium carbonate.

$$C \overset{NH_2}{\underset{NH_2}{\diagup \atop \diagdown}} O + 2H_2O \xrightarrow[\text{urease}]{\text{enzyme}} (NH_4)_2CO_3 \qquad (25\text{-}4)$$

The feces of animals contain appreciable amounts of unassimilated protein matter (organic nitrogen). It and the protein matter remaining in the bodies of dead animals and plants are converted to ammonia by the action of saprophytic bacteria, under either aerobic or anaerobic conditions.

$$\text{Protein (organic N)} + \text{bact.} \rightarrow NH_3 \qquad (25\text{-}5)$$

The ammonia released by bacterial action on urea and proteins may be used by plants directly to produce plant protein. If it is released in excess of plant requirements, the excess is oxidized by nitrifying bacteria. One group, known as the nitrite formers, convert ammonia under aerobic conditions to nitrites and derive energy from the oxidation.

$$NH_3 + 3O_2 \xrightarrow{\text{bact.}} NO_2^- + H^+ + H_2O \qquad (25\text{-}6)$$

The nitrites are oxidized by a second group of nitrifying bacteria called the nitrate formers.

$$2NO_2^- + O_2 \xrightarrow{\text{bact.}} 2NO_3^- \qquad (25\text{-}7)$$

The nitrates formed may serve as fertilizer for plants. Nitrates produced in excess of the needs of plant life are carried away in water percolating through the soil because the soil does not have the ability to hold them. This frequently results in relatively high concentrations of nitrates in ground waters.

Under anaerobic conditions nitrates and nitrites are both reduced. Presumably nitrates are reduced to nitrites and then reduction of nitrites occurs. Reduction of nitrites is carried all the way to ammonia by a few bacteria but most of them carry the reduction to nitrogen gas, which escapes to the atmosphere. This constitutes a serious loss of fertilizing matter in soils when anaerobic conditions develop. The formation of nitrogen gas by reduction of nitrates is sometimes a problem in the activated sludge process of sewage treatment. Prolonged detention of activated sludge in final settling tanks allows formation of sufficient nitrogen gas to buoy the sludge, if nitrates are present in adequate amounts. This is often referred to as the "rising" sludge problem.

## 25-2. Sanitary Significance of Nitrogen Data

Analyses for nitrogen in its various forms have been performed on potable and polluted waters ever since man became convinced that water was a vehicle for the transmission of disease. The determinations served as one basis of judging the sanitary quality of water for a great many years. Today nitrogen analyses are performed largely for other reasons.

**An Indicator of Sanitary Quality.** It has long been known that polluted waters will purify themselves provided that they are allowed to age for sufficient periods of time. The hazard to health or the possibility of contracting disease by drinking such waters decreases markedly with time and temperature increase, as shown in Fig. 25-2.

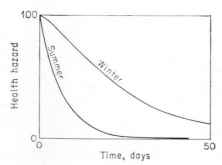

FIG. 25-2. Surface waters: health hazard in relation to age of pollution.

Prior to the development of bacteriological tests for determining the sanitary quality of water (about 1905), sanitary engineers and others concerned with the public health were largely dependent upon chemical tests to provide circumstantial evidence of the presence of contamination. The chloride test was one of these (see Sec. 21-2), but it gave no evidence of how recently the contamination had occurred. Chemists working with sewage and freshly polluted waters learned that most of the nitrogen is originally present in the form of organic (protein) nitrogen and ammonia. As time progresses, the organic nitrogen is gradually converted to ammonia nitrogen, and later on, if aerobic conditions are present, oxidation of ammonia to nitrites and nitrates occurs. The progression of events was found to occur somewhat as shown in Fig. 25-3, and more refined interpretations of the sanitary quality of water were based upon this knowledge. For example, waters that contained mostly organic and ammonia nitrogen were considered to have been recently polluted and, therefore, of great potential danger. Waters in which most of the nitrogen was in

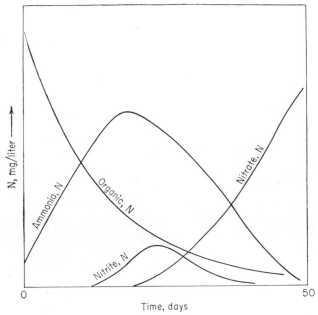

FIG. 25-3. Changes occurring in forms of nitrogen present in polluted water under aerobic conditions.

the form of nitrates were considered to have been polluted a long time previously and, therefore, offered little threat to the public health. Waters with appreciable amounts of nitrites were of highly questionable character. The bacteriological test for coliform organisms provides circumstantial evidence of much greater reliability concerning the hygienic safety of water, and it has eliminated the need for extended nitrogen analysis in most water supplies.

Of recent years (1940) it has been found that drinking waters with high nitrate content often cause methemoglobinemia in infants. From extended investigations in Iowa, Minnesota, and Ohio, where the problem has been most acute, it has been concluded that the nitrate content in terms of nitrogen should not exceed 20 mg/l in public water supplies.[1]

[1] K. F. Maxcy, Report on Relation of Nitrate Nitrogen Concentration in Well Waters to the Occurrence of Methemoglobinemia in Infants, *Natl. Acad. Sci.-Research Council Sanit. Eng. and Environment Bull.* 264, 1950.

**Nutritional and Related Problems.**    All biological treatment processes employed by sanitary engineers are dependent upon reproduction of the organisms employed, as discussed in Sec. 8-7.   In planning waste treatment facilities it becomes important to know whether the waste contains sufficient nitrogen for the organisms.   If not, any deficiency must be supplied from outside sources.   Determinations of ammonia and organic nitrogen are normally made to obtain such data.

Nitrogen is one of the fertilizing elements essential to the growth of algae.   Such growth is often stimulated to an undesirable extent in bodies of water that receive sewage or treatment plant effluents, because of the nitrogen and other fertilizing matter contributed by them.   Nitrogen analyses are an important means of gaining information on this problem.

**Control of Biological Treatment Processes.**    Determinations of nitrogen are often made to control the degree of purification produced in biological treatment processes.   Before the development of the BOD test, nitrite and nitrate tests were commonly used.   Significant nitrification was correlated with a high degree of stabilization.   With the use of the BOD test, it has been learned that effective stabilization of organic matter can be accomplished without carrying the oxidation into the nitrification stage.   This results in a material saving of time and air required; consequently tests for nitrites and nitrates are often used to control aeration practice.

## 25-3. Methods of Analysis

Since nitrogen exists in four forms that are of interest to sanitary engineers, a discussion of the determination of each form is required.   Because of differences in the amounts present in potable and polluted waters, methods applied to water may differ somewhat from those applied to sewage.   It is customary to report all results in terms of nitrogen so that values may be interpreted from one form to another without use of a factor.

**Ammonia Nitrogen.**    All nitrogen that exists as ammonium ion or in the equilibrium

$$NH_4^+ \rightleftharpoons NH_3 + H^+ \qquad (25\text{-}8)$$

is considered to be ammonia nitrogen.

*By Direct Nesslerization.*    In samples that have been properly clarified by a pretreatment method using zinc sulfate and sodium hydroxide, it is possible to obtain a measure of the amount of ammonia nitrogen by treatment with Nessler's reagent, which is a strongly alkaline solution of potassium mercuric iodide.   Its formula may be represented as $K_2HgI_4$ or simply $2KI \cdot HgI_2$.   It combines with $NH_3$ in alkaline solution to form a yellowish-brown colloidal dispersion whose intensity of color is directly proportional to the amount of $NH_3$ originally present.   The reaction may be represented by the equation

$$2K_2HgI_4 + NH_3 + 3KOH \rightarrow \quad \begin{array}{c} I \\ \diagup \\ Hg \\ \diagdown \\ O \\ \diagup \\ Hg \\ \diagdown \\ NH_2 \end{array} \quad + 7KI + 2H_2O \quad (25\text{-}9)$$

Yellowish-brown
colloid

The color developed with Nessler's reagent is easily matched by eye, and many people prefer to make visual comparisons rather than to depend upon photometric methods.   Nessler reagent prepared by different procedures and on different occasions varies somewhat in its sensitivity to ammonia.   It is usually good technique to prepare fresh visual standards or a new calibration curve each time a change is made in Nessler reagent.

*By Distillation.*   The direct Nesslerization procedure is subject to serious error from extraneous color and turbidity.   It is impractical to use it on many samples.   The distillation procedure is used to separate the ammonia from interfering substances, and measurement of ammonia nitrogen can then be made in a number of ways.

Ammonium ion exists in equilibrium with ammonia and hydrogen ion, as shown in Eq. (25-8).   At pH levels above 7, the equilibrium is displaced sufficiently to the right so that ammonia is liberated as a gas along with the steam produced when a sample is boiled, as follows:

$$NH_4^+ \overset{\Delta}{\rightarrow} NH_3\uparrow + H^+ \qquad (25\text{-}10)$$

If provision is made to condense the steam, ammonia will be absorbed in the condensate.   Removal of ammonia allows the hydrogen ions released in the decomposition of ammonium ion to accumulate in the residue, and a decrease in pH will result unless a buffer is present to combine with the hydrogen ions.   A phosphate buffer is added to maintain the pH in a range of 7.2 to 7.4.   Higher pH levels are not recommended because of the danger of some ammonia being released from organic sources at the temperature of boiling water.   Experience has shown that essentially all the free ammonia will be expelled by the time 200 ml of water has been distilled from solutions whose pH is maintained between 7.2 to 7.4, when samples of 500 ml or less are used.

For water samples that contain small amounts of ammonia nitrogen, the usual procedure is to measure the amount of nitrogen in the distillate by use of Nessler's reagent, as described above.  The calculation of ammonia nitrogen in terms of milligrams per liter must take into consideration the volume of distillate as well as the sample size.  If exactly 200 ml of distillate is obtained, the calculation can be made as shown in "Standard Methods."  Many analysts find it more convenient to distill an amount that exceeds 200 ml to avoid close attention at the end of the distillation.  The calculation can be made, provided that the volume of distillate is known, by the following method:

$$\text{mg/l } NH_3\text{---}N = \frac{V_D}{V_{DN}} \times N \times \frac{1,000}{s} \qquad (25\text{-}11)$$

where $V_D$ is the volume of distillate, $V_{DN}$ is the volume of distillate actually Nesslerized, $N$ is the amount of $NH_3$—N found in the Nesslerized portion of the distillate, and $s$ is the volume of sample used for the distillation.  $N$ should be expressed in milligrams.

When samples contain more than 1 mg/l of ammonia nitrogen, as is the case with sewage and many industrial wastes, it is best to absorb the ammonia in boric acid and measure the amount by back titration with standard acid.  The chemistry involved may be represented as follows: Boric acid is an excellent buffer.  It combines with ammonia to form ammonium and borate ions, as shown in the equation.

$$NH_3 + HBO_2 \rightarrow NH_4^+ + BO_2^- \qquad (25\text{-}12)$$

This causes the pH to increase somewhat, as was discussed under buffer action in Sec. 8-6, but the pH is held in a favorable range for absorption of ammonia by the use of an excess of boric acid.  The ammonia may then be measured by a back titration with a strong acid.  Actually, the acid measures the amount of borate ion present in the solution as follows:

$$BO_2^- + H^+ \rightarrow HBO_2 \qquad (25\text{-}13)$$

When the pH of the boric acid solution has been decreased to its original value, an amount of strong acid equivalent to the ammonia has been added.  The titration is most easily conducted by electrometric methods which eliminate the need for internal indicators.  The proper pH for the end point is best determined by diluting the specified volume of boric acid solution with ammonia-free distilled water in an amount equal to the volume of distillate desired and measuring the pH of the mixture.

**Organic Nitrogen.**  All nitrogen present in organic compounds may be considered organic nitrogen.  This includes the nitrogen in amino acids, amines, amides, imides, nitro derivatives, and a number of other compounds.  Most of these have very little significance in sanitary analysis unless specific industrial wastes are involved.

Most of the organic nitrogen that occurs in domestic sewage is in the form of proteins or their degradation products: polypeptides and amino acids. Therefore the methods employed in sanitary analysis have been designed to ensure measurement of these forms without particular regard to other organic forms. Actually most forms except the nitrogen in nitro compounds are measured by the method used.

Most organic compounds containing nitrogen are derivatives of ammonia, and destruction of the organic portion of the molecule by oxidation frees the nitrogen as ammonia. The Kjeldahl method employing sulfuric acid as the oxidizing agent is standard procedure. A catalyst is ordinarily needed to hasten the oxidation of some of the more resistant organic materials. The reaction that occurs may be illustrated by the oxidation of alanine ($\alpha$-aminopropionic acid). In the reaction, carbon and hydrogen are oxidized to carbon dioxide and water while the sulfate ion is reduced to sulfur dioxide. The amino group is released as ammonia but, of course, cannot escape from the acid environment and is held as an ammonium salt.

$$CH_3CHNH_2COOH + 7H_2SO_4 \xrightarrow[\text{cat.}]{\Delta} 3CO_2 + 6SO_2 + 8H_2O + NH_4HSO_4$$

Alanine                                                                     (25-14)

The oxidation proceeds rapidly at temperatures slightly above the boiling point of sulfuric acid (340°C). The boiling point of the acid is increased by addition of sodium or potassium sulfate.

The complete digestion of organic matter is essential if all organic nitrogen is to be released as ammonia. A misinterpretation often occurs as to what conditions exist when digestion is complete, and some explanation seems in order. This can best be done by listing the changes that samples undergo during digestion.

1. Excess water is expelled, leaving concentrated sulfuric acid to attack the organic matter.

2. Copious white fumes form in the flask at the time sulfuric acid reaches its boiling point. Digestion is just beginning at this stage.

3. The mixture turns black owing to the dehydrating action of the sulfuric acid on the organic matter.

4. Oxidation of carbon occurs. Boiling during this period is characterized by extremely small bubble formation due to the release of carbon dioxide and sulfur dioxide.

5. Complete destruction of organic matter is indicated by a clearing of the sample to a "water-clear" solution.

6. Digestion should be continued for at least 20 min after the samples appear clear to ensure complete destruction of all organic matter.

Once the organic nitrogen has been released as ammonia nitrogen, it may be measured in a manner similar to that described above in the discussion of ammonia nitrogen. The excess sulfuric acid must be neutralized and the pH of the sample adjusted to 7 or above. Usually phenolphthalein indicator is used and the pH raised well above 8.    Under such conditions, the equilibrium shown in Eq. (25-8) is displaced greatly to the right and ammonia can be distilled with ease.    The ammonia nitrogen in the distillate may be measured by Nesslerization or by absorption in boric acid and back titration with standard acid.    Calculation of organic nitrogen is made in the same manner as for ammonia nitrogen.

Many sanitary chemists prefer to use a $N/14$ solution of sulfuric acid for the measurement of ammonia and organic nitrogen when ammonia is distilled into boric acid.    Since each milliliter of $N/14$ acid is equivalent to 1.0 mg of nitrogen, its use eliminates the need for the 0.28 factor required when $N/50$ acid is used.    Furthermore, much smaller volumes of $N/14$ acid are needed for titration, an important factor in conserving reagent and preventing undue dilution of the sample during titration.

**Albuminoid Nitrogen.**    The albuminoid nitrogen determination is mainly of historic interest.    It was used extensively at one time to provide supplementary information on the sanitary quality of water, particularly when it was not convenient to measure organic nitrogen.    It measures certain forms of organic nitrogen that are released as ammonia nitrogen from alkaline solutions containing potassium permanganate.

**Nitrite Nitrogen**    Nitrite nitrogen seldom appears in concentrations greater than 1 mg/l even in sewage-treatment-plant effluents.    Its concentration in surface and ground waters is normally much below 0.1 mg/l. For this reason colorimetric methods are needed for its measurement. A modification of the Griess-Ilosvay diazotization method is used.    This employs the use of two organic reagents: sulfanilic acid and $\alpha$-naphthylamine.    The reactions involved may be represented as follows:

$$\text{Sulfanilic acid} + HNO_2 + HCl \rightarrow \text{A diazonium salt} + 2H_2O \qquad (25\text{-}15)$$

$$\text{diazonium salt} + \alpha\text{-Naphthylamine} \xrightarrow{HCl} \text{A red-colored azo dye} + HCl \qquad (25\text{-}16)$$

Under acid conditions nitrite ion as nitrous acid reacts with the amino group of sulfanilic acid to form a diazonium salt that combines with $\alpha$-naphthylamine to form a bright-colored pinkish-red azo dye. The color produced is directly proportional to the amount of nitrite nitrogen present in the sample, and determination of the amount can be made by comparison with color standards or by means of photometric measurement. Photometric measurement is preferred because standards for visual comparison are not permanent and must be prepared each time analyses are performed.

The $\alpha$-naphthylamine reagent used in the determination of nitrite nitrogen deteriorates rather rapidly. It is usually good practice to prepare fresh solutions each time determinations are made, or weekly when the reagent is used routinely.

**Nitrate Nitrogen.** The determination of nitrate nitrogen is probably one of the most difficult an analyst has to perform in order to obtain results in which he has real confidence. Two methods are recommended in "Standard Methods": the phenoldisulfonic acid and reduction methods. Both have severe limitations, and results obtained on natural samples can best be classed as semiquantitative. The need is great for a more refined and exact method of analysis.

*Phenoldisulfonic Acid Method.* Nitrates react with phenoldisulfonic acid to produce a nitro derivative that in alkaline solution rearranges its structure to form a yellow-colored compound with characteristics that conform to Beer's law.

The chemistry involved in the test has been explained in two ways, but the consensus appears to be that the phenoldisulfonic acid is converted to a mononitro derivative rather than to a trinitro derivative (picric acid). The reactions may be represented as follows:

$$+ \text{HNO}_3 \rightarrow \qquad\qquad + \text{H}_2\text{O} \qquad (25\text{-}17)$$

and

$$+ 3\text{KOH} \rightarrow \qquad\qquad + 3\text{H}_2\text{O} \qquad (25\text{-}18)$$

Colorless compound          A yellow-colored salt

The solution produced approaches a canary yellow in color and is quite difficult to compare visually. It can be measured best by photometric methods.

Chlorides interfere seriously with the determination of nitrates because of their reducing action. Under acid conditions such as occur when phenoldisulfonic acid is added in the nitrate test, chloride ion is expelled as HCl but some acts to reduce nitrate ion before it can escape from solution. The reactions involved are as follows:

$$Cl^- + H^+ \rightarrow HCl\uparrow \tag{25-19}$$
$$6Cl^- + 2NO_3^- + 8H^+ \rightarrow 3Cl_2\uparrow + 2NO\uparrow + 4H_2O \tag{25-20}$$

It would seem that chloride interference could be overcome by precipitation of the $Cl^-$ with $Ag^+$ and separation as AgCl. Although such treatment is recommended in "Standard Methods," the technique is difficult and results obtained are usually questionable. Excess $Ag^+$ is objectionable for two reasons. It catalyzes decomposition of nitrate ion when in the presence of ammonium ion during evaporation of the sample,

$$NH_4^+ + NO_3^- \xrightarrow[Ag^+]{\Delta} N_2O + 2H_2O \tag{25-21}$$

and excess $Ag^+$ is precipitated as black silver oxide when alkali is added to develop the yellow color. The latter difficulty may be overcome by adding small amounts of $NH_3$ or KCN to complex the $Ag^+$.

Nitrites are not ordinarily a consideration in nitrate determinations. In most waters their concentration is insignificant as compared with nitrates and corrections are impractical. In samples where nitrites reach significant amounts, appreciable amounts of $NH_4^+$ are normally present also. Under the conditions of the test for nitrates, ammonium nitrite is decomposed during the evaporation of the samples as follows:

$$NH_4^+ + NO_2^- \xrightarrow{\Delta} N_2 + 2H_2O \tag{25-22}$$

In most samples, the amount of $NH_4^+$ is far in excess of $NO_2^-$ and complete decomposition of nitrite is assured.

*Reduction Method.* Under alkaline conditions, both nitrates and nitrites are reduced to ammonia by aluminum. The method has met with a varying degree of success in the hands of different analysts, and many analysts are of the opinion that reduction of nitrates to ammonia is not quantitative. The explanation has been offered, without proof, that a variable percentage of the nitrate is reduced to nitrogen gas. The author's personal experience with the method has been very poor.

## 25-4. Applications of Nitrogen Data

At the present time, data concerning the nitrogen compounds that exist in water supplies are used largely in connection with disinfection

practice.    The amount of ammonia nitrogen present in a water determines to a great extent the chlorine needed to obtain free chlorine residuals in break-point chlorination and determines to some extent the ratio
of monochloramines to dichloramines when combined chlorine residuals
are involved.    Nitrate determinations are important in determining
whether ground-water supplies meet U.S. Public Health Service recommendations for the control of methemoglobinemia in infants.

Nitrogen data are extremely important in connection with sewage and
industrial waste treatment.    By controlling nitrification, aerobic-treat-
ment costs can be kept at a minimum.    Ammonia and organic nitrogen
determinations are important in determining whether sufficient available
nitrogen is present for aerobic biological treatment.    If not, they are
needed to calculate the amounts that must be supplied from outside
sources, an important economic consideration in many instances.

Where sewage sludges are sold for their fertilizing value, the nitrogen
content of the sludge is a major factor in determining their value for
such purposes.

The productivity of natural waters in terms of algal growths is related
to the fertilizing matter that gains entrance to them.    Nitrogen in its
various forms is a major consideration.    For this reason nitrogen data
are often part of the information needed in stream-pollution-control
programs.

# 26. Solids

## 26-1. General Considerations

The sanitary engineer is concerned with the measurement of solid matter in a wide variety of liquid and semiliquid materials ranging from potable waters through polluted waters, sewages, industrial wastes, and sludges produced in treatment processes. Strictly speaking, all matter except the water contained in liquid materials is classed as solid matter. The usual definition of *solids*, however, refers to the matter that remains as *residue upon evaporation* and drying at 103 to 105°C. All materials that exert significant vapor pressure at such temperatures are, of course, lost during the evaporation and drying procedures. The residue, or solids, remaining represent only those materials present in a sample that have a negligible vapor pressure at 105°C.

Because of the wide variety of inorganic and organic materials encountered in the analyses for solids, the tests are empirical in character and relatively simple to perform. Gravimetric methods are used in all cases, except for the measurement of settleable solids, and reference should be made to Sec. 4-3 in preparation for such determinations. The major problems in the analyses for solids are concerned with specific tests designed to gain information on the amounts of various kinds of solids present, e.g., dissolved, suspended, volatile, and fixed.

**Dissolved and Undissolved Solids.** The amount and nature of dissolved and undissolved matter occurring in liquid materials vary greatly. In potable waters, most of the matter is in dissolved form and consists mainly of inorganic salts, small amounts of organic matter, and dissolved gases. The total solids content of potable waters usually ranges from 20 to 1,000 mg/l, and, as a rule, hardness increases with total solids. In all other liquid materials, the amounts of undissolved colloidal and suspended matter increase with the degree of pollution. Sludges represent an extreme case in which most of the solid matter is undissolved, and the dissolved fraction is of minor importance. Determination of the amounts

302

of dissolved and undissolved matter is accomplished by making tests upon filtered and unfiltered portions of samples. The undissolved substances are usually referred to as *suspended matter* or *suspended solids*.

**Volatile and Fixed Solids.** One of the major objectives of performing solids determinations upon sewages, industrial wastes, and sludge samples is to obtain a measure of the amount of organic matter present. This test is accomplished by a combustion procedure in which organic matter is converted to carbon dioxide and water while the temperature is controlled to prevent decomposition and volatilization of inorganic substances as much as is consistent with complete oxidation of the organic matter. The loss in weight is interpreted in terms of organic matter.

The standard procedure is to conduct ignitions at 600°C. It is about the lowest temperature at which organic matter, particularly carbon residues resulting from pyrolysis of carbohydrates and other organic matter, as shown in Eq. (26-1), can be oxidized at reasonable speed.

$$C_x(H_2O)_y \xrightarrow{\Delta\Delta} xC + yH_2O\uparrow \qquad (26\text{-}1)$$

$$C + O_2 \xrightarrow{\Delta} CO_2 \qquad (26\text{-}2)$$

Also, at 600°C, decomposition of inorganic salts is minimized. Any ammonium compounds not released during drying are volatilized, but most other inorganic salts are relatively stable, with the exception of magnesium carbonate, as shown in the equation

$$MgCO_3 \xrightarrow[350°C]{\Delta} MgO + CO_2\uparrow \qquad (26\text{-}3)$$

In the determination of the volatile content of suspended solids, inorganic salts are not a consideration because they are removed during the filtration procedure. In sludge analysis, the ammonium compounds exist mainly as ammonium bicarbonate and are completely volatilized during the evaporation and drying procedures and are not present to interfere in a volatile-solids determination.

$$NH_4HCO_3 \xrightarrow{\Delta} NH_3\uparrow + H_2O\uparrow + CO_2\uparrow \qquad (26\text{-}4)$$

The other inorganic salts present in sludge are normally in such small amounts in relation to the amount of total solids that their influence is usually ignored.

Serious errors can be introduced in volatile-solids determinations by conducting ignitions at uncontrolled temperatures. For this reason it is standard practice to conduct combustions in a muffle furnace where the temperature can be accurately controlled. Calcium carbonate is decomposed at temperatures above 825°C, and, since it is a major component of the inorganic salts normally present in samples subjected to volatile-solids analysis, its decomposition can introduce significant errors.

Unless care is exercised in the initial stages, the determination of volatile solids in sludges is often subject to serious error because of physical or mechanical losses due to decrepitation during the procedure. Decrepitation may be eliminated by a preliminary controlled firing of samples with a bunsen burner to destroy all flammable materials before placing the samples in the muffle furnace.  If ignitions are properly performed, the weight loss incurred is a reasonably accurate measure of organic matter and the residue remaining represents the ash or fixed solids.

**Settleable Solids.**  The term *settleable solids* is applied to solids in suspension that will settle, under quiescent conditions, because of the influence of gravity.  Only the coarser suspended solids with a specific gravity greater than that of water will settle.  Sludges are accumulations of settleable solids.  Their measurement is important in engineering practice to determine the need for sedimentation units and the physical behavior of waste streams entering natural bodies of water.

### 26-2. Sanitary Significance of Solids Determinations

The amount of dissolved solids present in water is a consideration in its suitability for domestic use.  In general, waters with a total solids content of less than 500 mg/l are most desirable for such purposes, and the U.S. Public Health Service Standards recommend such a limit whenever possible.  Waters with higher solids content often have a laxative and sometimes the reverse effect upon people whose bodies are not adjusted to them.  This is important to people who travel and to the transportation companies who are interested in the welfare of their passengers. In many areas, it is impossible to find natural waters with a solids content under 500 mg/l; consequently it is impossible to meet the desired standards without some form of treatment.  In some instances, treatment to reduce the solids content is not practiced, and residents who regularly use such waters appear to suffer no ill effects.  The U.S. Public Health Service Standards recommend a limit of 1,000 mg/l on potable waters.

### 26-3. Determination of Solids in Water Supplies

Because of the wide variety of materials subjected to solids determinations, the tests applied vary somewhat and it is best to discuss them in terms of water, polluted waters and sludges.  Dissolved solids are the major concern in water supplies; therefore the total-solids determination is of greatest interest.  Suspended-solids tests are seldom made because of the small amounts present.  They are more easily evaluated by measurement of turbidity.

**Total Solids or Residue on Evaporation.**  The determination of total solids is easily made by evaporation and drying of a measured sample in a tared container.   The use of platinum dishes is highly recommended because of the ease with which they can be brought to constant weight before use.   Vycor ware is a good substitute.   The use of porcelain dishes is to be avoided because of their tendency to change weight.

The determination of volatile solids (organic content) is ordinarily not a consideration in waters intended for domestic use.   The results obtained cannot be interpreted in terms of organic matter with any degree of reliability.   In cases where the organic content of a water is important, it is usually best to obtain such information by means of a COD or BOD determination.

**Dissolved and Suspended Matter.**   In cases where turbidity measurements are not deemed adequate to provide the necessary information, the suspended solids may be determined by filtration through a Gooch crucible in the usual manner.   Because of the small amounts of suspended solids usually present in water supplies, the determination is subject to considerable error unless an abnormally large sample is filtered.   The preferred technique is to filter a sample of water through filter paper and determine total solids in the filtrate.   The difference between total solids in unfiltered and filtered samples is a measure of the suspended solids present.

## 26-4. Determinations Applicable to Polluted Waters and Domestic Sewage

The settleable- and suspended-solids determinations are of greatest value in assessing the strength of domestic sewage and lightly polluted waters.

**Settleable Solids.**   The determination of settleable solids is of particular importance in the analysis of sewage.   The test is ordinarily conducted in an Imhoff cone (see Fig. 26-1), allowing 1 hr settling time under quiescent conditions.   Samples should be adjusted to near room temperature and the test conducted in a location where direct sunlight does not interfere with normal settlement of the solids.   Results are measured and reported in terms of milliliters per liter of settleable solids.

**Total Solids or Residue on Evaporation.**   Total-solids determinations are ordinarily of little value in the analysis of polluted waters and domestic sewages because they are difficult to interpret with any degree of accuracy.   In most instances the dissolved solids present in the original water represent such a large and variable percentage of the total amount found in the polluted water or sewage that it is impossible to evaluate data, unless the amount of solids originally present in the carriage water is known.   The test was originally devised as a means of evaluating the amount of polluting matter present in sewage.   Since the BOD and COD tests are capable of evaluating the strength of such materials much more exactly, there is little justification for running total-solids tests for such purposes.

Some sewage treatment processes, particularly those involving sedimentation, are adversely affected by radical changes in the density of sewage. In coastal cities, sea water often gains access to sewer systems at times of high tide, and in industrial cities, intermittent discharge of

FIG. 26-1. Imhoff cones used to measure settleable solids.

highly mineralized wastes may occur. Both can cause significant changes in density. The total-solids test can be used to good advantage to detect such changes, although sea-water contamination can be detected more easily by the chloride determination.

**Suspended Solids.** The suspended-solids determination is extremely valuable in the analysis of polluted waters and sewage. It is one of the major parameters used to evaluate the strength of sewage and to determine the efficiency of treatment units. In stream-pollution-control work, all suspended solids are considered to be settleable solids, as time is not a limiting factor. Deposition is expected to occur through biological and chemical flocculation; therefore measurement of suspended solids is considered fully as significant as BOD.

The suspended-solids determination is subject to considerable error if proper precautions are not taken, as discussed in Secs. 4-1 and 4-3. Usually the sample size is limited to 50 ml or less because of difficulties encountered in filtration of larger samples. The weight of solids removed seldom exceeds 20 mg and is often less than 10 mg. Small errors in weighing or losses of filter mat can be quite significant. It is extremely important that the Gooch crucibles be carefully prepared and brought to constant weight before use. Sufficient sample should be filtered, if possible, to yield an increase in weight of about 10 mg. This often requires the filtration of 500 ml or more of samples of biologically treated sewages or lightly polluted waters.

The volatile content of suspended solids can be determined by direct ignition in the muffle furnace because the amount of solids involved is too small for decrepitation to occur. Suspended solids often contain as much as 80 per cent of volatile matter. The fixed solids remaining frequently weigh less than 2 mg. This illustrates why it is so very important to use Gooch crucibles that have been brought to constant weight. It often happens that a crucible plus fixed solids weighs less than the original tare weight. This indicates that the crucible used had not been brought to constant weight or that loss of filter mat occurred during the filtration process. A similar error can be caused by weighing crucibles before they have returned to room temperature.

Suspended solids are reported in terms of milligrams per liter, and volatile suspended solids are normally reported in terms of per cent of the suspended solids.

## 26-5. Determinations Applicable to Industrial Wastes

Industrial wastes include such a wide variety of materials that analyses for exploratory purposes should include all determinations that can possibly provide significant information. For this reason all the solids tests commonly applied to sewage are important. The settleable-solids test is particularly important as it serves as the principal basis of determining whether primary sedimentation facilities are required for treatment. In addition, the total-solids determination has special significance. Many industrial wastes contain unusual amounts of dissolved inorganic salts, and their presence is easily detected by the total-solids test. Their concentration and nature are a factor in determining the susceptibility of wastes to anaerobic treatment. Before the development of the COD test, the volatile content of total solids was used extensively to measure the amount of organic matter present. It was very helpful in assessing the amount of biologically inert organic matter, such as lignin in the case of wood-pulping waste liquors.

## 26-6. Determination of Solids in Sludges

The total- and volatile-solids determinations are important in the analysis of raw and digested sewage sludge. Both are subject to some error because of the loss of volatile organic compounds during the drying process. This factor is not particularly significant in samples of raw or well-digested sludges but it is important when partially digested sludges containing appreciable amounts of volatile acids are being analyzed. This loss often leads to faulty interpretation of volatile-solids destruction.

Because it is impossible to pipet samples of raw and digested sludges, it is common practice to weigh the samples into previously tared dishes. It is customary to use small porcelain evaporating dishes about 3 in. in diameter. It is important that the dishes be previously ignited to constant weight in order to obtain reliable results for volatile solids. Because of the rather nonuniform character of sludges, it is necessary to use relatively large samples of 25 to 50 gm, unless some method of homogenization has been employed. As a result, considerable amounts of residue are obtained upon evaporation of the samples. It is usually necessary to dry the samples at 103°C for several hours to be sure that all the moisture has had a chance to escape. Most analysts prefer to dry the samples overnight.

The volatile-solids content of sludges is an extremely important determination. Accurate results can be obtained provided that care is taken to control decrepitation, as described in Sec. 26-1.

The steps involved in the collection of data for total- and volatile-solids determinations are not always understood. A typical set of data and calculations are as follows:

| | | |
|---|---|---|
| Wt of dish on analytical balance | | 30.160 g |
| Wt of dish on trip balance | 30.5 g | |
| Wt of dish + sample | 70.8 | |
| Wt of sample | 40.3 | |
| Wt of dish + dry sludge solids | | 32.780 |
| Wt of sludge solids | | 2.620 |

Per cent solids in sludge $\dfrac{2.62}{40.3} \times 100 = 6.50\%$

| | | |
|---|---|---|
| Wt of dish + ash | | 30.720 |
| Wt of volatile matter | | 2.06 |

Per cent volatile matter $\dfrac{2.06}{2.62} \times 100 = 78.7\%$

It is unnecessary to report the per cent of fixed solids as it can be readily reckoned from the per cent of volatile solids.

The measurement of solids in activated sludges is a special case.

Because of the relatively low concentrations usually involved, serious errors can be introduced by measuring total solids, which would also include dissolved solids. It is customary to measure activated sludge by procedures used to determine suspended solids. This allows the dissolved solids to pass into the filtrate. A number of modifications are used to measure activated sludge solids but if volatile solids are desired, as is often the case, the test is best performed with the standard Gooch-crucible technique. The sample should be limited to 5 or possibly 10 ml because of filtration problems.

## 26-7. Applications of Solids Data in Sanitary Engineering Practice

In the realm of public and industrial water supplies, the total-solids determination is the only one of importance. It is used to determine the suitability of potential supplies for development. In cases where water softening is needed, the type of softening procedure used may be dictated by the total-solids content, since precipitation methods decrease and exchange methods increase the solids. Corrosion control is frequently accomplished by the production of stabilized waters through pH adjustment. The pH at stabilization depends to some extent upon the total solids present as well as the alkalinity and temperature.

The settleable-solids determination has two very important applications. First, it is used extensively in the analysis of industrial wastes to determine the need and design of primary settling tanks in plants employing biological treatment processes. The test is also widely used in sewage-treatment-plant operation to determine the efficiency of sedimentation units. It is fully as important in the operation of large treatment plants as in the smaller.

The suspended- and volatile-suspended-solids determinations are used to evaluate the strength of sewage and industrial wastes. The tests are particularly valuable in determining the amount of suspended solids remaining after settleable solids have been removed in primary settling units, for the purpose of determining the loading of remaining materials on secondary biological treatment units. In the larger treatment plants, suspended-solids determinations are used routinely as a measure of the effectiveness of treatment units. From the viewpoint of stream pollution control, the removal of suspended solids is usually as important as BOD removal. Both suspended- and volatile-suspended-solids determinations are used to control the aeration solids in the activated sludge process.

The total- and volatile-solids tests are the only solids determinations that are normally applied to sludges. They are indispensable in the design and operation of sludge-digestion, vacuum-filter, and incineration units.

# 27. Iron and Manganese

## 27-1. General Considerations

Both iron and manganese create serious problems in public water supplies. The problems are most extensive and critical in underground waters, but difficulties are encountered at certain seasons of the year in waters drawn from some rivers and some impounded surface supplies. Why some underground supplies are relatively free of iron and manganese and others contain so much has always been somewhat of an enigma that defied explanations when viewed solely from the viewpoint of inorganic chemistry. Recent developments and experiences have indicated that biochemical changes, or, more exactly, changes in environmental conditions brought about by biological reactions, are major considerations. Since both manganese and iron are present in insoluble forms in significant amounts in nearly all soils, any explanation of how appreciable amounts can gain entrance to water flowing through or coming in contact with the soil must consider how the iron and manganese are converted to soluble forms.

Iron exists in soils and minerals mainly as insoluble ferric oxide. It occurs in some areas also as ferrous carbonate (siderite), which is very slightly soluble. Since ground waters usually contain significant amounts of carbon dioxide (see Sec. 15-2), appreciable amounts of ferrous carbonate may be dissolved by the reaction shown in the equation

$$FeCO_3 + CO_2 + H_2O \rightarrow Fe^{++} + 2HCO_3^-  \qquad (27\text{-}1)$$

in the same manner that calcium and magnesium carbonates are dissolved. However, iron problems are prevalent where it is present in the soil as insoluble ferric compounds. Solution of measurable amounts of iron from such soils does not occur, even in the presence of appreciable amounts of carbon dioxide, as long as dissolved oxygen is present. Under reducing (anaerobic) conditions, however, the ferric iron is reduced to ferrous iron and solution occurs without difficulty.

Manganese exists in the soil principally as manganese dioxide which is very insoluble in water containing carbon dioxide. Under reducing (anaerobic) conditions, the manganese in the dioxide form is reduced from a valence of 4 to a valence of 2 and solution occurs, the same as with ferric oxides.

Evidence to indicate that iron and manganese gain entrance to water supplies through changes produced in environmental conditions as a result of biological reactions has stemmed from three sources, as follows:

1. Ground waters that contain appreciable amounts of iron and/or manganese are always devoid of dissolved oxygen and are high in carbon dioxide content. The iron and manganese are present as $Fe^{++}$ and $Mn^{++}$. The high carbon dioxide content indicates that bacterial oxidation of organic matter has been extensive, and the absence of dissolved oxygen shows that anaerobic conditions were developed.

2. Wells producing good-quality water, low in iron and manganese, for many years have been known to produce poor-quality water when organic wastes have been discharged on the soil around or near the well, thereby creating anaerobic conditions in the soil.

3. The iron and manganese problem in impounded surface supplies has been correlated with reservoirs that stratify but occurs only in those in which anaerobic conditions develop in the hypolimnion. The soluble iron and manganese released from the bottom muds are contained in the waters of the hypolimnion until the fall overturn occurs. At that time they are distributed throughout the reservoir and cause trouble in the water supply until sufficient time has elapsed for oxidation and sedimentation to occur under natural conditions.

In summary, the evidence seems clear that the development of anaerobic conditions is essential for appreciable amounts of iron and manganese to gain entrance to a water supply. Under anaerobic conditions, ferric and manganese compounds are reduced to soluble ferrous and manganous forms.

## 27-2. Sanitary Significance of Iron and Manganese

As far as is known, humans suffer no harmful effects from drinking waters containing iron and manganese. Such waters, when exposed to the air, so that oxygen can enter, become turbid and highly unacceptable from the aesthetic viewpoint, owing to oxidation of the $Fe^{++}$ to $Fe^{3+}$ which forms colloidal ferric hydroxide. Manganese undergoes a similar oxidation but usually at such a slow rate that it does not become a problem in household use. Both iron and manganese interfere with laundering operations and cause difficulties in distribution systems by supporting growths of iron bacteria. For these reasons the U.S. Public Health Service Standards recommend that public water supplies should not contain more than 0.3 mg/l of iron and/or manganese.

## 27-3. Methods of Determining Iron

A great many methods of determining iron have been developed. Precipitation methods are commonly used where quantities are relatively large, such as in some industrial wastes. However, in water supplies the amounts present are normally so small that colorimetric procedures are more satisfactory. The colorimetric procedures have a major advantage in that they are usually highly specific for the ion involved and a minimum of pretreatment is required.

The phenanthroline method is standard procedure for the measurement of iron in water at the present time. The method depends upon the fact that 1,10-phenanthroline combines with $Fe^{++}$ to form a complex ion which is orange red in color. The color produced conforms to Beer's law and is readily measured by visual or photometric comparison.

Water samples subjected to analysis have usually been exposed to the atmosphere; consequently some oxidation of $Fe^{++}$ to $Fe^{3+}$ and precipitation of ferric hydroxide may have occurred. It is necessary to make sure that all the iron is in a soluble condition. This is done by treating a portion of the sample with hydrochloric acid to dissolve the ferric hydroxide.

$$Fe(OH)_3 + 3H^+ \rightarrow Fe^{3+} + 3H_2O \qquad (27\text{-}2)$$

Since the reagent 1,10-phenanthroline is specific for measuring $Fe^{++}$, all iron in the form of $Fe^{3+}$ must be reduced to the ferrous condition. This is most readily accomplished by using hydroxylamine as the reducing agent. The reaction involved may be represented as follows:

$$4Fe^{3+} + 2NH_2OH \rightarrow 4Fe^{++} + N_2O + H_2O + 4H^+ \qquad (27\text{-}3)$$

Three molecules of 1,10-phenanthroline is required to chelate or form a complex ion with each $Fe^{++}$. The reaction may be represented as shown in the equation

1,10-phenanthroline                    Orange-red complex

By proper modifications of the test procedure, measurements of total, dissolved, and suspended iron can be made. These considerations are not normal, however, and, whenever they are, special precautions must be taken in sampling and transportation of samples to ensure that no changes occur before analyses are performed. Because of the possible errors that may result, it is best that the analyst assume full responsibility for sampling as well as for analysis.

## 27-4. Methods of Determining Manganese

In sanitary engineering practice, manganese is principally of concern in water supplies. Its concentration seldom exceeds a few milligrams per liter; therefore colorimetric methods are most applicable. Two methods are recommended in "Standard Methods"; both depend upon oxidation of the manganese from its lower states of valence to a valence of 7+ where it forms the highly colored permanganate ion. The color produced is directly proportional to the concentration of manganese present over a considerable range of concentration in accordance with Beer's law, and it is easily measured by eye or photometric means. Chlorides interfere because of their reducing action in an acid medium, and so provisions must be made to overcome their influence. Most other reducing agents are rendered inactive by the strong oxidizing agents used to form the permanganate ion.

**Persulfate Method.** The persulfate method is best suited for routine determinations of manganese because pretreatment of samples is not needed to overcome chloride interference. Ammonium persulfate is commonly used as the oxidizing agent. It is subject to deterioration during prolonged storage; for this reason, it is always good practice where samples are not run routinely to include a standard sample with each set of samples to verify the potency of the persulfate used.

Chloride interference is overcome in the persulfate method by adding $Hg^{++}$ to form poorly ionized $HgCl_2$. Since the ionization constant of $HgCl_2$ is about $2.6 \times 10^{-15}$, the concentration of chloride ion is decreased to such a low level that it cannot reduce the permanganate ions formed.

The oxidation of manganese in lower valences to permanganate by persulfate requires the presence of $Ag^+$ as a catalyst. The reaction involved in the oxidation may be represented as follows:

$$2Mn^{++} + 5S_2O_8^= + 8H_2O \xrightarrow{\text{Ag}^+} 2MnO_4^- + 10SO_4^= + 16H^+ \quad (27\text{-}5)$$

The color produced by the permanganate ion is stable for several hours provided that a good-quality distilled water is used for dilution purposes and reasonable care is taken to protect the sample from contamination by dust of the atmosphere.

**Periodate Method.** The periodate method is somewhat more sensitive to small amounts of manganese than the persulfate method, and the colored solutions produced are stable for longer periods of time. It is especially applicable where manganese concentrations are below 0.1 mg/l. Chlorides interfere, and it is often necessary to expel them as HCl by evaporating the sample with sulfuric acid to the point where the sulfuric acid begins to distill.   This is recognized by the formation of white fumes resulting from the condensation of water vapor in the atmosphere by the sulfuric acid as it distills.

The oxidation of manganese from its lower valence states to permanganate by periodate is normally accomplished without the aid of a catalyst. However, where small amounts of manganese are involved, the use of $Ag^+$ as a catalyst is recommended.   The reaction involved may be represented as follows:

$$2Mn^{++} + 5IO_4^- + 3H_2O \rightarrow 2MnO_4^- + 5IO_3^- + 6H^+ \qquad (27\text{-}6)$$

In practice an excess of periodate is used and in its presence the permanganate ion is stable.

### 27-5. Applications of Iron and Manganese Data in Sanitary Engineering Practice

In explorations for new water supplies, particularly from underground sources, iron and manganese determinations are an important consideration.   Supplies may be rejected on this basis alone.   When supplies containing amounts in excess of 0.3 mg/l are developed, the engineer must decide whether treatment is justified and, if so, the best method of treatment.   The ratio of iron to manganese is a factor that determines the type of treatment used, as well as the amount of organic matter present in the water.   The efficiency of treatment units is determined by routine tests for iron and manganese.   They are also used to aid in the solution of problems in distribution systems where iron-fixing bacteria are troublesome.

Corrosion of cast-iron and steel pipelines often produces "red-water" troubles in distribution systems.   The iron determination is helpful in assessing the extent of corrosion and aiding in the solution of these problems.   Research on corrosion and methods of corrosion control require the use of many types of tests to evaluate the extent of metal loss.   The iron determination is one of them.

# 28. Fluoride

## 28-1. General Considerations

The sanitary engineer has at least a dual interest in the determination of fluorides. It is his responsibility to design and operate units for the removal of fluorides from water supplies that contain excessive amounts and, on the other hand, it becomes his responsibility to supervise the addition of fluorides to optimum levels in water supplies that are deemed to be deficient in fluorides by local health agencies. In some areas, particularly in the neighborhood of aluminum-processing plants, contamination of the atmosphere and vegetation by fluorides has been a serious problem. Control methods have had to be employed to protect cattle and other herbivorous animals from damage to bones and teeth.

**Significance of High Fluorides in Water Supplies.** A disfigurement in the teeth of humans known as *mottled enamel* (dental fluorosis) has been recognized for many years. U.S. immigration authorities, at an early date, noticed that people arriving from certain areas of Europe were severely afflicted whereas people from other areas showed little or no evidence of mottling. This led dental authorities to believe that the diseased condition was due to a local factor. Shortly after this information became known, reports of mottled enamel among people native to the United States began to appear. These cases came largely from cities in the Great Plains and Rocky Mountain states, but no real clue was offered to explain the cause of the defective teeth until about 20 years later.

Substantial evidence to suspect fluorides as the cause of mottled enamel was obtained by Churchill of the Aluminum Co. of America in 1930.[1] The city of Bauxite, Arkansas, was one of the communities that had reported a high incidence of mottled enamel among its people. Churchill, through spectrographic analysis, found appreciable amounts of fluoride ion present in the Bauxite water supply. In collaboration with McKay,

[1] H. V. Churchill, *Ind. Eng. Chem.*, **23**, 996 (1931).

a dentist of Colorado Springs, Colorado, he studied waters from five areas where mottling was endemic and from 40 areas where it was not a problem. From these studies it was concluded that excessive fluoride levels in drinking water are the cause of mottled enamel. Their data showed that mottling did not appear unless the fluoride-ion concentration was in excess of 1.0 mg/l and that the degree and severity of mottling increased as the fluoride level rose.

As soon as excessive amounts of fluorides in water supplies had been established as the cause of dental fluorosis, research on methods of removal were initiated. Two methods have been developed and used in practice: (1) defluorite, i.e., $Ca_3(PO_4)_2 \cdot Ca(OH)_2$, and (2) activated alumina. Both of these methods are expensive, and it is generally considered impractical to provide facilities for fluoride removal unless the concentration exceeds 4 mg/l. At the present time only five cities in the United States have fluoride removal plants. Development of cheaper methods would make fluoride removal a practical matter for many other cities.

**Significance of Low Fluorides in Water Supplies.** As a result of the great interest focused on the fluoride content of public water supplies in relation to the dental fluorosis problem, a great deal of information became available on fluorides. It was natural that the dental profession would use this information to determine whether fluorides were correlated with other dental diseases.

In 1938, Dean[1] presented information which demonstrated that dental caries is less prevalent when mottled enamel occurs. This led to extensive correlation studies on dental caries versus fluoride levels in public waters at many places in the United States. The results obtained, as summarized by Dean[2], are presented in Fig. 28-1. From this information, a dental caries–fluoride hypothesis evolved: Approximately 1 mg/l of fluoride ion is desirable in public waters for optimal dental health. At decreasing levels, dental caries becomes a serious problem and, at increasing levels, dental fluorosis becomes a problem.

The dental caries–fluoride hypothesis has served as the basis for programs of supplementing public water supplies having low fluoride levels with fluorides to bring the concentration up to about 1 mg/l. Because there was some question about the physiological effects of supplemental fluorides, as well as their efficacy as a substitute for "natural" fluorides for controlling dental caries, extensive 10-year pilot studies were conducted at Newburgh, New York, Grand Rapids, Michigan, and several other cities. The results of the investigations have been unanimous in demonstrating the safety of supplemental fluoridation and that added

[1] H. T. Dean, *Public Health Repts.* (*U.S.*), **53**, 1443 (1938).
[2] H. T. Dean, *J. Am. Water Works Assoc.*, **35**, 1161 (1943).

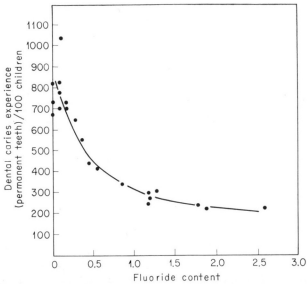

FIG. 28-1. Relationship between dental caries and fluoride level in drinking water. (*After Dean.*)

fluorides are as effective in controlling dental caries as so-called "natural" fluorides. The program for fluoridation of public water supplies deficient in natural fluorides has been sponsored by many organizations interested in the public health, including the American Dental and Medical Associations. There has been considerable opposition to the program from several quarters, but the program has advanced with a steady growth. In 1957 over 1,500 public water supplies in the United States serving over 30 million people were being supplemented with fluorides. Control of additions is based upon the fluoride determination.

**Fluorides and Air Pollution.** Cryolite ($Na_3AlF_6$) is used as a solvent for $Al_2O_3$ in the electrolytic method of producing aluminum. At operating temperatures, the cryolite is molten and exerts a considerable vapor pressure. As a result, appreciable amounts of fluorides escape to the atmosphere through exhaust systems. The fluorides condense to form a smoke, and much of the particulate matter settles on vegetation and the soil in the immediate area. Considerable damage to livestock has occurred in certain areas of the United States. The problem has been solved in most instances by use of electrostatic precipitation units.

## 28-2. Chemistry of Fluorine and Its Compounds

Fluorine is the most active element known and is not used in the elemental form in sanitary engineering practice. It forms simple fluoride compounds and many complex ions. The principal forms in which fluorides are added to public water supplies are

NaF                  $Na_2SiF_6$ (sodium silicofluoride)
$CaF_2$              $H_2SiF_6$ (hydrofluosilicic acid)
$H_2F_2$

All the compounds and complex ions containing fluorine dissociate to yield fluoride ion. At the concentrations of about 1 mg/l involved in water treatment practice, it is generally considered that hydrolysis of the fluosilicate ion is essentially complete, as shown in the equation

$$SiF_6^= + 3H_2O \rightleftharpoons 6F^- + 6H^+ + SiO_3^= \qquad (28\text{-}1)$$

On this basis, the fluoride in silicofluorides can be determined by any method that is sensitive to fluoride ion.

## 28-3. Methods of Determining Fluorides

Standard procedures for the measurement of fluorides at the present time are all modifications of one colorimetric method. They are all subject to interferences from other ions, and it is often necessary to separate the fluorides from the interfering ions before making the colorimetric test. The separation is accomplished by a distillation procedure such as that used in the determination of ammonia nitrogen. In the case of fluorides, however, the distillation is performed from acidified solutions. Under the conditions, all fluoride ion is converted to poorly ionized hydrogen fluoride, according to the equation

$$F^- + H^+ \xrightarrow{\Delta} HF\uparrow \qquad (28\text{-}2)$$

The hydrogen fluoride is evolved with the steam and held in the condensate.

Samples of water that do not contain significant amounts of interfering ions and distillates obtained from the purification procedure may be analyzed by any one of three modifications of a colorimetric method that involves the bleaching of a preformed color by the fluoride ion. The preformed color is the result of the action between zirconium ion and alizarin dye. The color produced is commonly referred to as a "lake," and the intensity of the reddish color produced is reduced if the amount of zirconium present is decreased. Fluoride ion combines with zirconium ion to form a stable complex ion $ZrF_6^=$, and the intensity of the color lake decreases accordingly. The reaction involved may be represented as

$$\underset{\text{Reddish color}}{(Zr - \text{alizarin lake})} + 6F^- \rightarrow \text{alizarin} + \underset{\text{Yellow}}{ZrF_6^=} \qquad (28\text{-}3)$$

The bleaching action is a function of the fluoride-ion concentration and is directly proportional to it. Thus Beer's law is satisfied in an inverse manner. Comparisons are best made visually. The bleaching action of fluorides is slow, and a 1-hr contact period is recommended before comparisons are made. Because temperature and time are important variables, it is necessary that standards be prepared for making comparisons each time analyses are to be made. The Megregian-Maier modification allows photometric measurements to be used but care must be exercised to keep contact time and temperature the same as employed in developing the calibration curve. Good practice requires that at least one standard be included with samples each time photometric measurements are made. Most analysts prefer to prepare several standards and make visual comparisons to avoid the strict time limitations imposed by the photometric procedure.

The present methods of measuring fluorides are reasonably accurate and satisfactory for all practical purposes when sufficient attention is paid to necessary detail. It would be advantageous to have a more rapid method of analysis and one with greater sensitivity.

## 28-4. Application of Fluoride Data

Because of the public health significance of fluorides in water supplies intended for human use, determination of fluorides has become extremely important. In situations where fluorides are added to provide an optimum level for the control of dental caries, it is necessary to know the amount of natural fluorides present so that proper amounts of supplemental fluoride can be added. In all cases where supplementation is practiced, it is necessary to maintain surveillance on the finished water to be sure that proper amounts of chemicals are being fed. The usual practice is to collect samples on the distribution system as well as at the treatment plant.

In areas where natural fluorides exceed the U.S. Public Health Service recommended limit of 1.5 mg/l, the fluoride content of a water may determine the suitability of a supply for development. In cases where high fluoride waters must be used, local authorities, in cooperation with the engineer, must decide whether fluoride-removal facilities are to be installed. The size and design of such units will depend upon the level of fluorides present in the water. Fluoride determinations, of course, serve as the basis of determining when removal units require regeneration.

# 29. Sulfate

## 29-1. General Considerations

The sulfate ion is one of the major anions occurring in natural waters. It is of importance in public water supplies because of its cathartic effect upon humans when it is present in excessive amounts. For this reason the U.S. Public Health Service Standards recommend an upper limit of 250 mg/l in waters intended for human consumption. Sulfates are important in both public and industrial water supplies because of the tendency of waters containing appreciable amounts to form hard scales in boilers and heat exchangers.

Sulfates are of considerable concern in sewage and industrial wastes because they are indirectly responsible for two serious problems often associated with the handling and treatment of sewage. These are odor and sewer-corrosion problems resulting from the reduction of sulfates to hydrogen sulfide under anaerobic conditions, as shown in the following equations:

$$SO_4^= + \text{org. matter} \xrightarrow[\text{bact.}]{\text{anaerobic}} S^= + H_2O + CO_2 \qquad (29\text{-}1)$$

$$S^= + 2H^+ \rightleftharpoons H_2S \qquad (29\text{-}2)$$

A knowledge of the sulfur cycle, as represented in Fig. 29-1, is essential to an understanding of the transformations that occur.

**Odor Problems.** In the absence of dissolved oxygen and nitrates, sulfates serve as a source of oxygen (or as a hydrogen acceptor) for biochemical oxidations produced by anaerobic bacteria. Under anaerobic conditions, the sulfate ion is reduced to sulfide ion which establishes an equilibrium with hydrogen ion to form hydrogen sulfide in accordance with its primary ionization constant $K_1 = 5.7 \times 10^{-8}$. The relationships existing between $H_2S$, $HS^-$, and $S^=$ at various pH levels in a $10^{-3}$ molar solution are shown in Fig. 29-2. At pH values of 8 and above, most of the reduced sulfur exists in solution as $HS^-$ and $S^=$ ions and the amount of free $H_2S$ is so small that its partial pressure is insignificant and odor

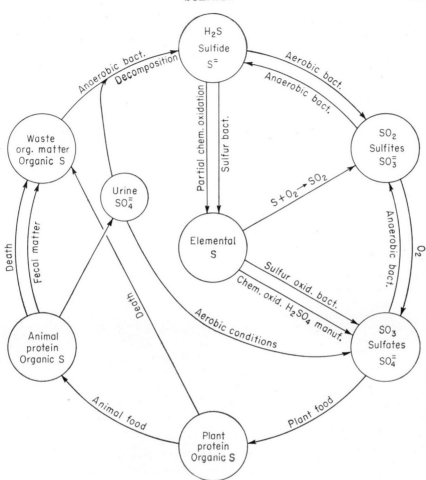

FIG. 29-1. The sulfur cycle.

problems do not occur. At pH levels below 8, the equilibrium shifts rapidly toward the formation of un-ionized $H_2S$ and is about 80 per cent complete at pH 7. Under such conditions the partial pressure of hydrogen sulfide becomes great enough to cause serious odor problems whenever sulfate reduction yields a significant amount of sulfide ion.

**Corrosion of Sewers.** In many areas of the United States—particularly in the southern states where sewage temperatures are high, detention times in the sewers are long, and sulfate concentrations are appreciable—"crown" corrosion of concrete sewers has been an important problem. The difficulty is always associated with reduction of sulfates to hydrogen sulfide, and the hydrogen sulfide is often blamed for the corrosion. Actually $H_2S$, or hydrosulfuric acid as its aqueous solutions are called, is a weaker acid than carbonic acid and has little effect on good concrete. Nevertheless, "crown" corrosion of gravity-type sewers does occur, and hydrogen sulfide is indirectly responsible.

Gravity-type sewers provide an unusual environment for biological changes in the sulfur compounds present in sewage. Sewers are really part of a treatment system, for biological changes are constantly occurring during transportation. These changes require oxygen, and, if sufficient amounts are not supplied through natural reaeration from air in the sewer, reduction of sulfates occurs and sulfide ion is formed. At the usual pH level of domestic sewage, most of the sulfide is converted to hydrogen sulfide and some of it escapes into the atmosphere above the sewage. Here it does no damage if the sewer is well ventilated and the walls and crown are dry. In poorly ventilated sewers, however, moisture collects on the walls and crown. Hydrogen sulfide dissolves in this water in accordance with its partial pressure in the sewer atmosphere. As such it does no harm.

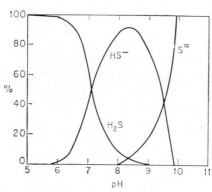

FIG. 29-2. Effect of pH on hydrogen sulfide–sulfide equilibrium ($10^{-3}$ molar solution, 32 mg $H_2S/l$).

Bacteria capable of oxidizing hydrogen sulfide to sulfuric acid are ubiquitous in nature and are always present in domestic sewage. It is natural that some of these organisms should infect the walls and crown of sewers at times of high flows or in other manner. Because of the aerobic conditions normally prevailing in sewers above the sewage, these bacteria oxidize the hydrogen sulfide to sulfuric acid,

$$H_2S + 2O_2 \xrightarrow{\text{bact.}} H_2SO_4 \qquad (29\text{-}3)$$

and the latter, being a strong acid, attacks the concrete. This effect is particularly serious in the crown where drainage is at a minimum. Figure 29-3 summarizes the important aspects of odor and corrosion problems in sewer systems.

## 29-2. Methods of Analysis

Three methods of determining sulfates, employing gravimetric, turbidimetric, and volumetric procedures, are currently used. The choice of method depends to a considerable extent upon the purpose for which the determination is being made and the concentration of sulfates in the sample.

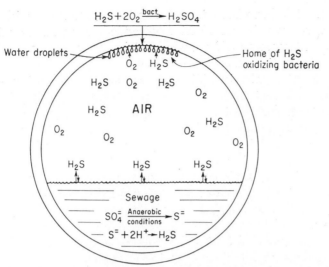

FIG. 29-3. Formation of hydrogen sulfide in sewers and "crown" corrosion resulting from oxidation of hydrogen sulfide to sulfuric acid.

**Gravimetric.** The gravimetric method is considered to yield the most accurate results and is the standard procedure for measuring sulfates. The quantitative aspects of this method depend upon the fact that barium ion combines with sulfate ion to form poorly soluble barium sulfate as follows:

$$Ba^{++} + SO_4^= \rightarrow \underline{BaSO_4} \qquad (29\text{-}4)$$

The precipitation is normally accomplished by adding barium chloride in slight excess to samples of water acidified with hydrochloric acid and kept near the boiling point. The samples are acidified to eliminate the possibility of precipitation of $BaCO_3$, which might occur in highly alkaline waters maintained near the boiling temperature. Excess barium chloride is used to produce sufficient common ion to precipitate sulfate ion as completely as possible.

Because of the great insolubility of barium sulfate ($K_{sp} = 1.98 \times 10^{-10}$), there is a considerable tendency for much of the precipitate to form in a colloidal condition that cannot be removed by ordinary filtration procedures. Digestion of the samples at temperatures near the boiling point for a few hours usually results in a transfer of the colloidal to crystalline forms, in accordance with the principle discussed in Sec. 6-7, and filtration can then be accomplished. The crystals of barium sulfate are usually quite small; for this reason, a special grade of filter paper (suitable for sulfate determinations) should be used. Some analysts prefer to use Gooch crucibles with asbestos mats. With reasonable care to make sure that all crystals have been transferred to the filter and with sufficient washing to remove all excess barium chloride and other salts, this method is capable of measuring sulfates with a high order of accuracy. Its major limitation is the time required.

**Turbidimetric.**  The turbidimetric method of measuring sulfates is based upon the fact that barium sulfate tends to precipitate in a colloidal form and that this tendency is enhanced in the presence of appreciable amounts of sodium chloride.  By standardizing the procedure used to produce the colloidal sol of barium sulfate, it is possible to obtain results that are quantitative and acceptable for a great many purposes. The method is very rapid and has wide application since samples with sulfate concentrations greater than 10 mg/l can be analyzed by taking smaller portions and diluting them to the recommended 50-ml sample size.  Because of the variables that enter into a determination of this sort, it is recommended that at least one standard sample of sulfate ion be included in each set of samples to verify that conditions used in the test are comparable to those used in establishing the calibration curve.

**Volumetric.**  A number of volumetric methods have been proposed for the determination of sulfates.  All of them suffer from a lack of sensitivity and precision and are not applicable to natural waters of potable character.  They are used in analysis of boiler and other saline waters for control purposes.

## 29-3. Applications of Sulfate Data

The sulfate content of natural waters is an important consideration in determining their suitability for public and industrial water supplies. The amount of sulfate in sewage and industrial wastes is a factor of concern in determining the magnitude of problems that can arise from reduction of sulfates to hydrogen sulfide.  In anaerobic digestion of sludges and industrial wastes, the sulfates are reduced to hydrogen sulfide, which is evolved with methane and carbon dioxide.  If the gas is to be used in gas engines, the hydrogen sulfide content should not exceed 50 grains/100 cu ft.  A knowledge of the sulfate content of the sludge or waste fed to digestion units provides a means of estimating the hydrogen sulfide content of the gas produced.  From this information, the designing engineer can determine whether scrubbing facilities will be needed to remove hydrogen sulfide and the size of the units required.

Many organic compounds contain sulfur as sulfates, sulfonates, or sulfides.  During aerobic treatment of such wastes, complete utilization or dissimilation results in release of the organically bound sulfur as sulfate ion.  Sulfate determinations have been used in research work as one means of demonstrating the biological assimilability of alkyl sulfates and alkyl benzene sulfonates used in the production of synthetic detergents.

# 30. Phosphorus and Phosphate

## 30-1. General Considerations

The phosphate determination has grown rapidly in importance in the field of sanitary engineering practice as engineers have realized the many ways in which phosphorus compounds affect phenomena with which they are concerned. The only inorganic compounds of phosphorus of significance in sanitary engineering practice are the phosphates or their molecularly dehydrated forms, usually referred to as polyphosphates. Organically bound phosphorus is a minor consideration.

**Water Supplies.** Polyphosphates are used in some public water supplies as a means of controlling corrosion. They are also used in some softened waters for stabilization purposes to eliminate the need for recarbonation.

All surface water supplies support growths of minute aquatic organisms. The free swimming and floating organisms are called *plankton* and are of great interest to sanitary engineers. The plankton are composed of animals, *zooplankton*, and plants, *phytoplankton*. The latter are predominately algae, and, being chlorophyll-bearing organisms, their growth is influenced greatly by the amount of fertilizing elements in the water. Research has shown that nitrogen and phosphorus are both essential for the growth of algae and that limitation in amounts of these elements is usually the factor that controls their rate of growth. Where both nitrogen and phosphorus are plentiful, algal blooms occur which may produce a variety of nuisance conditions. Experience has shown that such blooms do not occur when nitrogen and/or phosphorus is present in very limited amounts. The critical level for phosphorus has been established as somewhere near 0.01 mg or 10 $\mu$g/l.

**Sewage and Industrial Waste Treatment.** Domestic sewage is relatively rich in phosphorus compounds. Prior to the development of synthetic detergents, the content of inorganic phosphorus usually ranged from 2 to 3 mg/l and organic forms varied from 0.5 to 1.0 mg/l. Most of the inorganic phosphorus was contributed by human wastes as a result

325

of the metabolic breakdown of proteins and elimination of the liberated phosphates in the urine.  The amount of phosphorus released is a function of protein intake and, for the average person in the United States, this release is considered to be about 1.5 g/day.[1]

Most heavy-duty synthetic detergent formulations designed for the household market contain large amounts of polyphosphates as "builders." Many of them contain from 12 to 13 per cent phosphorus or over 50 per cent of polyphosphates.  The use of these materials as a substitute for soap has greatly increased the phosphorus content of domestic sewage. It has been estimated from sales of polyphosphates to the detergent industry that domestic sewage probably contains from two to three times as much inorganic phosphorus at the present time as it did before synthetic detergents became widely used.

The organisms involved in biological processes of sewage and industrial waste treatment all require phosphorus for reproduction and synthesis of new cell tissue.  Domestic sewage contains amounts of phosphorus far in excess of the amount needed to stabilize the limited quantity of organic matter present.  This fact is demonstrated by the presence of appreciable amounts in effluents from treatment plants.  Many industrial wastes, however, do not contain sufficient quantities of phosphorus for optimum growth of the organisms used in treatment.  In such cases, deficiencies may be supplied by the addition of inorganic phosphates.

**Fertilizing Value of Sludges.**  A major problem in sewage treatment practice is the disposal of sludges remaining from aerobic and anaerobic treatment processes.  All sludges contain nitrogen and phosphorus in significant amounts and have value for fertilizing purposes.  The total phosphorus content of digested sludges is ordinarily about 1 per cent and that of heat-dried activated sludge about 1.5 per cent.  In the United States, where phosphate fertilizers are relatively abundant and cheap, most sludges are sold on the basis of their nitrogen content and little or no credit is given for the phosphorus.

**Boiler Waters.**  Phosphate compounds are widely used in steam power plants to control scaling in boilers.  If complex phosphates are used, they are rapidly hydrolyzed to orthophosphate at the high temperatures involved.  Control of phosphate levels is accomplished through determinations of orthophosphate.

## 30-2. Phosphorus Compounds of Importance

Phosphorus compounds of wide variety are encountered in sanitary engineering practice.  A list of the more important ones is given in Table 30-1.

[1] C. N. Sawyer, Factors Involved in Disposal of Sewage Effluents to Lakes, *Sewage and Ind. Wastes*, **26**, 317 (1954).

TABLE 30-1. PHOSPHORUS COMPOUNDS COMMONLY ENCOUNTERED IN
SANITARY ENGINEERING PRACTICE

| Name | Formula |
|------|---------|
| Orthophosphates: | |
| Trisodium phosphate | $Na_3PO_4$ |
| Disodium phosphate | $Na_2HPO_4$ |
| Monosodium phosphate | $NaH_2PO_4$ |
| Diammonium phosphate | $(NH_4)_2HPO_4$ |
| Polyphosphates: | |
| Sodium hexametaphosphate | $Na_3(PO_3)_6$ |
| Sodium tripolyphosphate | $Na_5P_3O_{10}$ |
| Tetra sodium pyrophosphate | $Na_4P_2O_7$ |

All the polyphosphates (molecularly dehydrated phosphates) gradually hydrolyze in aqueous solution and revert to the ortho form from which they were derived. The rate of reversion is a function of temperature and increases rapidly as the temperature approaches the boiling point. The rate is also increased by lowering the pH, and advantage is taken of this fact in the preparation of samples for the determination of complex phosphates. The hydrolysis of complex phosphates is also influenced by bacterial enzymes. The rate of reversion is very slow in pure waters but is more rapid in sewage. Experiments have shown that pyrophosphates are hydrolyzed more rapidly in sewage than tripolyphosphates. A matter of several hours and possibly days is required for the complete reversion of tripolyphosphate to orthophosphate, particularly at low temperatures. No information is currently available on the rate of reversion of the polyphosphates during biological treatment of sewage.

From the considerations given above, it should be obvious that determinations for phosphorus or phosphates must employ procedures to measure polyphosphates if a true measure of the total inorganic forms present is to be obtained.

### 30-3. Methods of Determining Phosphorus or Phosphate

The sanitary engineer is often interested in knowing the amounts of ortho, poly, and organic phosphorus present. Fortunately, it is possible to measure orthophosphate with very little interference from polyphosphates because of their stability under the conditions of pH, time, and temperature used in the test. Both poly and organic forms of phosphorus are converted to orthophosphate for measurement.

**Orthophosphate.** Phosphorus occurring as orthophosphate ($H_2PO_4^-$, $HPO_4^=$, $PO_4^\equiv$) can be measured quantitatively by gravimetric, volumetric, or colorimetric methods. The gravimetric method is applicable where large amounts of phosphorus are present, but such situations do not occur in sanitary engineering practice. The volumetric method is applicable when phosphate concentrations exceed 50 mg/l, but such concentrations are seldom encountered except in boiler waters and digester supernatant liquors. The method involves formation of a precipitate, filtration, careful washing of the precipitate, and titration. The procedure is time-consuming, and most analysts prefer to use a colorimetric method, possibly at some sacrifice of accuracy.

Two colorimetric methods are used for measuring orthophosphate. They are essentially the same in principle but differ in the nature of the reducing agent used for final color development. The chemistry involved is essentially as follows: Phosphate ion combines with ammonium molybdate under acid conditions to form a complex compound known as ammonium phosphomolybdate.

$$PO_4^{\equiv} + 12(NH_4)_2MoO_4 + 24H^+ \rightarrow (NH_4)_3PO_4 \cdot 12MoO_3$$
$$+ 21NH_4^+ + 12H_2O \quad (30\text{-}1)$$

When large amounts of phosphates are present, the phosphomolybdate forms a yellow precipitate that can be filtered and used for volumetric determination. At lower concentrations of phosphates, a yellow colloidal sol is formed which has been proposed as a basis of colorimetric measurement of intermediate concentrations. With concentrations of phosphates under 10 mg/l, the usual range in sanitary analysis, the yellow color of the colloidal sol is not discernible and other means of color development are necessary.

The molybdenum contained in ammonium phosphomolybdate is readily reduced to produce a blue-colored sol that is proportional to the amount of phosphate present. Excess ammonium molybdate is not reduced and, therefore, does not interfere. Either amino-naphthol-sulfonic acid or stannous chloride may be used as the reducing agent. The colored compound formed has never been isolated, and its formula is unknown. It is referred to as molybdenum or heteropoly blue in most cases. The chemistry involved with stannous chloride as the reducing agent may be represented in a qualitative manner as follows:

$$(NH_4)_3PO_4 \cdot 12MoO_3 + Sn^{++} \rightarrow (\text{molybdenum blue}) + Sn^{4+} \quad (30\text{-}2)$$

The choice of reducing agent is largely a personal matter. The amino-naphthol-sulfonic acid is difficult to dissolve, and fresh solutions must be prepared frequently. Many analysts prefer to use stannous chloride solutions which are more easily prepared and have a much longer effective life, provided that they are protected from the atmosphere by a layer of mineral oil. The increased sensitivity of the stannous chloride method is a definite advantage. Samples whose phosphate content is greater than 3 mg/l can readily be analyzed by taking smaller portions for analysis and diluting to the proper volume. If the stannous chloride has been in contact with air to allow significant oxidation of stannous ion to stannic ion, a turbidity develops in samples when the reducing agent is added, because of the hydrolysis of $SnCl_4$ to $Sn(OH)_4$, which precipitates. Any indication of turbidity should cast doubt on the quality and effectiveness of the stannous chloride.

**Polyphosphates.** Polyphosphates may be converted to orthophosphates by boiling samples that have been acidified with sulfuric acid for at least 30 min. The hydrolysis may be hastened by heating in an autoclave at 20 psi. Because of the acid added to the sample to hasten hydrolysis, an ammonium molybdate solution containing less acid must be used in the determination. The orthophosphate formed from the polyphosphate is measured in the presence of orthophosphates originally present in the sample by one of the methods applicable to orthophosphates. The amount of polyphosphate is obtained by difference as follows:

$$\text{Total inorganic phosphate} - \text{orthophosphate} = \text{polyphosphate} \quad (30\text{-}3)$$

**Organic Phosphorus.** Sanitary engineers are often interested in measuring the amount of organic phosphorus present in industrial wastes or in sludges. This analysis requires that the organic matter be destroyed so that the phosphorus is released as phosphate ion. The organic matter may be destroyed by a wet oxidation,[1] similar to that used in the determination of organic nitrogen, or it may be destroyed by a dry combustion procedure. If a dry combustion procedure is used, it is essential that enough basic ash-forming substances be present to hold the phosphate in the ash; otherwise phosphorus will be lost as $P_2O_5$ as follows:

$$\text{Org-P} + O_2 \xrightarrow{\Delta\Delta} CO_2\uparrow + H_2O\uparrow + P_2O_5\uparrow \quad (30\text{-}4)$$

The loss of phosphorus can be avoided by adding small amounts of a magnesium chloride solution to the sample before ignition. The magnesium chloride loses hydrogen chloride during the early stages of the ignition,

$$MgCl_2 \cdot 6H_2O \xrightarrow{\Delta} MgO + 2HCl\uparrow + 5H_2O \quad (30\text{-}5)$$

and the magnesium oxide remaining combines with phosphate or $P_2O_5$ to form magnesium pyrophosphate according to the equation

$$2 \text{ Org-P} + 2\tfrac{1}{2}O_2 + 2MgO \rightarrow Mg_2P_2O_7 + CO_2\uparrow + H_2O\uparrow \quad (30\text{-}6)$$

The organic phosphorus is held in the ash as a pyrophosphate. It must be hydrolyzed to orthophosphate before it can be measured. Once this has been accomplished, measurement can be made by any of the methods

[1] "Official Methods of Analysis of the Association of Official Agricultural Chemists," 7th ed., p. 8, 1950.

applied to orthophosphate. All forms of phosphorus (total) are measured in an organic phosphorus determination. Therefore the organic phosphorus is obtained as follows:

$$\text{Total phosphorus} - \text{inorganic phosphorus} = \text{Org-P} \qquad (30\text{-}7)$$

## 30-4. Applications of Phosphorus Data

Phosphorus data are becoming more and more important in sanitary engineering practice as engineers appreciate its significance as a vital factor in life processes. In the past, the data have been used principally to control phosphate dosages in water systems for corrosion prevention and in boilers for control of scale. Phosphorus determinations are extremely important in assessing the potential biological productivity of surface waters, and in some areas limits are being established on amounts of phosphorus that may be discharged to receiving bodies of water. It is fairly certain that phosphorus determinations will become routine procedure in stream pollution studies in many areas. Because of the importance of phosphorus as a nutrient in biological methods of sewage treatment, its determination is essential with many industrial wastes and in the operation of waste treatment plants.

# 31. Grease

## 31-1. General Considerations

The grease content of sewage, certain industrial wastes, and sludges is an important consideration in the handling and treatment of these materials for ultimate disposal. Grease is singled out for special attention because of its poor solubility in water and its tendency to separate from the aqueous phase. Although this characteristic is advantageous in facilitating the separation of grease by use of flotation devices, it does complicate the transportation of wastes through pipelines, their destruction in biological treatment units, and their disposal into receiving waters.

Wastes from the meat-packing industry, particularly where hard fats from the slaughtering of sheep and cattle are involved, have resulted in serious decreases in the carrying capacity of sewers. Such experiences, and other factors related to treatment or ultimate disposal, have served as the basis for ordinances and regulations governing the discharge of greasy materials to sewer systems or receiving waters and have forced the installation of preliminary treatment facilities by many industries for the recovery of grease or oil before discharge is permitted.

A number of problems are caused by grease in sewage treatment practice. Very few plants have provisions for the separate disposal of grease to scavengers or by incineration; consequently that which separates as scum in primary settling tanks is normally transferred with the settled solids to disposal units. In sludge digestion tanks, the grease tends to separate and float to the surface to form dense scum layers, because of its poor solubility in water and its low specific gravity. Scum problems have been particularly severe where high-grease-content wastes, such as those from the meat-packing and oil and fat industries, have been admitted to public sewer systems. The vacuum filtration of sludge is also complicated by high grease content.

Not all the grease is removed from sewage by primary settling units. Appreciable amounts remain in the clarified sewage in a finely divided

331

emulsified form.   During subsequent biological attack in secondary treatment units or in the receiving stream, the emulsifying agents are usually destroyed and the finely divided grease particles become free to coalesce into larger particles which separate from the water.   In activated sludge plants, the grease often accumulates into "grease balls" which give an unsightly appearance to the surface of final settling tanks. Both trickling filters and the activated sludge process are adversely affected by unreasonable amounts of grease which seems to coat the biological forms sufficiently to interfere with oxygen transfer from the liquid to the interior of the living cells.   This is sometimes described as a "smothering" action.

Separation of floating grease in final settling tanks has been a problem in some treatment plants employing high-rate processes.   This has been attributed to short-term contact of the waste with limited amounts of biological growths which destroy the emulsifying agents present but do not have sufficient adsorptive powers to hold the grease that is released, nor time to oxidize it.   As a result, the grease is free to separate under quiescent conditions such as occur in final settling tanks or receiving waters.

### 31-2. Grease and Its Measurement

The term *grease* applies to a wide variety of organic substances that are extracted from aqueous solution or suspension by petroleum ether.[1] Hydrocarbons, esters, oils, fats, waxes, and high-molecular-weight fatty acids are the major materials dissolved by petroleum ether.   All these materials have a "greasy feel" and are associated with the problems in sewage treatment related to grease.

Petroleum ether[2] has been selected for the solvent in grease determinations because it is a good solvent for all the materials normally associated with the term "grease" and has a minimum solvent power for other organic compounds.   Chloroform, diethyl ether, and other solvents have been used in the past but are less desirable than petroleum ether in one or more respects.   Chloroform, for example, dissolves carbohydrates to a limited extent.

The method of determining grease by means of petroleum ether extraction does not measure low-molecular-weight hydrocarbons such as gasoline.   Preparation of the sample for extraction requires that it be dried at 103°C.   As a result, all materials with boiling points below this temperature are lost as well as significant amounts of all other materials

---

[1] A mixture of pentane and hexane (bp, 35 to 54°C).

[2] Pure hexane has recently become readily available and it is expected that it will become the recommended solvent in the coming eleventh edition of "Standard Methods for the Examination of Water, Sewage and Industrial Wastes."

that have appreciable vapor pressures at 103°C. Such compounds, except in unusual cases, are normally present in relatively small amounts in sewage and are of little concern except in wastes from the petroleum industry. Most of the materials generally classed as "grease" have very low vapor pressures at 103°C and can be recovered essentially 100 per cent by petroleum ether extraction. In cases where drying oils are present, some oxidation occurs at the unsaturated linkages during the drying procedure and may render them insoluble. Such oils, however, do not normally occur in domestic sewage to any great extent.

Although the methods employed for the determination of grease may seem highly unrefined and inaccurate, they are the result of years of effort to obtain a reasonable measure of those things in water, sewage, industrial wastes, and sludges that tend to separate from the aqueous phase and create special problems. Once the sanitary engineer becomes fully acquainted with the purposes of the grease determination and understands the relative significance of volatile versus nonvolatile materials, he can usually adjust his thinking to the terms of the test method and its limitations.

## 31-3. Methods of Analysis

All the common methods of determining grease depend upon a preferential solution of the greasy materials using petroleum ether extractions and are subject in some degree to the limitations discussed above. The methods employed for water, polluted waters, and sludges differ somewhat, and separate discussions are needed.

**Water.** The oil or grease content of relatively clean waters is not a routine determination and is seldom performed except in special cases where accidental contamination has occurred. The choice of method of analysis depends upon the volatility of the contaminants. High-boiling-point materials may be measured by the direct extraction method given in "Standard Methods," but all materials with appreciable vapor pressures at 70°C must be measured by a special distillation procedure or the use of infrared analysis.

**Sewage and Industrial Wastes.** Oils, fats, waxes, and fatty acids are the principal substances classed as grease in sewage. Industrial wastes may contain simple esters and, possibly, a few other compounds in the same category.

The term "oil" represents a wide variety of substances ranging from low- to high-molecular-weight hydrocarbons of mineral origin, spanning the range from gasoline through heavy fuel and lubricating oils. In addition, it includes all glycerides of animal and vegetable origin that are liquid at ordinary temperatures. The fatty acids occur principally in a precipitated form as calcium and magnesium soaps. As such, they are insoluble in petroleum ether.    Samples are acidified with hydrochloric acid to a pH of about 1.0 to release the free fatty acids.    The reaction involved may be represented by the equation

$$Ca(C_{17}H_{35}COO)_2 + 2H^+ \rightarrow 2C_{17}H_{35}COOH + Ca^{++} \qquad (31\text{-}1)$$

The high-molecular-weight fatty acids are relatively insoluble in water and are separated with other components of grease in the filtration procedure involved.

Filtration is considered acceptable practice since it effectively separates those materials normally referred to as grease and allows low-molecular-weight and soluble materials, which are of no consequence, to escape in the filtrate.    Drying of the filtered material removes water so that the petroleum ether can penetrate the sample readily and accomplish separation of the grease in the 4-hr extraction period normally provided.    It also eliminates the possibility of appreciable amounts of water being carried into the extract and, thereby, simplifies the drying procedure. A Soxhlet type of extractor which provides intermittent batchwise extraction is used (Fig. 31-1).

**Sludges.**    Sludges are frequently of such consistency and character that they are difficult to filter, and prolonged periods are often required to dry them sufficiently for solvent extraction.    The current standard procedure involves the use of a chemical dehydration technique that eliminates the need for filtration and drying.    The method consists of weighing a definite amount of sample, acidifying it to release fatty acids as shown in Eq. (31-1), and then adding a quantity of $MgSO_4 \cdot H_2O$ sufficient to combine with all free water by forming higher hydrated forms, $MgSO_4 \cdot 7H_2O$ being the ultimate.    With the water in a chemically bound form, the sample is pulverized to facilitate extraction of grease.    A Soxhlet extractor, as shown in Fig. 31-1, is used to separate the grease from the $MgSO_4 \cdot 7H_2O$ and the organic matter that is not grease.

### 31-4. Applications of Grease Data

In sanitary engineering practice, grease determinations are made more or less routinely for a number of purposes.    Many municipalities and other local authorities have ordinances for the regulation of the discharge of grease-bearing industrial wastes to sewer systems or to receiving waters and, of course, use grease and oil determinations for regulatory purposes. Industries that must treat their wastes to remove such materials use the test or some modification of it to determine the effectiveness of treatment units and to keep a record of the grease content of their discharges.

One of the major purposes of sewage treatment facilities is to remove unsightly and obnoxious floating matter, of which grease is a major consideration.    Grease determinations on raw and settled sewages give a measure of the effectiveness of primary settling tanks, and determinations

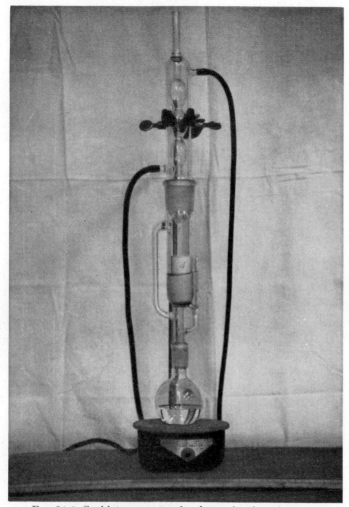

Fig. 31-1. Soxhlet apparatus for determination of grease.

on final effluents provide a record of the efficacy of secondary treatment units as well as the amounts actually discharged to receiving waters. The latter is particularly important in cases where disposal is into recreational areas.

Grease determinations are used extensively in sludge disposal practice. Determinations on the raw and digested sludges, when properly adjusted to volumes involved in a given plant, allow calculation of grease destruction during anaerobic digestion. When scum problems occur in digestion units, determinations of grease often yield information of considerable value. The grease content of sludge is a factor in determining its suitability for use as a fertilizer, and purchasers often require a guarantee that the percentage shall not exceed a certain value.

# $32.$ Volatile Acids

## 32-1. General Considerations

The volatile-acids determination is widely used in the control of anaerobic digestion processes. In the biochemical decomposition of organic matter that occurs, saprophytic bacteria of wide variety hydrolyze and convert the complex materials to low-molecular-weight compounds, as discussed in Secs. 8-8 to 8-10. Among the low-molecular-weight compounds formed, the short-chain fatty acids, such as acetic, propionic, and butyric, are important components. An accumulation of these low-molecular-weight acids can have a disastrous effect upon anaerobic digestion if the buffering capacity of the system is exceeded and the pH falls to unfavorable levels.

In anaerobic digestion units that are operating in a stabilized condition, two groups of bacteria work in harmony to accomplish the destruction of organic matter. The saprophytic organisms carry the degradation to the acid stage and then the methane-forming bacteria complete the conversion into methane and carbon dioxide. When a sufficient population of methane-forming bacteria is present and environmental conditions are favorable, they utilize the end products produced by the saprophytic bacteria as fast as they are formed. As a result, acids do not accumulate beyond the neutralizing ability of the natural buffers present and the pH remains in a favorable range for the methane bacteria. Under such conditions the volatile-acid content of digesting sludges usually runs in the range of 100 to 250 mg/l, expressed as acetic acid.

Methane-forming bacteria are ubiquitous in nature and some are always present in sewage and sewage sludge. Their population, however, is very small compared with that of the saprophytic bacteria. This disparity in numbers is the reason for the troubles encountered in starting digestion units without benefit of "seeding" sludge. Raw sewage sludge has a relatively low buffering capacity, and when it is allowed to ferment anaerobically, volatile acids are produced so much faster than the few methane bacteria present can consume them that the buffers are soon spent and free acids exist to depress the pH. At pH values below 6, methane bacteria are seriously inhibited but the saprophytic bacteria are not until pH levels fall to about 5. Under such unbalanced conditions, the volatile-acids concentration continues to increase to levels of 2,000 to 6,000 mg/l or more, depending upon the solids content of the sludge. Active methane digestion may never develop in such mixtures unless the sludge is diluted or neutralizing agents, such as lime, are added to produce a favorable pH for the methane bacteria. The volatile-acids determination, in conjunction with pH measurements, is valuable in control of environmental conditions during the initiation of methane digestion.

Successful operation of anaerobic digestion units depends upon maintaining a satisfactory balance between the methane and saprophytic bacteria. The methane bacteria appear to be the most susceptible to changes in environmental conditions and food load. They are affected much more radically by changes in pH and temperature than the saprophytic bacteria. Inhibitions caused by changes in either of these factors result in a decreased rate of destruction of volatile acids; consequently volatile acids begin to accumulate in the system. The saprophytic bacteria are known to reproduce more rapidly than the methane bacteria. Under increased food loads, volatile acids may be formed faster than the slow-growing methane organisms can take care of them. This discrepancy results in an accumulation of volatile acids in the system. Sludge must be removed or transferred from digestion units on occasion; however, removal of too large an amount will deplete the methane organism population to levels where volatile acids cannot be destroyed as fast as they are formed and accumulations will develop. Volatile-acid determinations are extremely important in detecting the presence of unbalanced conditions in digestion units caused by any of the factors mentioned above. The onset of unfavorable conditions can be detected almost immediately, and usually several days in advance of other methods, such as through pH measurements.

## 32-2. Theoretical Considerations

According to Knoop's beta-oxidation theory, the biological degradation of long-chain fatty acids results in multiple cleavage of the molecules to form two-carbon-atom units of acetic acid. With compounds containing an even number of carbon atoms initially, it would be predicted that acetic acid should be the sole end product but, in any dynamic system, all intermediate forms of even-numbered carbon atoms would be present to some extent.   Kaplovsky[1] has found that acetic and butyric acids are the principal volatile acids present during digestion of sewage sludge. Propionic acid is a minor component.   In subsequent studies with industrial wastes,[2] he found propionic and valeric acids to be present in significant amounts at some stages in the digestion of yeast and meat-packing wastes but not in the case of paperboard-mill wastes.   Thus it seems clear that the kinds and amounts of volatile acids present are a function of the nature of the substrate undergoing decomposition.

The biological degradation of high-molecular-weight compounds through beta oxidation results in greatly multiplying the number of carboxyl groups.   For example, complete degradation of one molecule of stearic acid produces nine molecules of acetic acid, or, in other words, the acidity is increased ninefold.   All the low-molecular-weight acids have ionization constants greater than $1.0 \times 10^{-5}$ and, therefore, are stronger acids than carbonic acid whose primary ionization constant is about $1 \times 10^{-7}$.   Since the major buffer system in digesting sludge is due to bicarbonates, the short-chain fatty acids destroy the bicarbonate buffer as they accumulate.   As the buffer is destroyed, carbon dioxide is released and the pH falls gradually.   When all the buffer has been consumed, further formation of acids decreases the pH very rapidly.   For these reasons it is necessary to maintain buffer capacity by adding basic materials from outside sources or to exercise some control over the rate of volatile-acid formation if pH conditions favorable to methane-forming bacteria are to be maintained.

TABLE 32-1. VAPOR PRESSURES OF VOLATILE ACIDS AT 100°C

| Acid | Vapor pressure at 100°C, mm Hg* |
|------|---------------------------------|
| Formic | 753 |
| Acetic | 417 |
| Propionic | 183 (calc.) |
| Butyric | 70 (calc.) |
| Valeric | 28 |
| Hexanoic | 10.6 |
| Heptanoic | 4.1 |
| Octanoic | 1.6 |

* Data from "International Critical Tables," McGraw-Hill Book Company, Inc., New York.

All the low-molecular-weight fatty acids have boiling points above 100°C.   However all members up to octanoic acid have significant vapor pressures at 100°C, the boiling point of water, as shown in Table 32-1.

[1] A. J. Kaplovsky, Volatile Acid Production during Digestion of Seeded, Unseeded and Limed Fresh Solids, *Sewage and Ind. Wastes*, **23**, 713 (1951).

[2] A. J. Kaplovsky, Volatile Acid Production during Digestion of Several Industrial Wastes, *Sewage and Ind. Wastes*, **24**, 194 (1952).

If mixtures containing these acids are distilled without any attempt at fractionation, the distillate will contain appreciable amounts of the acids. In any event, the distillation of volatile acids is never complete. Because of this, the procedures used must be highly standardized in order to distill a uniform fraction of the acids, and factors must be included in computations to obtain a measure of volatile acids in the sample.

## 32-3. Methods of Determining Volatile Acids

Two methods of determining volatile acids are in current use. Both are distillation procedures based upon the general principle discussed above.

**Direct Distillation.** The direct-distillation method is used for the routine determination of volatile acids in most instances. The method is rapid and sufficiently accurate for all practical purposes, since it is not usually necessary to know volatile-acid concentrations more accurately than $\pm 50$ mg/l.

Digesting sludges normally have a pH in the range of 6.5 to 7.5, and under such conditions organic acids exist largely in ionic form as fixed salts. It is impossible to distill acids from mixtures in this pH range. By the addition of a strong nonvolatile acid, such as sulfuric, the ions of the organic acids are converted to un-ionized acids as represented by acetate ion in the equation

$$\underset{\text{Ion of organic acid}}{CH_3COO^-} + H^+ \rightarrow \underset{\text{Free un-ionized acid}}{CH_3COOH} \qquad (32\text{-}1)$$

Usually sufficient acid is added to reduce the pH below 1.0.

It would be expected from the vapor-pressure data in Table 32-1 that the low-molecular-weight acids would distill most readily because of their greater vapor pressures. This is not the case, however. Formic, acetic, and propionic acids are the most difficult to separate by distillation in dilute aqueous solution.[1] This is because aqueous solutions are not ideal in character. Molecular association occurs between the acid and water molecules and varies with the particular acid. As a result, binary mixtures of all three classes described in Sec. 6-6 are formed.

Formic acid and water form a Class II mixture, and water is the major component of the vapor phase when dilute solutions are distilled. Acetic acid and water form a Class I mixture, and the vapor phase is predominantly water vapor. Fractionation of the vapor in each case produces a distillate that is essentially pure water and the acids remain in the undistilled liquor. It is for this reason that fractionation of the vapors must be kept at a minimum in the volatile-acids determination.

---

[1] A. M. Buswell and S. L. Neave, Laboratory Studies on Sludge Digestion, *Illinois State Water Survey Bull.* 30, p. 76, 1930.

Propionic, butyric, and other fatty acids that are soluble in water form Class III mixtures. The distillate contains the acid and water in a constant ratio until all the acid is distilled.

It is unnecessary to separate sludge from samples prior to distillation if care is used to prevent excessive heating of the walls of the distillation flask above the level of the mixture in the flask. If this is allowed to happen, some decomposition of sludge may occur in the strong acid environment, which may give rise to the production of organic acids. Also, reduction of sulfuric acid may occur with production of sulfur dioxide. The latter, being an acid anhydride, will dissolve in the distillate to produce sulfurous acid and give abnormally high results. There is little chance of this happening when electric heaters are used but it frequently happens if uncontrolled gas flames are used for heat.

The distillation rate is an important consideration in this determination and should be closely controlled. At low rates of distillation considerable fractionation may occur in the neck of the flask and the volatile acids will not carry over in the distillate as desired. Care must be taken to stop the distillation when the appropriate amount of distillate has been formed. The residue remaining in the flask is in contact with the excess sulfuric acid used and the acid becomes more concentrated as the distillation progresses. If the distillation is carried too far, the sulfuric acid will cause decomposition of the sludge and be reduced as described above.

Approximately 70 per cent of the volatile acids contained in sludge samples is distilled from samples treated by the recommended procedure. This matter is taken into account in calculations of the volatile acids present.

**Steam Distillation.** Many of the limitations of the direct-distillation method can be overcome by use of a steam-distillation procedure. In this method, sludge solids are separated, and the determination of volatile acids is made on the sludge liquor. Steam is generated in a separate unit, and excessive heating of the sample containing sulfuric acid is avoided. Sufficient heat is usually supplied to the distillation flask containing the sample to prevent dilution by condensation, and the accessory heat is controlled in a manner to prevent concentration of the sample. The distillation may be continued as long as desired, and essentially complete recoveries of acid can be obtained in the distillate.

The steam-distillation procedure requires considerable time, and its use is not ordinarily justified except for research purposes.

### 32-4. Applications of Volatile-acid Data

Volatile-acid determinations have been valuable in providing information concerning the anaerobic degradation of organic matter and the environmental conditions best suited for optimum activity of methane-producing bacteria. Much research on anaerobic processes, particularly in regard to the nature of the substrate undergoing decomposition, remains to be done before anaerobic treatment can be applied intelligently to a wide variety of industrial wastes. The volatile-acids determination, because of its ability to detect when methane organisms fail to keep pace with the saprophytic organisms, will continue to be a valuable test in research work.

The value of volatile-acid data in routine control of anaerobic digestion units at sewage treatment plants and other installations has been amply demonstrated. These data are needed especially in the control of units that are operating at or near design capacity. With the development of high-rate digestion processes, the test will become more important in the future as corrective measures will, undoubtedly, have to be made more promptly. The volatile-acid test offers the most promise of providing pertinent information as quickly as possible and at reasonable expense.

# 33. Gas Analysis

### 33-1. General Considerations

Anaerobic decomposition of sludges and of some liquid wastes, particularly those with BOD values exceeding 1,500 mg/l, is considered to be the most economical method of treatment when the organic materials involved are amenable to attack by methane-forming bacteria. Anaerobic processes are popular because operating costs are low, although capital investments are usually high.

The gas produced in anaerobic digestion of sewage sludge usually contains from 33 to 38 per cent carbon dioxide, from 55 to 65 per cent methane, small amounts of hydrogen, some nitrogen, and traces of hydrogen sulfide, and it has a heating value in the neighborhood of 600 Btu/ cu ft. The caloric value of the gas produced is normally in excess of the heat requirements for maintaining proper temperatures in the digestion units. The excess gas has value for producing power for useful work.

The composition of gas produced during anaerobic digestion varies somewhat with the environmental conditions in the digester. It changes rapidly during the period that digestion is being initiated, such as when digesters are first started, and when normal digestion is inhibited. For digesters operating in a routine manner and being fed a given substrate regularly, the composition of the gas produced is fairly uniform; however, the ratio of carbon dioxide to methane varies radically with the character of the substrate undergoing decomposition. Buswell and Boruff[1] have shown that methane fermentation of the three common classes of organic materials produces carbon dioxide and methane in the following

---

[1] A. M. Buswell and C. S. Boruff, The Relation Between the Chemical Composition of Organic Matter and the Quality and Quantity of Gas Produced During Sludge Digestion, *Sewage Works J.*, **4,** 454 (1932).

ratios:

|  | Carbon dioxide | Methane |
|---|---|---|
| Carbohydrates | 50 | 50 |
| Low-MW fatty acids | 38 | 62 |
| High-MW fatty acids | 28 | 72 |
| Proteins | $\begin{cases} 24 \\ 31 \end{cases}$ | 76<br>69 |

Because of the wide variety of organic substances (usually of unknown composition) that are subjected to methane fermentation, it has become common practice to analyze the gases produced to determine their fuel value and, in some cases, to maintain a check on the behavior of the digestion units.   The idea has been advanced that the onset of digestion troubles is accompanied by an increase in the carbon dioxide content of the gas produced and that this test can be used in place of the volatile-acids determination to detect such conditions.   As a result, a limited analysis of digester gas to determine its carbon dioxide content is becoming common.   Experience will demonstrate whether carbon dioxide measurements can substitute for volatile-acids determinations in this capacity. Because of the influence of the substrate on the ratio of carbon dioxide to methane in the gas produced, it is reasonable to assume that interpretations based upon carbon dioxide content alone may lead to faulty conclusions.

## 33-2. Methods of Analysis

Gas analysis is normally accomplished by gasometric (volumetric) procedures, except for the measurement of hydrogen sulfide which occurs in amounts too small to be measured in this way.   Early methods of analysis employed separate measurement of carbon dioxide and oxygen followed by a slow simultaneous combustion of hydrogen and methane. The analysis was completed by measuring the amount of carbon dioxide produced during the combustion of the methane and then applying a knowledge of Gay-Lussac's law of combining volumes (Sec. 2-8) to determine the amounts of methane and hydrogen present in the mixture.

The Orsat apparatus, employing a slow-combustion unit, shown in Fig. 33-1, is most commonly used in gas analysis.   Its operation in the determination of hydrogen and methane is somewhat hazardous because of the possibility of explosions.   Other devices, such as the Burrell apparatus shown in Fig. 33-2, provide for separate oxidation of hydrogen and methane.   Hydrogen is oxidized by passing the gas through a heated unit charged with cupric oxide, and methane is oxidized in a separate unit by bringing a mixture of it and oxygen in contact with a catalyst at rela-

FIG. 33-1. Orsat gas-analysis apparatus equipped with slow-combustion chamber. (*Metcalf & Eddy.*)

tively low temperatures.    Explosion hazards are completely eliminated.

**Carbon Dioxide.**    Carbon dioxide is measured by bringing a sample of known volume, usually 100 ml, into contact with a solution of  potassium hydroxide.    The carbon dioxide reacts with the hydroxide to form potassium carbonate, as shown in the equation

$$CO_2 + 2KOH \rightarrow K_2CO_3 + H_2O \qquad (33\text{-}1)$$
$$\text{1 vol.} \qquad\qquad\quad \text{0 vol.}$$

In the reaction, the carbon dioxide disappears from the gaseous phase, and the potassium carbonate formed remains in the liquid phase; therefore the loss in volume of the gas is equal to the carbon dioxide content.

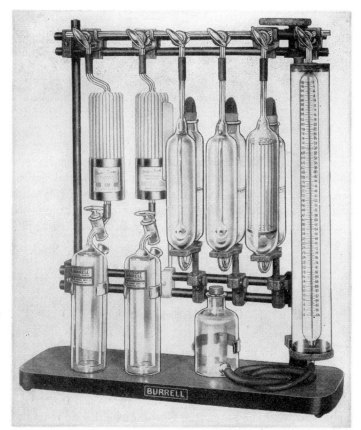

Fig. 33-2. Burrell gas-analysis apparatus equipped for separate low-temperature oxidation of hydrogen and catalytic oxidation of methane. (*Burrell Corp.*)

Actually, any hydrogen sulfide present in the gas also combines with the potassium hydroxide,

$$H_2S + 2KOH \rightarrow K_2S + H_2O \qquad (33\text{-}2)$$
$$\text{1 vol.} \qquad\qquad \text{0 vol.}$$

but the volume of hydrogen sulfide is usually so small that its effect may be ignored.

Potassium hydroxide is used instead of sodium hydroxide to absorb carbon dioxide because of the greater solubility of potassium carbonate. If sodium hydroxide is used, sodium carbonate tends to precipitate. Some of it usually floats and clogs the capillary passages.

**Oxygen.** Theoretically, there is very little possibility of oxygen being present in the gas produced by anaerobic digestion units. However, small amounts may gain entrance to the sample during the sampling procedure and when charging the gas-analysis apparatus.    It is, therefore, good practice to analyze for oxygen.    The presence of more than 0.1 to 0.2 per cent usually indicates poor technique in sampling and in transferring the sample to the gas-analysis apparatus.

Oxygen in sludge gas may be measured by the use of any of three reagents: (1) alkaline pyrogallol, a strongly alkaline solution of pyrogallic acid (pyrogallol); (2) acid cuprous chloride solution; and (3) chromous chloride solution.

Under alkaline conditions, pyrogallol (1,2,3-trihydroxy benzene) is oxidized by oxygen.    The end products of the reaction have not been clearly defined but are, presumably, carbon dioxide and organic acids, both of which are held as potassium salts in the absorbing solution.    If all carbon dioxide has been removed from the sample before bringing it in contact with the alkaline pyrogallol, any decrease in sample volume will be due to removal of oxygen.

Acid solutions of cuprous chloride have been used to determine oxygen. Their capacity is quite limited, and solutions must be renewed frequently. The reaction involved is

$$4Cu^+ + O_2 + 4H^+ \rightarrow 4Cu^{++} + 2H_2O \qquad (33\text{-}3)$$
$$\underset{\text{1 vol.}}{} \qquad \qquad \underset{\text{0 vol.}}{}$$

Under the acid conditions prevailing, the oxygen appears as water which has zero volume as far as the gaseous phase or sample volume is concerned.

Chromous chloride solutions are also used to measure oxygen.    They are especially effective and must be carefully protected from the air when units are charged with the reagent.    Chromous chloride reacts with oxygen according to the reaction

$$4Cr^{++} + O_2 + 4H^+ \rightarrow 4Cr^{3+} + 2H_2O \qquad (33\text{-}4)$$
$$\underset{\text{1 vol.}}{} \qquad \qquad \underset{\text{0 vol.}}{}$$

**Hydrogen.**    Hydrogen may be determined separately in the presence of methane by passing the gas mixture over cupric oxide maintained at a temperature in the range of 290 to 300°C.    Under such conditions, hydrogen is oxidized to water but methane is not oxidized.    The water vapor formed condenses at the temperatures to which the sample must be reduced for subsequent volume measurements, and, therefore, loss in volume after contact with heated cupric oxide is a measure of the hydrogen present.

**Methane.**    After removal of hydrogen, methane may be determined in the residual gas by slow combustion or by catalytic oxidation.    In either case, oxygen is required, but the technique for each is very different.

*Catalytic Oxidation.*    A mixture of the gas containing methane and oxygen is used in this method, and the oxidation is performed catalytically at temperatures below the kindling point; consequently an explosion does not occur. The volume of oxygen required is determined from the equation

$$CH_4 + 2O_2 \rightarrow CO_2 + 2H_2O \qquad (33\text{-}5)$$
$$\text{1 vol.} \quad \text{2 vol.} \quad \text{1 vol.} \quad \text{0 vol.}$$

It will be noted that 2 volumes of oxygen is required to oxidize 1 volume of methane and that 1 volume of carbon dioxide is produced. The two volumes of water vapor produced are reduced to zero volume at the temperature at which final gas volumes are measured. Since 2 volumes of oxygen is required for each volume of methane, at least $2\frac{1}{2}$ volumes should be used to provide a sufficient excess to carry the reaction to completion.

After the analyses for carbon dioxide, oxygen, and hydrogen are finished, the volume of residual gas containing methane is about 60 to 70 ml, if a 100-ml sample is used initially. It is impossible to mix 60 or 70 ml of gas with two and one-half times its volume of oxygen in the equipment provided. The maximum-size sample of methane that may be used in a 100-ml buret and be mixed with two and one-half times its volume of oxygen is about 28 ml. The usual procedure is to waste sufficient residual gas to leave a sample ranging in size from 20 to 25 ml. Some analysts prefer not to waste the gas but store the excess in the oxygen absorption pipet as a reserve supply in case it is needed. Oxygen is next admitted to the sample in proper amount and then the mixture is brought in contact with the catalyst.

The methane content of the gas used for the combustion may be determined in two ways. Inspection of Eq. (33-5) will show that 2 volumes of oxygen is used for each volume of methane oxidized and 1 volume of carbon dioxide results. A contraction in gas volume occurs that is equal to the amount of oxygen used. Since this is equal to two times the methane,

$$\text{Volume of methane} = \tfrac{1}{2} \text{ total contraction}$$

The residual gas after measurement to determine total contraction still contains carbon dioxide in a volume equal to the methane originally present. It may be measured by bringing it into contact with potassium hydroxide and measuring the residual gas to get the volume absorbed.

Final calculations of methane content must be based upon an adjustment of the values obtained on the test portion of the methane-bearing sample to the total volume. For example, if 65 ml remained after carbon dioxide, oxygen, and hydrogen were removed and 25 ml was used for the methane determination, the values should be multiplied by a factor of 65/25 to obtain the percentage of methane.

*Slow Combustion.* The separate determination of methane by the slow-combustion method is not common. The procedure is essentially the same as for a combination of hydrogen and methane. Analysis of the data is exactly as described under catalytic oxidation.

**Hydrogen and Methane by Combustion.** Mixtures of oxygen and methane or oxygen, hydrogen, and methane are explosive when temperatures are raised to the kindling point. Therefore *mixtures are not used* in this method of analysis. The procedure used to prevent explosions and still allow combustion to occur is gradually to introduce the mixture of hydrogen and methane into an atmosphere of oxygen in the region of a heating element maintained above the kindling point. The hydrogen and methane burn as fast as they enter the oxygen chamber, and an explosive mixture never develops. It is imperative that the heating element be maintained above the kindling point at all times and that the flow of gas to be burned not be interrupted.

The usual procedure used in determining hydrogen and methane by slow combustion is to store all the gas remaining after removal of carbon dioxide and oxygen in the oxygen absorption pipet. A volume of oxygen equal to at least two and one-half times the volume of hydrogen and methane to be burned is measured and then transferred completely to the combustion pipet. The proper-size sample of hydrogen and methane gas is next measured in the gas buret and then transferred slowly into the combustion pipet with the heating element red-hot. A continuous flame should be maintained until all the sample has been transferred.

Calculation of the amount of hydrogen and methane in the sample is based upon Eq. (33-5) and the equation for the oxidation of hydrogen [Eq. (33-6)].

$$2H_2 + O_2 \rightarrow 2H_2O \tag{33-6}$$
$$\text{2 vol.} \quad \text{1 vol.} \quad \text{0 vol.}$$

The volume of gas remaining after combustion is measured and, when deducted from the volume of oxygen plus gas used, gives a value known as total contraction. The volume of methane is ascertained by passing the residual gas through potassium hydroxide to absorb carbon dioxide. The loss in volume is equal to the methane, from Eq. (33-5). Since 2 volumes of oxygen is used for each volume of methane during combustion, the contraction due to methane is equal to two times the volume of methane. Then

Total contraction − contraction due to methane

= contraction due to hydrogen    (33-7)

From Eq. (33-6), it may be seen that 2 volumes of hydrogen combines with 1 volume of oxygen to produce 2 volumes of water vapor, which condenses at the temperature of the measurements to zero volume.  Or, in other words, two-thirds of the contraction caused by formation of water is due to hydrogen and one-third to oxygen.  This fact provides the basis for calculating hydrogen as follows:

$$\text{Hydrogen} = \tfrac{2}{3} \text{ contraction due to hydrogen} \qquad (33\text{-}8)$$

Since the determination of hydrogen and methane is based upon a fractional part of the sample remaining after removal of carbon dioxide and oxygen, proper corrections must be applied, as discussed above under catalytic oxidation.

**Nitrogen.**  Nitrogen is a relatively inert gas and remains unchanged at the end of the usual gas-analysis procedure.  It is assumed that it is the only component of any significance that behaves in this manner. It is customary to total the carbon dioxide, oxygen, hydrogen, and methane percentages and subtract them from 100.  The difference represents inert gases and is reported as nitrogen.

## 33-3. Sources of Error

There are five major sources of error in gas analysis, as follows:

**Collection, Storage, and Handling of Samples.**  Unless special care is taken in the collection of samples, contamination by air occurs.  Samples should always be collected in glass or metal tubes, particularly if an appreciable time elapses before analysis can be made.  Gum-rubber balloons are not suitable because they are pervious to hydrogen and methane.  Transfer of gas from the sample tube to the gas-analysis apparatus requires the use of a displacing fluid, and some modification of the sample is apt to occur.  Also, some air may gain entrance.

**Confining Fluid.**  Mercury is the ideal confining fluid because of the insolubility of all gases in it but, because of its great density and cost, it is seldom used, except in precision-type instruments.  For ordinary purposes, a high degree of accuracy is not needed, and less ideal confining fluids can be used.  Water has much too great a solvent power for all the gases involved to serve satisfactorily.  However, it has been found that an aqueous solution containing 20 per cent sodium sulfate and 5 per cent sulfuric acid has markedly reduced solvent powers.  This is the mixture normally used in portable equipment but does introduce some error in analysis.

**Incomplete Combustion of Methane.**  During the combustion of methane, a high concentration of oxygen is present at the start of the combustion, but, as the combustion proceeds, the oxygen concentration decreases markedly owing to use and to dilution by the carbon dioxide formed.  Unless a volume of oxygen at least two and one-half times the size of the gas sample is used, an oxygen deficiency may occur.  Incomplete combustion is a common cause of high nitrogen values and of low methane values.

**Temperature Changes.**    In gas analysis, small changes in temperature can cause serious errors.    This is a special problem during the measurement of hydrogen and methane where the reactions are conducted at high temperatures.    There is always a tendency to measure the volume remaining after combustion before the temperature of the gas has returned to the original value.    This may lead to positive errors in some instances and negative errors in others.

**Volume of Capillaries.**    In most instances the volume of the capillaries does not introduce a serious error.    However, in the determination of hydrogen and methane by the slow-combustion procedure, the volume of unburned gas in the capillaries may represent 1 to 2 per cent of the sample measured for burning.

### 33-4. Hydrogen Sulfide

The measurement of hydrogen sulfide is particularly important in cases where sludge gas is to be used for fuel in gas engines.    Most engine manufacturers specify that the gas used should not have more than 50 grains of $H_2S$/100 cu ft (1.14 mg/l), in order to prevent harm from corrosion.

Hydrogen sulfide is commonly measured in sludge gas by means of the Tutweiler apparatus shown in Fig. 33-3.    The procedure is essentially as follows: A sample of gas is introduced into the apparatus which contains a small amount of starch indicator.    Small amounts of a standard iodine solution are added intermittently, with vigorous shaking between additions of iodine.    The iodine reacts with hydrogen sulfide as shown in the equation

$$H_2S + I_2 \rightarrow 2HI + S° \qquad (33\text{-}9)$$

When sufficient iodine has been added to oxidize all the hydrogen sulfide, excess iodine is indicated by the typical blue color produced by starch indicator.    The strength of the iodine solution is selected to facilitate calculation of hydrogen sulfide in terms of grains per 100 cu ft.

In the absence of a Tutweiler apparatus for measuring hydrogen sulfide in gases, the determination can be made in a satisfactory manner with routine laboratory equipment (see Fig. 33-4), employing excess iodine solution to oxidize the hydrogen sulfide by the following procedure:

1. Equip a 1-liter separatory funnel as shown in Fig. 33-4 to allow for collection of a gas sample.

2. Transfer 1,000 ml of approximately $N/100$ iodine solution to the separatory funnel.

3. Connect the separatory funnel to the gas supply.

4. Withdraw exactly 900 ml of iodine solution into a graduated cylinder, taking special care to prevent agitation of the iodine solution within the separatory funnel during the transfer.

Fig. 33-3. Tutweiler apparatus used to determine hydrogen sulfide in sludge gas. (*Burrell Corp.*)

5. Disconnect from the gas supply and allow the gas within the separatory funnel to adjust to atmospheric pressure before final closure of the gas inlet.

6. Agitate the gas sample with the 100-ml portion of iodine solution remaining in the separatory funnel to allow all hydrogen sulfide to be oxidized to sulfur.

7. Titrate 50-ml portions of the iodine solution withdrawn from the separatory funnel to make room for the gas sample and of the iodine solution remaining in the separatory funnel after removal of hydrogen

sulfide with $N/100$ thiosulfate solution.    The portions used for the titration should be acidified with 1 ml of dilute ($N/1$ or 10 per cent) sulfuric acid before the titration is started.    The difference in the titrations is a measure of the hydrogen sulfide oxidized by the iodine.

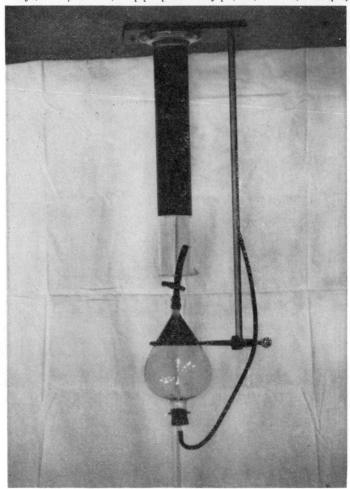

Fig. 33-4.  Apparatus constructed from regular laboratory equipment for measuring hydrogen sulfide in sludge gas.

8. Calculations are based upon a 900-ml sample of gas, titration of one-half of the iodine solution used to react with the hydrogen sulfide, and the use of a $N/100$ thiosulfate solution for titration.    The equivalent weight of hydrogen sulfide is 17, since two electrons are lost in the conversion of $S^= \longrightarrow S°$.    Therefore each milliliter of a $N/100$ thiosulfate

solution is equivalent to 0.17 mg of hydrogen sulfide and

$$(\text{ml}_1 - \text{ml}_2) \times 0.17 \times 2 \times \frac{1,000}{900} = \text{mg H}_2\text{S/l}$$

One cubic foot = 28.3 liters, and one grain = 64.8 mg. Therefore,

$$\frac{\text{mg/l} \times 2830}{64.8} = \text{grains/100 cu ft}$$

## 33-5. Applications of Gas-analysis Data

In the past, gas analyses have been used largely in research studies and at the larger sewage treatment plants where information on the fuel value of gas was important. They will continue to serve in these capacities in the future. In addition, there is a strong possibility that carbon dioxide measurements may be of considerable help in the control of digestion units as a supplement to information provided by volatile-acids and other determinations or as a replacement for some of them.

The determination of hydrogen sulfide will continue to be an important consideration wherever sludge gas is used for fuel in gas engines, particularly in areas where the sulfate content of sewage is high.

# Index